geography now

SENIOR AUTHOR

Graham Draper

AUTHORS

Wayne Andrew

Bert Duncan

Angie Roth

THOMSON

NELSON

Australia   Canada   Mexico   Singapore   Spain   United Kingdom   United States

THOMSON
NELSON

Geography Now

Senior Author
Graham Draper

Authors
Wayne Andrew
Bert Duncan
Angie Roth

Director of Publishing
Beverley Buxton

General Manager
Carol Stokes

Publisher
Doug Panasis

Managing Editor, Development
Karin Fediw

Program Manager
Norma Pettit

Developmental Editor
Gillian Scobie

Production Editor
Carolyn Pisani

Assistant Production Editor
Christi Davis-Martell

Copyeditor
Susan Till

Proofreaders
Dianne Broad
Elizabeth Salomons
Linda Szostak

Indexer
Noeline Bridge

Production Coordinator
Susan Ure

Design Director
Ken Phipps

Interior Design
Kyle Gell Design

Cover Design
Johanna Liburd

Compositor
ArtPlus Ltd.

Photo Research and Permissions
Terri Rothman

Printer
Transcontinental Printing Inc.

Reviewers
Ian Brimble
York Catholic District School Board

Kathryn Dertinger
Peel District School Board

Gina M. Dowdall
Upper Canada District School Board

Brian Gallagher
York Catholic District School Board

Brian Heaton
Limestone District School Board

Lou Iaccino
York Region District School Board

Craig I. W. Marlatt
Durham District School Board

Rachelle Y. Séguin
Limestone District School Board

Jessica Young-Keffer
Renfrew County District School Board

Aboriginal Content Reviewer
Brenda Davis
Six Nations of the Grand River Territory

Literacy Consultants
Pina Sacco
York Catholic District School Board

Lori Lisi
York Catholic District School Board

Contents

Using *Geography Now*

Getting Started

Unit Opener

Each unit begins with two pages that show one image from the unit. This image gives you a visual impression of what the unit is about. Also, read the expectation statements that you will be evaluated on during the unit.

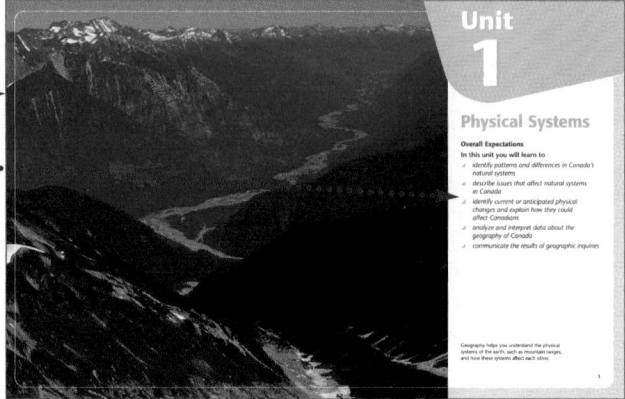

Key Words and Glossary

Key Words are the new words that you need to know.

They are explained in the book and also defined in the **Glossary** on pages 269–275.

Preview the Key Words list before you begin reading. Try to figure out their meanings in context as you read. Look back over the Key Words list from time to time to help you check your understanding of the vocabulary.

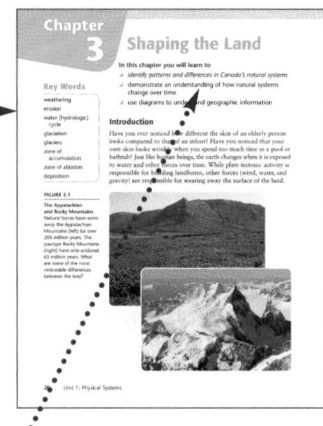

Expectations

Expectations are statements about what you need to demonstrate that you know by the time you finish each chapter.

The statements in *italic type* are overall expectations. They are important because you will be graded on these understandings. Look carefully at the first word in each expectation. These verbs help you see what you need to do and understand.

Literacy Focus

Literacy Skill

Literacy Skills are helpful hints that will make ··············▶ it easier for you to read, understand, and communicate ideas.

The skills are linked to information or activities in the chapter in which they are found. Learning each of the skills contained in this book will help you become a more effective learner.

Literacy Strategy

The Literacy Strategy margin notes provide tools to ··············▶ help you to better understand what you have read.

They also help you to organize the ideas and apply them to other situations. Use these strategies to help you use *Geography Now*.

Appendix: Literacy Hints

The Literacy Hints in the appendix are designed to ··············▶ help you better understand content and apply skills.

The hints deal with broad literacy skills that you can use in most subject areas; in fact, throughout your life.

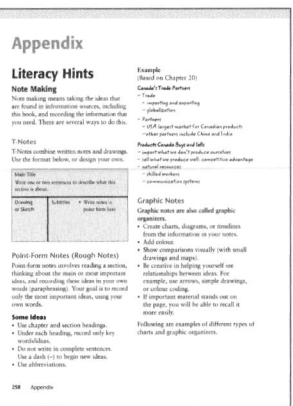

Expanding Your Understanding

GeoCareers

The GeoCareers feature shows you ways that the geographic information you are learning about can be useful in the work world.

The features give information about how you can prepare for such a career.

GeoTechnology

GeoTechnology features give examples of how digital information can be used and changed to help solve geographic problems.

These features help you to see how our tools for exploring geographic conditions continue to improve.

FASTFact

Facts can create interest in and help expand your understanding of a topic. The FASTFact feature gives little nuggets of information for you to use.

Try to see how the fact connects to the whole discussion in that chapter.

FAST *Fact*

An average Canadian over 65 years of age uses three times the amount of health care of an average Canadian under that age.

Case Study

Sometimes it is helpful to see one example of what we have been discussing in more detail. Each Case Study feature connects to the broader discussions in the chapter, but digs a little deeper into just one situation.

GEOCAREERS
Meteorologist

Chris Scott became interested in weather when a hailstorm destroyed his family's crops in 1983. This inspired Chris to study Atmospheric Science and Atmospheric Chemistry at York University. He then became a meteorologist. A meteorologist investigates the natural forces that shape our weather and climate. Chris collected data for Environment Canada before he started reporting the forecast for The Weather Network.

FIGURE 4.5

Chris Scott of The Weather Network
Chris uses technology (computers, radar, satellites) to discover how natural processes and human activities affect our atmosphere. He can then warn others of severe weather.

GEOTECHNOLOGY
Statistics Canada

We are bombarded every day with statistics, such as
- the number of people without jobs
- the amount spent by tourists
- crime rates

Much of this information comes from Statistics Canada. This agency collects statistics about the whole of Canada plus the provinces and territories.

Statistics Canada conducts a census every five years to gather statistical information. Households must fill out census forms and give information about race, education, employment, and so on. The agency also uses about 350 other surveys to collect information on all aspects of life in Canada. This includes information about businesses, travel patterns, and spending habits.

Researchers and businesses can get this information by downloading data from Statistics Canada's Web site. They can also get it from print resources in many public libraries. Anyone can access the Web site. Click free resources, such as Canadian Statistics or Community Profiles. More specific data can be purchased from Statistics Canada.

CASE STUDY
Doctor Shortages in Rural Areas

Many people who live in small towns and rural areas cannot find family doctors. The number of doctors outside of large cities has decreased by over 15 percent since 1994. At the same time, the populations in these areas have increased by 4 percent. By 2010, there will be a shortfall of 1337 doctors in rural parts of Ontario alone. This situation is predicted to get worse right through to 2021. At that point, the doctor shortage should begin to improve.

Why is there a shortage of doctors? Several factors have caused this shortage:
- Doctors, like many of the population, are getting older and are retiring.
- More medical students are choosing to specialize. This means they have to work in large hospitals in big cities.
- To cut costs, governments have reduced enrollments in medical schools.
- Canadian doctors are moving to the United States. For every 19 Canadian medical graduates who go to the U.S., only one American doctor moves north.

In recent years, some provinces have boosted the number of spaces in medical schools and have made it easier for foreign doctors to work in Canada. Critics say that these efforts are "too little, too late." They predict that the doctor shortage is going to get worse.

Checking Your Progress

Check It Over

The Check It Over questions provide a guide for you to check your understanding ·········▶ of the ideas at the end of each section of a chapter.

If you can't answer the questions, reread the section and write down the main ideas in your own words.

CHECK IT OVER

1. Think about one person you know who lives in Canada but was born in another country. Answer these questions to the best of your ability:
   a) Around what year did the person come to Canada?
   b) Why did the person leave his or her home country to come to Canada?
   c) Where did the person live once he or she arrived here in Canada?
2. Choose one of the children in Figure 8.1. Pretend you are that person. Write a one-paragraph journal entry. In it, identify some emotions that you would be feeling as you and your family arrived in Canada.

Think It Over

The Think It Over ···············▶ questions at the end of each chapter help you to connect your new understandings to other ideas that you have.

You will find that some questions ask you to see links, make predictions, express opinions, or do research. Your teacher may use some of these questions for assessment and evaluation purposes.

THINK IT OVER

Knowledge and Understanding

1. There are four definitions of the word *system* in Column A and four example activities in Column B in the table below. The definitions and examples are incorrectly matched. Copy the definitions into your notebook and match them with the correct examples.

Column A	Column B
a set of things or parts forming a whole	the respiratory system
a plan or scheme or method	banking system
an orderly way of getting things done	railway system
the animal body as an organized whole	betting system

Thinking and Communication

2. Make a diagram to show some ways that physical and human systems interact. You might take one activity that you enjoy doing and figure out the interactions that support your activity.
3. Suppose a student in grade 6 asked you what was meant by a *system*. What would you tell that student? Include three main points in your explanation.
4. Make up a cartoon to show something humorous that occurs when physical and human systems interact. You might use one of the following situations as a starting point:
   • a person at a bus stop getting caught in the rain
   • heavy snowfall trapping a family in their home
   • your electricity getting cut off because of a windstorm

Unit

1

Physical Systems

Overall Expectations

In this unit you will learn to

◢ identify patterns and differences in Canada's natural systems

◢ describe issues that affect natural systems in Canada

◢ identify current or anticipated physical changes and explain how they could affect Canadians

◢ analyze and interpret data about the geography of Canada

◢ communicate the results of geographic inquiries

Geography helps you understand the physical systems of the earth, such as mountain ranges. It also helps you to see how these systems affect each other.

1

Systems and How They Work

Key Words

system
drainage system
interaction
smog

In this chapter you will learn to

◢ *identify patterns in Canada's natural and human systems*

◢ *describe some characteristics of systems*

Introduction

How many times have you heard people use the word system in conversation?

- The computer system is down.
- He's really interested in the solar system.
- My satellite TV system is great!
- The education system prepares students for the future.

System is one of those words that has a number of different meanings. It is also one of those words that people sometimes use without really understanding its meaning.

FIGURE 1.1

www.CartoonStock.com

System Been Down Long?
What does the word *system* refer to in this cartoon?

Turn to the Table of Contents and you will see that two of the unit titles contain the word *system*. Throughout *Geography Now*, we will study both physical systems and human systems, so it is important to clearly understand the meaning of *system*.

The *Gage Canadian Intermediate Dictionary* lists six different meanings for *system*. They appear below in the table. The first meaning is the one most useful for studying Geography.

Meaning	Example
1. a set of things or parts forming a whole	a computer system
2. an ordered group of facts, principles, or beliefs	the legal system
3. a plan or scheme or method	a weight-loss system
4. an orderly way of getting things done	an assembly-line system
5. the animal body as an organized whole	the digestive system
6. a group of heavenly bodies forming a whole that follows certain natural laws	the solar system

FIGURE 1.2

Different Meanings of System
Give one more example for each of the meanings in the chart.

This chapter will focus on understanding systems by looking at

- characteristics (particular features) of systems
- some ways in which systems shape geography

CHECK IT OVER

1. Give two examples of systems that you use or see in your day-to-day life.
2. Give two examples of problems that can occur when systems do not work properly.

Literacy Strategy

Answering text questions
Before reading the text, read the questions you need to answer. As you read the text, use sticky notes to identify parts of the text that will help you answer the questions.

Characteristics of Systems

In this book we will use this definition of *system:* "A system is a set of things or parts forming a whole."

If you think about a computer system, the "set of things or parts" is fairly obvious: the processor, monitor, keyboard, mouse, printer, and so on. But what makes up "forming a whole"?

"Forming a whole" is about the connections among the parts. For example, you look at your computer monitor and use the keyboard to search on the Internet for song lyrics. You use the mouse to tell the processor to download a song you have found on the Internet. The processor saves the song onto your MP3 player. You use the sound from your MP3 player to listen to the song as you are doing your Geography homework. "Forming a whole" happens when the parts work together to do a job.

FAST *Fact*

A system's whole is greater than the sum of its parts.

FIGURE 1.3

The Parts of a Drainage System
When a **drainage system** works well, water from all parts of the land finds its way to the oceans. **Note:** A drainage divide is a high point in the landscape that funnels water downward into a stream valley.

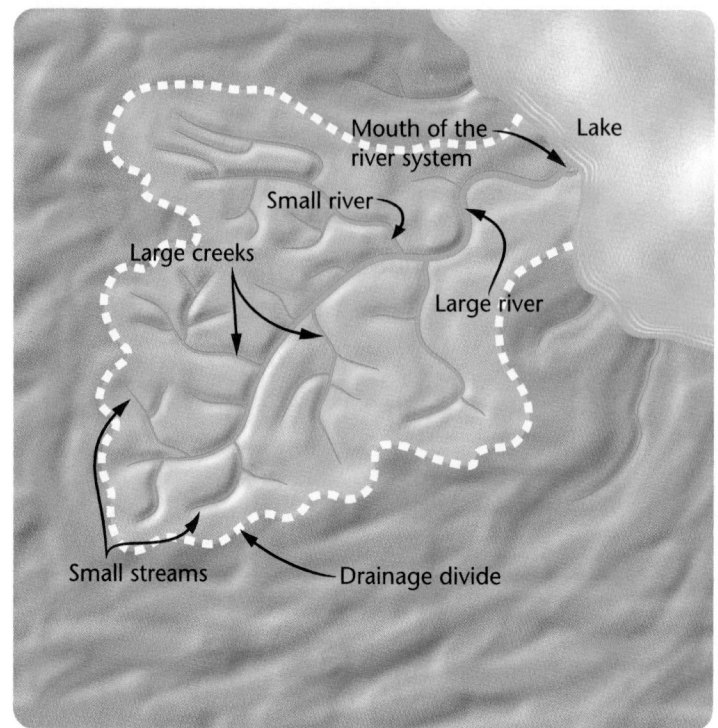

All systems have these five characteristics:

The size of parts varies. The parts and connections that make up systems are different sizes. For example, streams drain into small rivers that drain into larger rivers. Those flow into oceans. The large and small parts are needed to reach all places.

The purpose of parts varies. The parts of a system have different jobs. Small streams *collect* water from the land, rivers *transport* the water towards the ocean, and the oceans *store* the water.

The importance of parts varies. Some parts of a system have more important roles than other parts. A large river is very important to how a drainage system works. If it doesn't flow properly, it will cause significant problems such as flooding. On the other hand, a change in a small stream will not affect a drainage system very much.

The number of parts varies. A system may contain many of one part and only one or two of another part. A drainage system may have a great number of small streams but only one ocean.

Systems interconnect. Systems do not exist on their own, but interact with other systems. For example, the water system is needed to cycle water to the land; the rivers transport the water; parts of the drainage system are used to generate hydroelectric power.

LITERACY SKILL

Working With Vocabulary

Most school subjects have technical vocabulary. These words are used to express ideas and content related to the subject. Geography has plenty of technical terms that you will need to know. Here are two ideas to help you to remember and use Geography terms.

Word Signs: Make small sketches or diagrams to help you "see" the meaning of the words. These sketches do not need to be complicated. They should simply capture something of the meaning of each word, for example, a sketch of a TV to remind you of the word *system*. You could add the sketches to your notebook as you learn new words.

Acrostic Devices: Acrostic devices are arrangements of words to help you remember the meaning or spelling of technical words. Here is an acrostic device that has been used for generations to help students spell *Geography*:

> **G**eorge
> **E**lliot's
> **O**ld
> **G**randmother
> **R**ode
> **A**
> **P**ig
> **H**ome
> **Y**esterday

Again, list your acrostic devices in your notebook, or add the acrostic devices to your notebook as the new words are introduced.

CHECK IT OVER

3. Think about a system you know. List the parts of the system. Describe some of the ways that the parts are connected to form a whole.

4. Look at the auto parts distribution system shown in Figure 1.4 on page 6. The purpose of this system is to move car parts from the makers to the stores' customers. Give examples from this system to show each of the five characteristics of systems.

5. What does the statement in the FASTFact on page 3 mean?

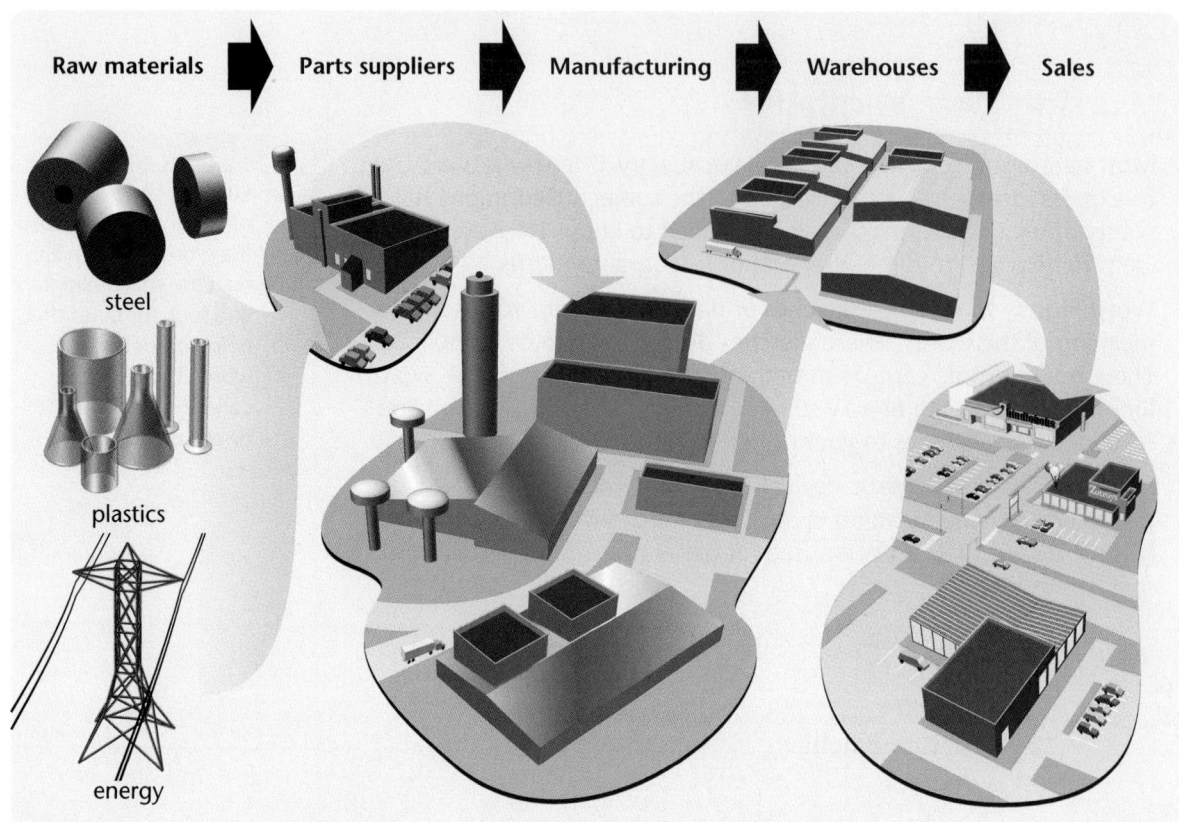

Raw materials ➤ Parts suppliers ➤ Manufacturing ➤ Warehouses ➤ Sales

steel

plastics

energy

FIGURE 1.4

How an Auto Parts Distribution System Works
When the distribution system works well, customers get their parts quickly and efficiently.

Systems and Geography

Human activities need physical, or natural, systems. We are able to build homes, produce food, and drive cars because of resources that we take from the physical environment. This means that human systems depend on physical systems to a great extent. On the other hand, physical systems don't depend on humans. A river system does not need human involvement to work.

Examples of Physical Systems	Examples of Human Systems
• river systems	• transportation networks
• atmospheric circulation	• communication systems
• energy cycles	• manufacturing systems
• food chains	• election systems
• animal reproductive systems	• settlements

Let's take a look at the interaction or connections among physical and human systems. Suppose you decided to buy a new flat-screen, high-definition television. You find just the one you want at an electronics store. After it is delivered and set up, you sit down to enjoy a movie. But then someone asks, "What systems were used to help provide you with this television?" You find the question so interesting that you turn the TV off and begin some research. Figure 1.6 on page 8 shows what you were able to find out about physical and human systems.

Physical and human systems interact in many ways. To make it possible for someone to buy a television, humans have to build manufacturing, transportation, and sales equipment. Building this equipment changes physical systems.

Humans have more and more power to change physical systems. We cut down forests, pave over wetlands, change the course of rivers, pollute the air, and threaten the existence of species. The greater we are in number, and the more we use our natural resources, the greater the impact on physical systems.

As you work your way through this book, look for

- examples of physical and human systems
- ways in which these systems interact
- problems that occur due to the human use of physical systems

Processes	Physical Systems Involved	Human Systems Involved
Manufacturing: Making the television set	• Energy powers the different manufacturing processes. • Natural resources provide the raw materials. • Land is used for the manufacturing facilities.	• Design the electronic components. • Get the natural resources, like chemicals and minerals. • Make the components. • Package the television for shipping. • Manufacturing wastes are removed.
Marketing: Making customers want to buy the television	• Energy powers all the different marketing stages. • Natural resources provide materials for ads and flyers.	• Plan an advertising campaign. • Produce materials such as flyers. • Advertise on television and in newspapers and magazines.
Transportation: Shipping the television to the store	• Metals, plastics, and rubber are used to make the trucks and other vehicles. • Fuels provide energy for shipping.	• Load the television into a container and ship it to Canada. • Unload the container at a warehouse in a large city. • Transport the television to your local store.
Sales: Selling the television to the customers	• Energy is used for heat and lighting in the store.	• Hire and train sales staff. • Provide assistance to customers. • Make credit available to customers.
Service: Helping the customers to enjoy their television	• Fuel powers the vehicle that delivers the television. • Energy powers the television.	• Deliver the television and set it up. • Repair the television when it breaks down. • Provide programming, movies, and videogames. • The television is disposed of when it is no longer useful.

FIGURE 1.6

Physical and Human Systems Involved in Buying a Television
Which are more important in this situation, physical or human systems? Explain your answer.

CHECK IT OVER

6. a) Write a definition for the term *physical systems*. Give two examples.

    b) Write a definition for the term *human systems*. Give two examples.

7. Use examples to prove that humans need physical systems but physical systems don't need humans.

8. List some of the physical and human systems that are used so that you can buy a donut at a local coffee shop.

CASE STUDY

Smog in Canada

Smog occurs when human systems interact with physical systems to produce poor air quality. Smog is a hazy blend of smoke and fog that forms during the warm summer months. Emissions (exhaust) from cars, smokestacks, and electrical generating stations are pumped into the air. Energy from the sun turns the smoke into a haze. Air masses (large volumes of air) carry the smog well beyond the areas where it occurs.

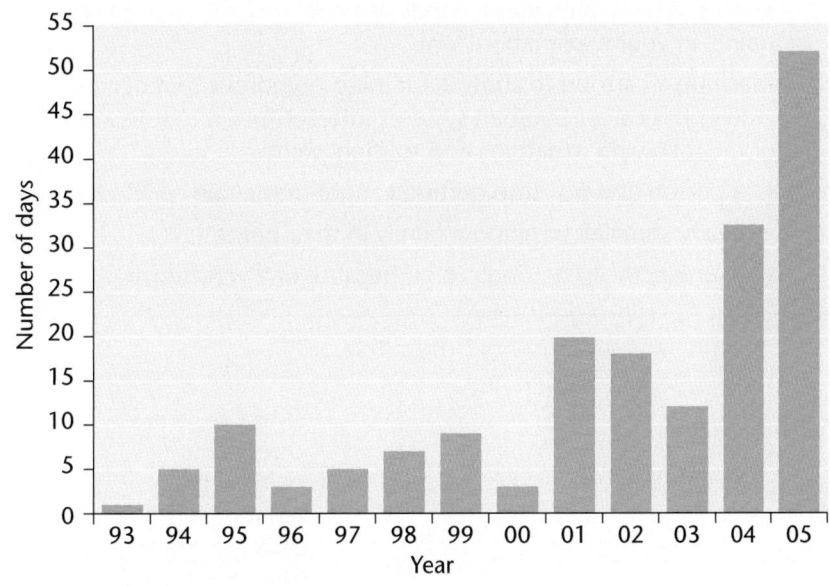

FIGURE 1.7

Smog Alert Days in Toronto, 1993–2005
Do the bars show a pattern?

Smog has negative health effects. In some cases, people who already have breathing problems can die from the poor air quality.

Suggest two actions to reduce the problem of smog.

THINK IT OVER

Knowledge and Understanding

1. Match the correct definition of *system* from Column A with the example given in Column B.

   Column A

   a set of things or parts forming a whole

   a plan or scheme or method

   an orderly way of getting things done

   the animal body as an organized whole

   Column B

   the respiratory system

   banking system

   railway system

   betting system

Thinking and Communication

2. Make a diagram to show some ways that physical and human systems interact. You might take one activity that you enjoy doing and figure out the interactions that support your activity.

3. Suppose a student in grade 6 asked you what was meant by a *system*. What would you tell that student? Include three main points in your explanation.

4. Make up a cartoon to show something humorous that occurs when physical and human systems interact. You might use one of the following situations as a starting point:
   - a person at a bus stop getting caught in the rain
   - heavy snowfall trapping a family in their home
   - your electricity getting cut off because of a windstorm

Forces Building the Land

Chapter 2

In this chapter you will learn to

⊿ *show you understand how natural systems change over time*

⊿ use terms related to regions

⊿ use different types of maps to interpret geographic inquiry

Introduction

What if you could take a giant vacuum and remove all the water from the earth? You would be amazed to see that very large mountains and deep valleys exist on the ocean floors just the way they do on land. All the earth's surface is made up of different landforms—mountains, valleys, hills, plains, and lowlands, to name a few. How did all these landforms get there? What caused the surface of the earth to be the way it is?

In this chapter we will look at how the surface of the earth was shaped and built. We will discuss how rocks formed under an ocean could end up at the tops of mountains. We will also investigate the major forces that create landforms. The topics we will look at are

- the ability of parts of the earth's crust to move around

- how volcanoes and earthquakes are formed by plate tectonics

- the geologic age of the earth

Key Words

plates

plate tectonics

region

seismologist

convection currents

subduction zones

geologic time

FIGURE 2.1

The Coast Mountains of British Columbia
Geologists (scientists who study the earth) have discovered that the rocks at the peaks of some mountains were formed at the bottoms of oceans.

CHECK IT OVER

1. Brainstorm a list of landforms in your area. How have they influenced the way people live?

2. Suggest ways that landforms influence where people live.

LITERACY SKILL

Reading Maps

Step 1: Get a general impression of the map. What is the title? Which way is north? What do the colours show? What type of map is this?

Step 2: Examine the map. What do the symbols show? Does the legend (a list that explains symbols or colours on a map or chart) explain all the symbols? What parts of the map are hard to figure out?

Step 3: Interpret the map. What patterns do you see on the map? What information doesn't fit the patterns?

Step 4: Make connections. How does this map connect to you personally? How does this map connect to ideas in the textbook? How can you use this map to help you understand the topic the class is discussing?

Step 5: Write your observations. What are three observations that you can make about the map?

Moving Continents
大陸

Six major **plates** cover the earth's surface. These plates are large slabs of rock that make up the earth's crust (outer layer of the earth). For billions of years, they have been moving around on the earth's surface because of forces known as **plate tectonics**. This plate movement has had an important role in creating the mountains, shields (large area made of Precambrian rock), and plains in Canada and in the rest of the world.

Mountains on the east and west coasts of Canada show that plate tectonics have shaped our landforms. The mountains were formed by plates crashing into each other. This caused the land to buckle and create the Appalachians (on the east coast) and the Western Cordillera (on the west coast).

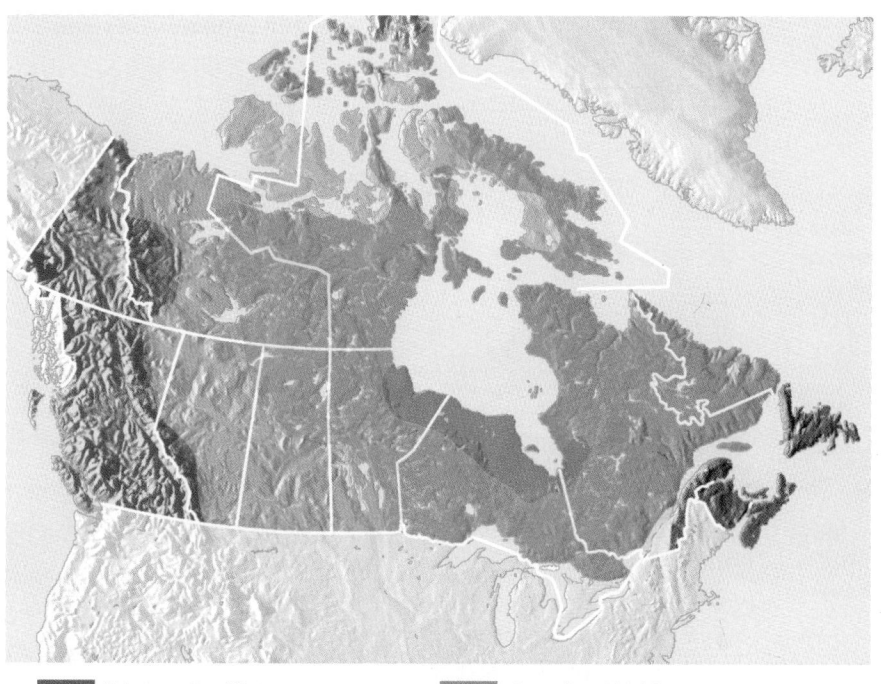

FIGURE 2.2

The Landform Regions in Canada
A **region** is a part of the earth's surface that has characteristics different from other regions nearby. The Interior Plains region has flat to rolling landforms. The Western Cordillera region has high, sharp-peaked mountains.

- Western Cordillera
- Interior Plains
- Innuitian Mountains
- Hudson Bay Lowlands
- Canadian Shield
- Appalachian Mountains
- Great Lakes-St. Lawrence Lowlands
- Arctic Lowlands

CHECK IT OVER

3. Look at Figure 2.2. Around Hudson Bay, the land is close to sea level. The mountains in the Western Cordillera are thousands of metres high. What does this tell us about the land from the Western Cordillera to Hudson Bay?

4. List the landform regions found in each province and territory using a table with the following headings:

Provinces and Territories	Landform Regions

   Note that provinces and territories can have up to three landform regions.

5. Draw a diagram of the landforms of Canada as you travel from west to east across the country. Include mountains, hills, plains, shield, and lowlands. Mark on your diagram where one landform region ends and another one starts.

6. Tectonic forces formed large mountain ranges. Explain how mountain building is similar to two cars crashing into each other head-on.

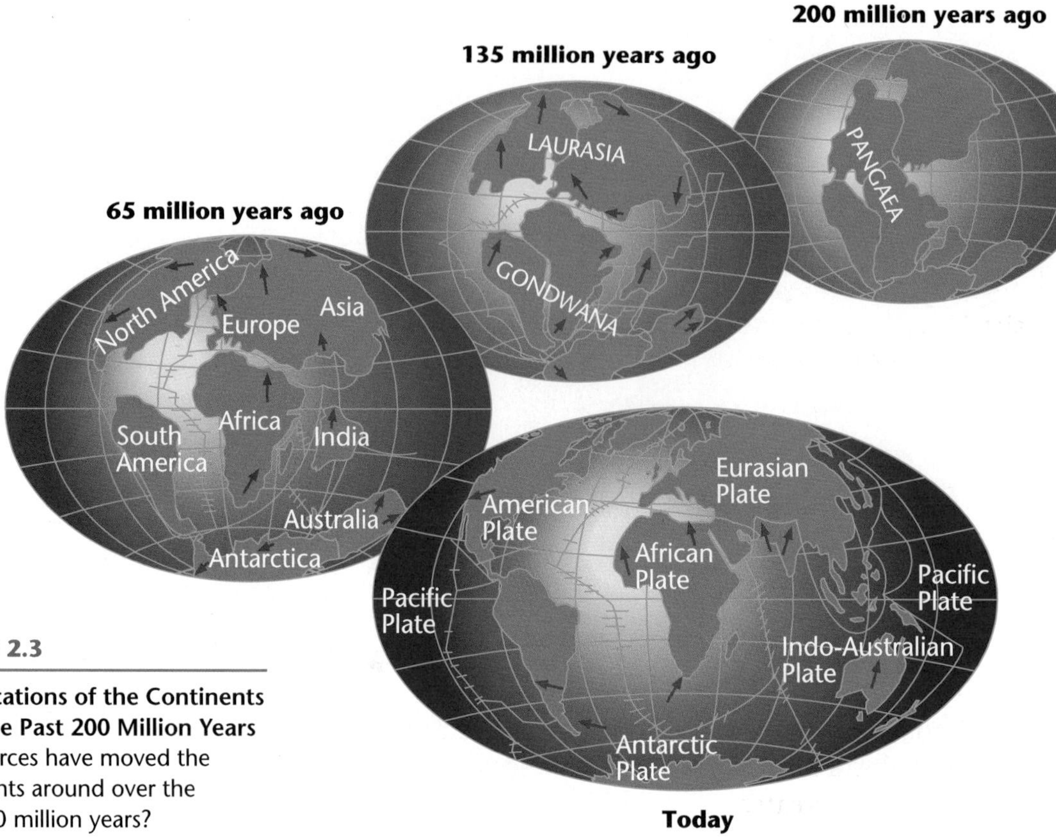

200 million years ago

135 million years ago

LAURASIA

GONDWANA

PANGAEA

65 million years ago

North America

Europe

Asia

South America

Africa

India

Australia

Antarctica

Eurasian Plate

American Plate

African Plate

Pacific Plate

Pacific Plate

Indo-Australian Plate

Antarctic Plate

Today

FIGURE 2.3

The Locations of the Continents Over the Past 200 Million Years
What forces have moved the continents around over the past 200 million years?

CHECK IT OVER

7. On a world map, the coastlines of Africa and South America look like they would fit together like pieces of a jigsaw puzzle. Using Figure 2.3, identify two other places where today's continents were once joined with other continents.

8. The Western Cordillera (65 million years old) has higher mountains with sharper peaks than the Appalachians (200 million to 300 million years old). Suggest three ways the Appalachian Mountains have become more worn down and rounded over time.

CASE STUDY

The Sudbury Basin

Sudbury sits in a huge crater in the Canadian Shield and holds one of the earth's richest known deposits of nickel and copper. The huge hole (60 km wide and 15 km deep) was formed by a 10 km-wide meteorite that slammed into the earth's crust about 2 billion years ago. This large crater became filled with magma (melted rock), which contained large amounts of metals. These metals are still mined today. The meteorite was one of the largest ever to hit the earth.

Global Hotspots

Heat from the earth's core forms convection currents. These currents move the continental plates around on the earth's surface. Convection currents can cause plates to move apart or come together. When plates move apart from one another, magma rises through the open space and then cools, forming a ridge. When plates come together, there can be two results. If they crash into each other, they form a mountain chain. If one plate slides below another, a volcano is created.

FIGURE 2.4

Convection Currents
The flow of energy inside the earth can be illustrated by heating water in a pan. Why do the convection currents form circles? How hot do you think the convection currents have to be to move the plates?

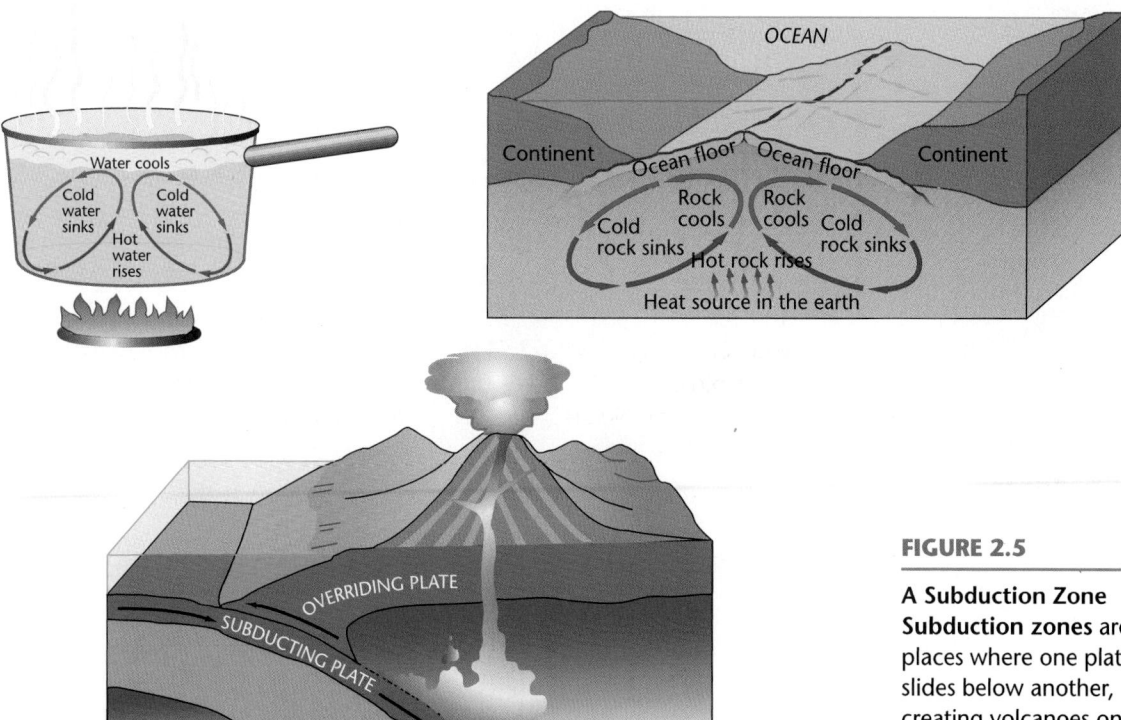

FIGURE 2.5

A Subduction Zone
Subduction zones are places where one plate slides below another, creating volcanoes on the surface.

CHECK IT OVER

9. Explain why large earthquakes occur near subduction zones.
10. Describe how a subduction zone is formed. What types of plates are involved?
11. Why do you think plates found at a subduction zone form bigger mountains than those found at other plate boundaries?

FIGURE 2.6

The Locations of Earthquakes and Volcanoes
Earthquakes and volcanoes occur near the edges of plates. Point out on this map where the earthquakes and volcanoes take place. The numbers on the map refer to the populations of large cities.

Earthquakes and volcanoes typically occur on the boundaries of continental plates, like those found around the Pacific "Ring of Fire." Some of the world's biggest cities are located along this hotbed of seismic activity.

Continental plates are very thick and move at about the rate a fingernail grows. When they collide, they usually crumple up along their leading edges. That welds the two continents into a larger unit. For example, the Himalayas are the largest mountain chain in the world and home to Mount Everest, the world's highest peak. The Himalayas were created when the Indo-Australian plate collided with the Eurasian plate (see Figure 2.3).

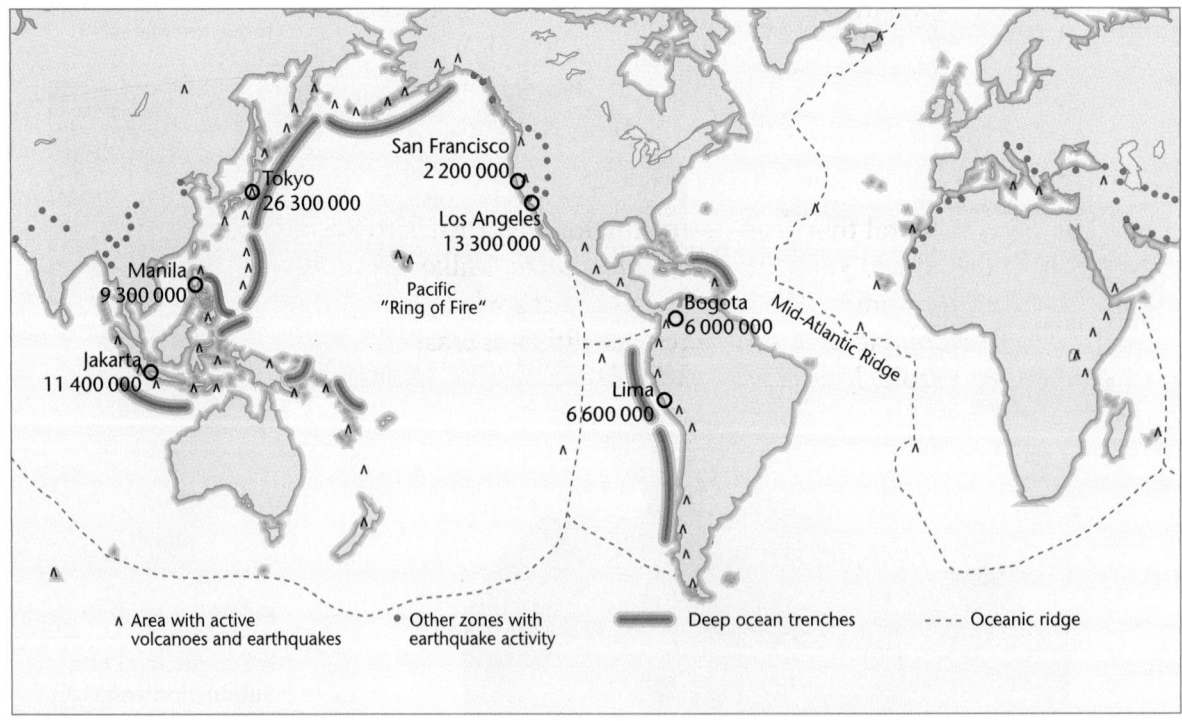

GEOCAREERS

Seismologist

A **seismologist** is a scientist who studies seismic waves. Seismic waves are waves of energy caused when rock suddenly breaks within the earth or when an explosion occurs. One of a seismologist's jobs is to find ways to reduce the damage that would occur if an earthquake hit. Seismologists do this by helping to improve construction standards. Some seismologists work for oil companies to help them deal with seismic waves from human-made explosions. To become a seismologist, you need a degree in Geophysics, with a major in Seismology.

CHECK IT OVER

12. Explain what is meant by the saying, "Earthquakes don't kill people. Buildings do."

13. Suggest some ways cities in the Ring of Fire could prepare for earthquakes and volcanoes.

14. List the cities in the Pacific Ring of Fire from largest to smallest population. Would the most populated city experience the most damage from an earthquake? Give reasons for your answer.

Geologic Time

Geologic time is the total time from the formation of the earth to the present day. One hundred years seems like a long time. Millions, even billions, of years seem impossible to imagine. That's why scientists have divided the geologic time scale into four different eras: Precambrian, Paleozoic, Mesozoic, and Cenozoic.

FIGURE 2.7

Geologic Time Line

The geologic age of the earth is estimated to be 4.6 billion years. This long period of time has been broken into four eras, and the eras have been divided into shorter periods. How long ago did the Cambrian period take place? How many millions of years did the Paleozoic era last?

Literacy Strategy

How to read a timeline
There are two types of timelines, horizontal (across) and vertical (up and down). Figure 2.7 is a vertical timeline that must be read from the bottom to the top and back to the bottom.

FAST Fact

The oldest rocks in the Canadian Shield are over 2.5 billion years old. They were formed during the Precambrian era. It is hard to know the actual age of the rocks because they have undergone heat, pressure, and weathering changes.

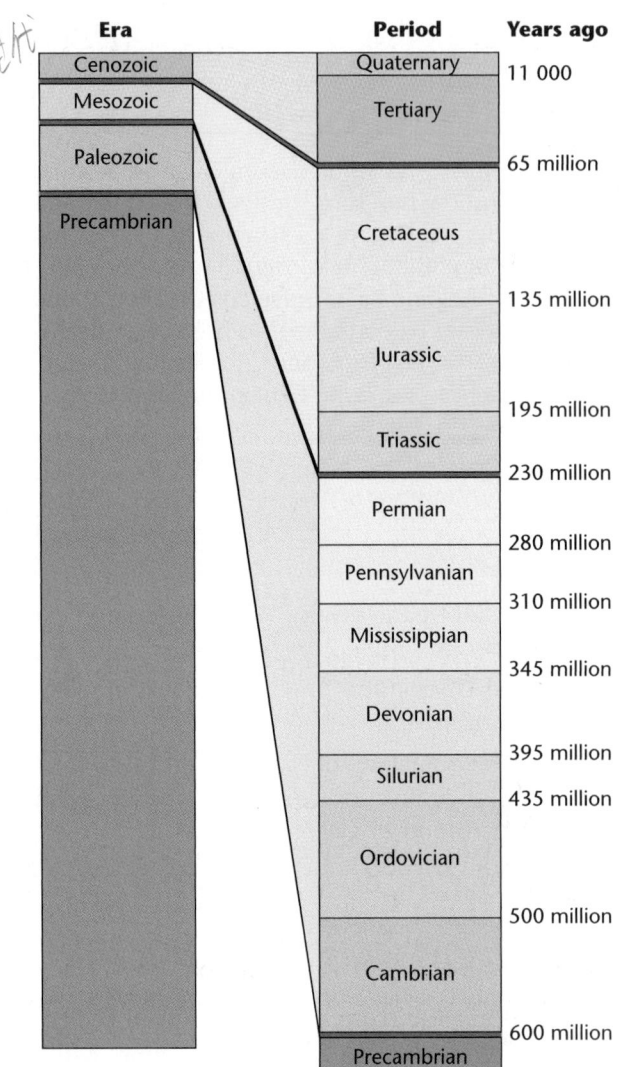

Era	Period	Years ago
Cenozoic	Quaternary	11 000
Mesozoic	Tertiary	
Paleozoic		65 million
Precambrian	Cretaceous	
		135 million
	Jurassic	
		195 million
	Triassic	
		230 million
	Permian	
		280 million
	Pennsylvanian	
		310 million
	Mississippian	
		345 million
	Devonian	
		395 million
	Silurian	
		435 million
	Ordovician	
		500 million
	Cambrian	
		600 million
	Precambrian	

CHECK IT OVER

15. What is the oldest era in the geological timeline?

16. Complete the following chart. For the third column, add an important event that took place during that era. You can research this information using the search terms of geologic time, events, and eras.

Era	Length of Time	Significant Event
Precambrian era		
Paleozoic era		
Mesozoic era		
Cenozoic era		

2

17. Historical events such as Canada becoming a country (1867), the *Titanic* sinking (1912), humans first landing on the moon (1969), and you being born are a part of the Cenozoic era. Consider these events in geologic time. How long ago did these events happen? Where would you place these events on the time line in Figure 2.7? What do you notice?

18. British Columbia is mostly mountainous while Alberta is mostly flat or hilly. Identify three ways that living in these distinct landscapes would be different. Some topics to think about are transportation, locations of cities, and farming.

19. The west side of North America has seen a great deal of tectonic activity over the past 100 million years, including earthquakes and the formation of mountains and volcanoes. Use classroom resources or the Internet to find one physical characteristic of each landform region. Write it beside the landform region name.

 THINK IT OVER

Knowledge and Understanding

1. Which is the largest of Canada's landform regions? Describe its location in Canada.

2. List each of the landform regions in Canada. Beside each one, write one characteristic that you connect to that area of Canada.

3. Suppose you were talking on the phone to a friend, describing the way mountains are created at a subduction zone. Write down three points that you would want to make in your explanation. Your answer should include information about locations and processes.

4. a) List the four eras of geologic time.

   b) Explain why geologic time has been divided into eras.

   c) Divide human time into "eras," explaining your ideas.

Thinking and Communication

5. Using the Key Words from the list at the beginning of the chapter, write a short story that explains how landform regions came to be and what impact they have had on the earth and human activities (such as jobs).

6. It is difficult for us to understand geologic time. Write a short paragraph to describe geologic time so that a child would understand. Use as many words from the Key Words list as you can.

Chapter 3

Shaping the Land

In this chapter you will learn to

◢ *identify patterns and differences in Canada's natural systems*

◢ demonstrate an understanding of how natural systems change over time

◢ use diagrams to understand geographic information

Key Words

weathering

erosion

water (hydrologic) cycle

glaciation

glaciers

zone of accumulation

zone of ablation

deposition

Introduction

Have you ever noticed how different the skin of an elderly person looks compared to that of an infant? Have you noticed that your own skin looks wrinkly when you spend too much time in a pool or bathtub? Just like human beings, the earth changes when it is exposed to water and other forces over time. While plate tectonic activity is responsible for building landforms, other forces (wind, water, and gravity) are responsible for wearing away the surface of the land.

FIGURE 3.1

The Appalachian and Rocky Mountains Natural forces have worn away the Appalachian Mountains (top) for over 200 million years. The younger Rocky Mountains (bottom) have only endured 65 million years. What are some of the most noticeable differences between the two?

In this chapter we will explore how running water and moving ice have shaped and changed the land. We will consider how it is possible for glaciers to deposit enough broken rock and land fragments to form local landform features and good farming land. The topics we will look at in this chapter are

- the ability of water to move rock and land debris
- how glaciers form and create landforms
- the effect of human interaction on land erosion and glacier melting

The Work of Water

Water wears away rocks and minerals. This process is called weathering. Weathering breaks rocks into pieces in two ways:

- mechanically: when water fills cracks, freezes, then expands and puts pressure on the rocks
- chemically: when water dissolves some of the chemicals found in rock

When moving water, ice, or wind carries away these small weathered pieces of rock, it is called erosion. Erosion involves movement, while weathering does not.

LITERACY SKILL

Reading Diagrams

Geographers often use diagrams to make things simpler. Illustrators choose what they want the reader to focus on and highlight those key points in the illustration. In a diagram, you can see the details more clearly than you would on a map or even in a photograph. In Figure 3.2, the illustrator has paid particular attention to

- the ways water moves
- the ways water is stored

These are the elements that you as the reader should focus on. Look at Figures 3.3(a) and (b). Identify what you consider to be the key topics that the illustrator has focused on.

Literacy Strategy

Reading diagrams
Read all labels, captions, and phrases. Follow any arrows and lines. Look for the use of colours or symbols to help you find important information in the diagram.

FIGURE 3.2

The Water (Hydrologic) Cycle
Water on the earth is constantly recycled from one form to another. Water makes its way from oceans, lakes, and rivers into the atmosphere (evaporation and transpiration, which is vapour from plants) where it is released in the form of rain (precipitation). Rain wears away the land through the weathering process. Moving water and glaciers carry pieces of rocks away through the process of erosion. Recharge is the area where water is absorbed. Infiltration and percolation is the area where water is filtered into the ground. The **water cycle** is also called the hydrologic cycle. (Note that the numbers are in millions of cubic metres of water per day.)

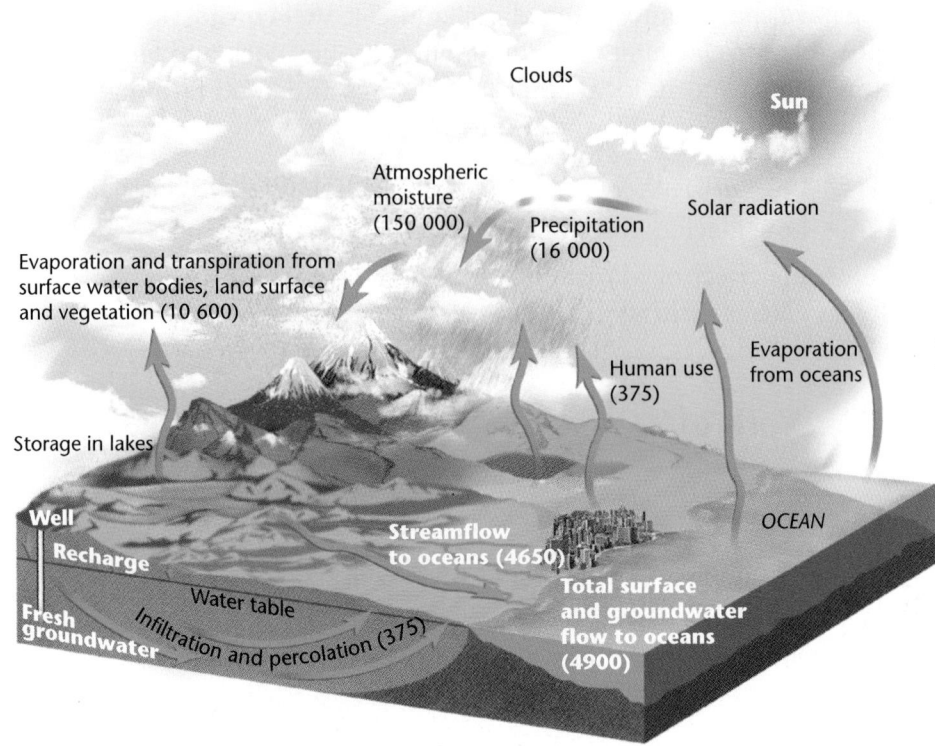

Clouds

Sun

Atmospheric moisture (150 000)

Precipitation (16 000)

Solar radiation

Evaporation and transpiration from surface water bodies, land surface and vegetation (10 600)

Human use (375)

Evaporation from oceans

Storage in lakes

Well

Recharge

Fresh groundwater

Streamflow to oceans (4650)

OCEAN

Water table

Infiltration and percolation (375)

Total surface and groundwater flow to oceans (4900)

CHECK IT OVER

1. Define *weathering* and *erosion*. What is the difference between the two?

2. Examine Figure 3.2. This diagram shows the ways water is moved and stored.
   a) List the ways water is stored.
   b) List the ways water is moved and give the volumes for each method.
   c) Explain why the movement of water is called a *cycle*.
   d) Which parts of the hydrologic cycle contribute most to erosion? Explain your answer.

3. Create a word web (similar to the ones on pages 41 and 44) with the word *water* in the centre. Brainstorm as many ways as you can how water changes land over time. Add these ideas to the web.

The Work of Ice

Glaciation occurs when snow freezes. Glaciers are created when more snow falls in winter than can be melted during the following summer. As snow builds up, the glacier becomes heavy and turns the bottom layers into ice. Once the glacier is heavy enough, gravity pulls it downwards or outwards. This causes rock underneath the glacier to be broken (weathering) and carried away with melt water (erosion).

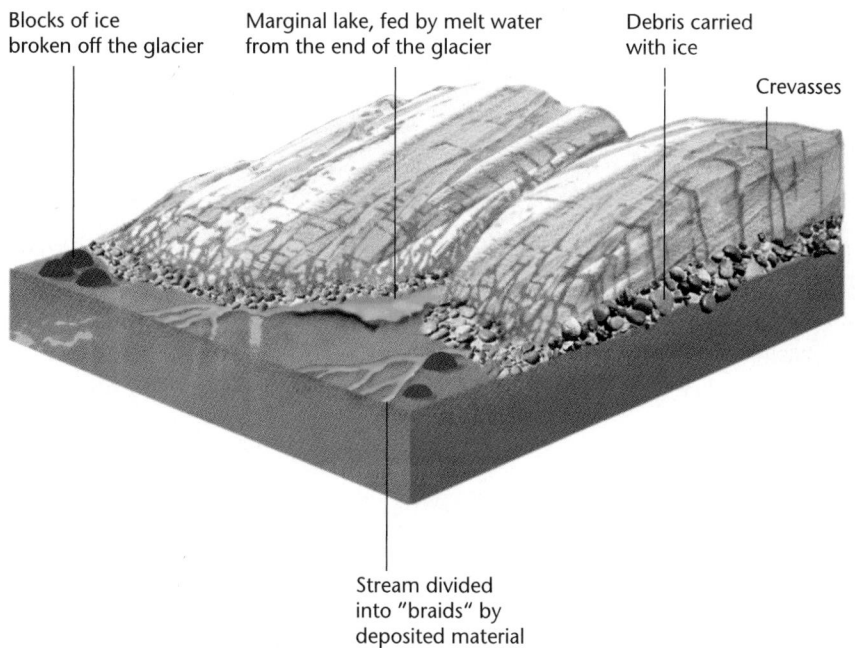

Blocks of ice broken off the glacier

Marginal lake, fed by melt water from the end of the glacier

Debris carried with ice

Crevasses

Stream divided into "braids" by deposited material

FIGURE 3.3(a)

During Glaciation
Glaciers have two distinct zones: the **zone of accumulation** where the amount of snow added is more than the amount melted, and the **zone of ablation**, where snow is melting. Glaciers flow from the accumulation zone to the ablation zone.

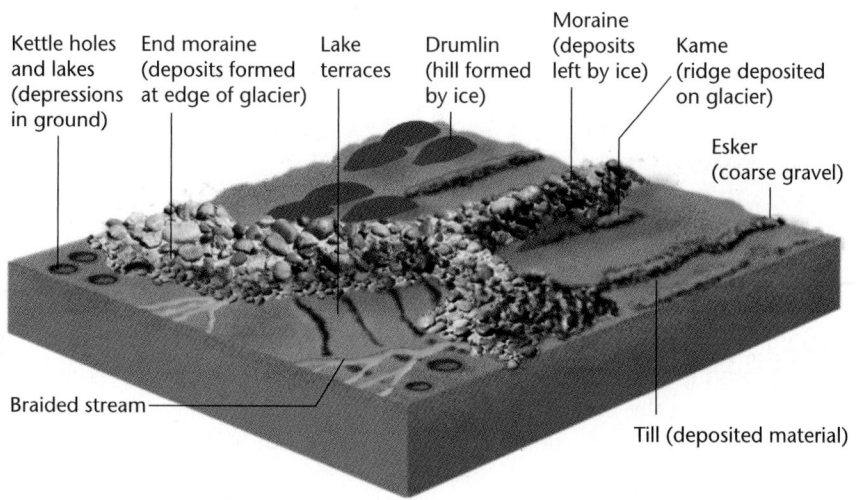

Kettle holes and lakes (depressions in ground)

End moraine (deposits formed at edge of glacier)

Lake terraces

Drumlin (hill formed by ice)

Moraine (deposits left by ice)

Kame (ridge deposited on glacier)

Esker (coarse gravel)

Braided stream

Till (deposited material)

FIGURE 3.3(b)

After Glaciation
Moving glaciers scrape up materials from the mass of ice and deposit them as glacial landforms. Melt water (water from melting glaciers or snow) flows away from the snout (front part) of the glacier, carrying debris with it.

4. Explain how a glacier is formed and how it moves.

5. a) Using Figure 3.3(a), describe what the melting side (zone of ablation) of a glacier and its front edge looks like.

    b) Describe the appearance of each of the landforms created by glaciers.

6. Which of the glacial landforms found in Figure 3.3(b) are found in your region?

7. How might a landform created by tectonic forces look different from a landform created by a glacier?

Deposition by Glaciers

Glaciers can completely change a landscape. During the last ice age (over 14 000 years ago), Canada was almost entirely covered in ice! As the glaciers moved, they eroded a lot of rock. This rock material was left behind in a process known as deposition. Sand, gravel, and clay are examples of material (till) deposited by glaciers.

8. Sand, gravel, and clay are important materials in our lives. List 10 jobs that are related to these materials deposited by glaciers.

9. Are there still glaciers in the part of Canada where you live? Check Figure 3.4 for the answer.

10. Canada's farmland is found largely in the south. Explain, in your own words, how the nutrient-rich soil ended up there.

CASE STUDY

Columbia Icefield

The Columbia Icefield is located on the boundaries of Banff and Jasper National Parks and has an area of over 325 km². An ice field is a large area covered in ice. A glacier is a moving mass of ice. Snow feeds over eight glaciers in the area. The Columbia Icefield is known as a true "continental divide." Its melt waters form rivers that feed into the Atlantic, Pacific, and Arctic Oceans. Ice found here is as old as 400 years. The ice field attracts tourists from around the globe.

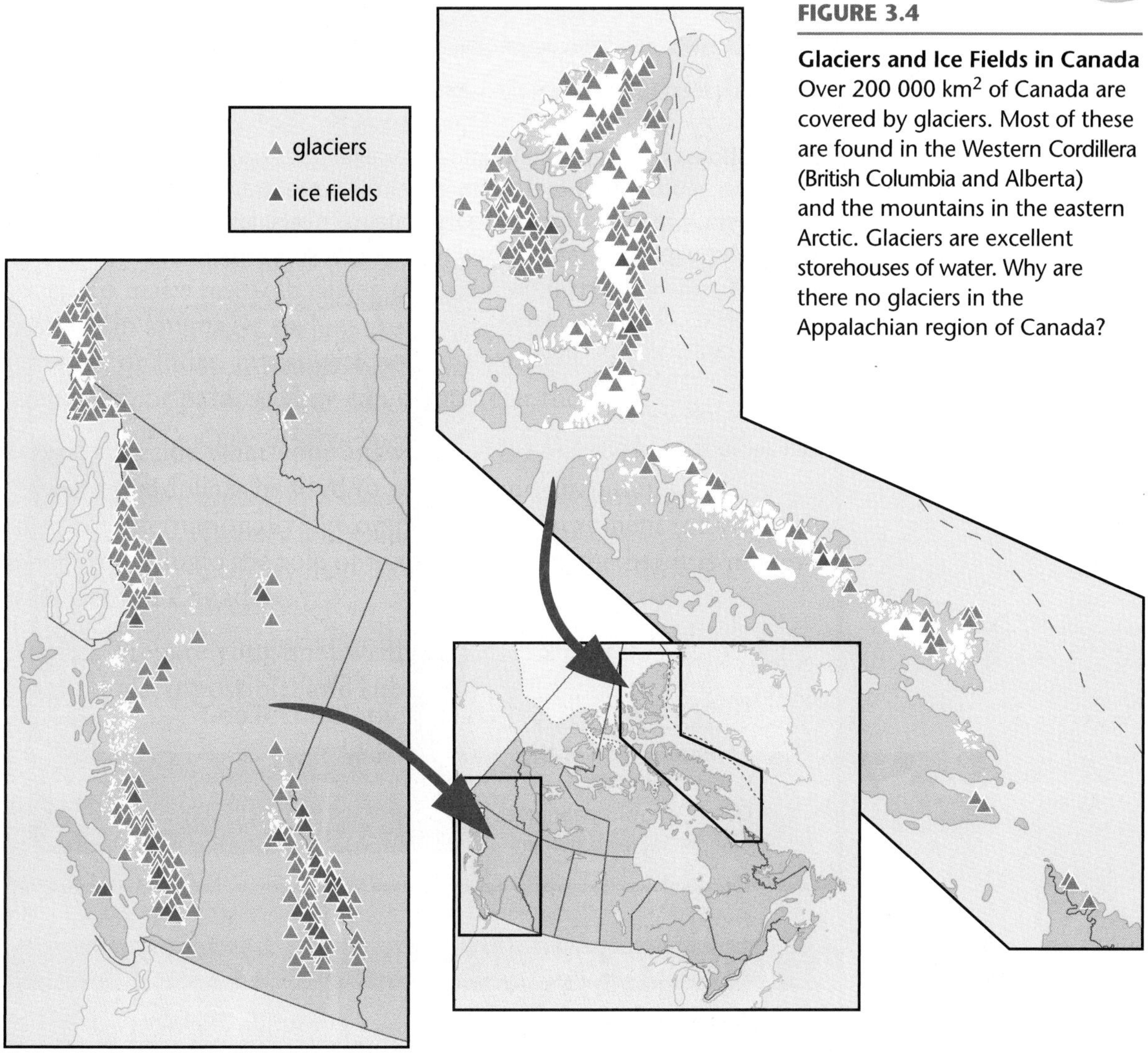

FIGURE 3.4

Glaciers and Ice Fields in Canada
Over 200 000 km^2 of Canada are covered by glaciers. Most of these are found in the Western Cordillera (British Columbia and Alberta) and the mountains in the eastern Arctic. Glaciers are excellent storehouses of water. Why are there no glaciers in the Appalachian region of Canada?

▲ glaciers
▲ ice fields

CHECK IT OVER

11. Glaciers are melting faster now than ever before. Give three ways human beings have contributed to this situation in recent years.

12. Anticipate five problems caused by glaciers melting quickly.

13. How have glaciers had an impact on the amount of farmland in Canada?

Aerial Photography

Aerial photos record the changing natural features on the earth's surface. They can capture residential and industrial areas, transportation routes, and physical features, including mountains, rivers, lakes, forests, and farms. Aerial photos can be used to make maps, plan cities, or research environmental issues. Some people even like to use aerial photography in their homes as wall art. This aerial photograph shows a glacier in the Yukon.

FIGURE 3.5

Air Photograph of the Kaskawulsh Glacier
Describe the appearance of a glacier from the air.

 THINK IT OVER

Knowledge and Understanding

1. Use your knowledge of the water cycle and glaciers to explain how a glacier is capable of slowing down the water cycle.
2. Explain how a glacier is formed and how it moves.
3. Give one example from this chapter of how natural systems change over time.

Thinking and Communication

4. You are an environmentalist studying the effects of global warming on the melting of glaciers. Write a proposal to the government outlining changes that you feel will slow down the melting process.
5. Design a tourism poster that advertises bus tours to the Columbia Icefield. Include an illustration and key words that will attract people to this area.

Climate Factors and Patterns

Chapter 4

In this chapter you will learn to

⊿ *identify patterns and diversity in Canada's natural systems*

⊿ use terms about regions

⊿ describe factors that influence climate

⊿ use different types of maps and graphs

Key Words

weather

climate

hythergraph

meteorologist

latitude

air mass

relief precipitation

rain shadow

leeward

windward

Introduction

When a bride asks, "What's the weekend weather forecast?" she wants to know if it's going to rain. What will the temperature be for her upcoming wedding? Weather is the day-to-day report of precipitation (rain or snow) and temperature. It can usually be predicted up to 10 days in advance.

The same bride would not ask, "What's the weekend climate forecast?" Climate is the long-term pattern of weather for a city, country, or region. There are many different climate regions around the globe and within Canada. It is rainy and cool on the west coast of Canada, dry on the Prairies, hot in summer and cold and snowy in winter in central Canada, and cool and wet in the Maritimes.

This chapter will focus on climate. We will learn about

- patterns in climate across Canada
- global factors that create climate patterns
- local factors that shape climate patterns

✓ CHECK IT OVER

1. Brainstorm a list of 5 to 10 situations in which people may be concerned about the weather. Share your list with someone else in the class and add his or her ideas to your list.

2. What types of weather do you prefer? Why?

3. What comes to mind when you think about the climate of Australia? the Caribbean? Russia? Tell whether you think each is warm or cold, wet or dry.

Literacy Strategy

Brainstorming
Brainstorming means coming up with as many ideas about a topic as possible. Begin by writing down all your ideas. Then add to, subtract from, join, and change ideas to come up with the new ones. Finally, reflect on your ideas and choose the best ones.

Climate Patterns

The temperature and precipitation for a place can be recorded throughout the year and used to describe climate patterns. Figure 4.1 shows three common ways of describing climate:

- temperatures during the coldest time of the year
- temperatures during the warmest time of the year
- the total amount of annual precipitation

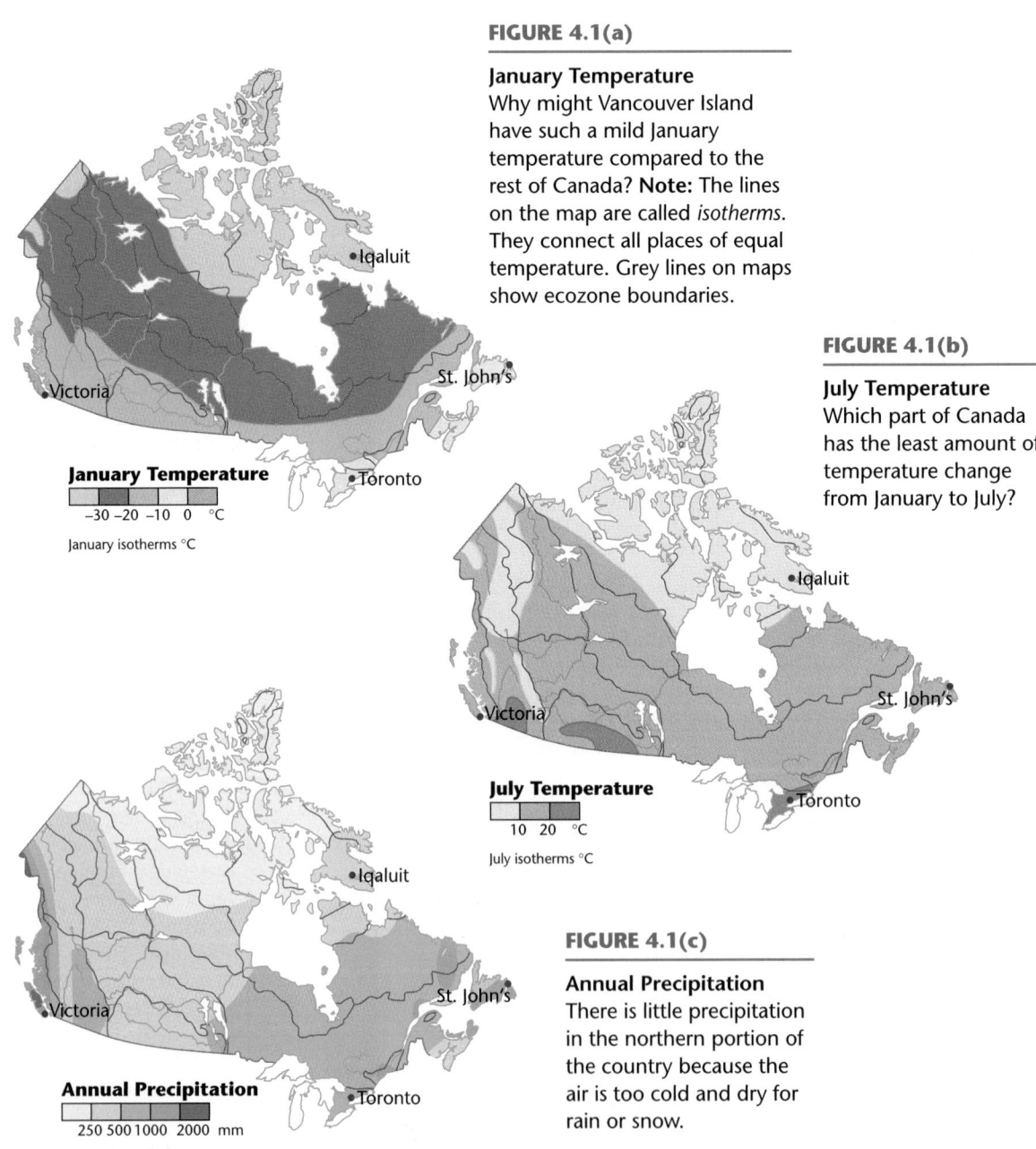

FIGURE 4.1(a)

January Temperature
Why might Vancouver Island have such a mild January temperature compared to the rest of Canada? **Note:** The lines on the map are called *isotherms*. They connect all places of equal temperature. Grey lines on maps show ecozone boundaries.

January Temperature
−30 −20 −10 0 °C
January isotherms °C

FIGURE 4.1(b)

July Temperature
Which part of Canada has the least amount of temperature change from January to July?

July Temperature
10 20 °C
July isotherms °C

FIGURE 4.1(c)

Annual Precipitation
There is little precipitation in the northern portion of the country because the air is too cold and dry for rain or snow.

Annual Precipitation
250 500 1000 2000 mm

LITERACY SKILL

Reading Graphs

Step 1: Get a general impression of the graph. What is the title? What type of graph is this?

Step 2: Examine the graph. What do the axes represent? What are the intervals? Are there any colours or lines that communicate relevant information?

Step 3: Interpret the graph. Do you notice any patterns or trends that are revealed in the data? What data do not follow the pattern or trend, or stand out?

Step 4: Make connections. How can this graph connect to you personally? How does this graph connect to the topic being discussed?

Step 5: Write your observations. What observations can you make *from* the graph? What observations can you make *about* the graph?

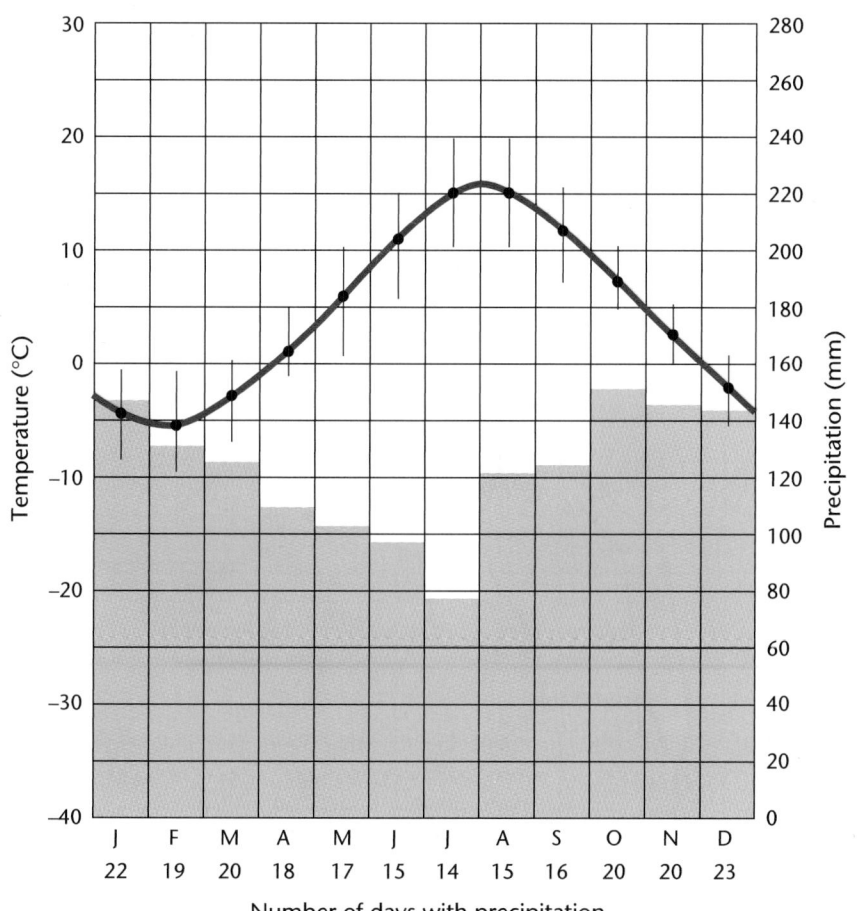

FIGURE 4.2(a)

A Climate Graph for St. John's, Newfoundland and Labrador
Cities located near oceans may have higher levels of precipitation and more moderate temperatures.

FIGURE 4.2(b)

A Circular Graph for Winnipeg, Manitoba
Notice how this circular graph shows Winnipeg's cold, dry winters and warm, moist summers.

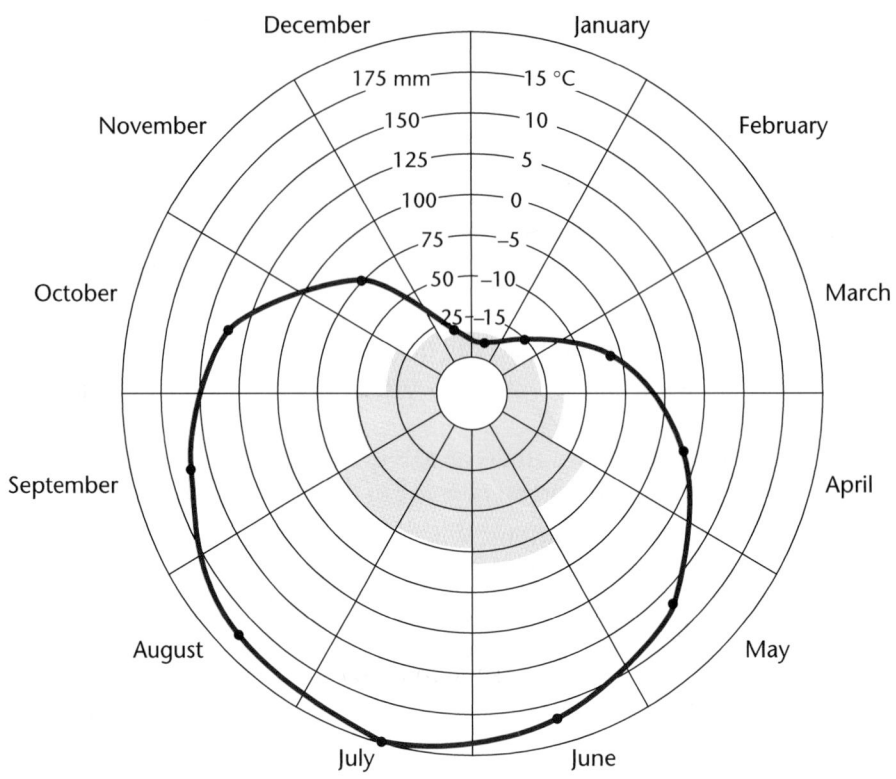

FIGURE 4.2(c)

A Hythergraph for Montreal, Quebec, and Kugluktuk (Coppermine), Nunavut
A **hythergraph** is a grid that shows temperature and precipitation. It is particularly useful for comparing the climates of two or more places. Data plotted close to the corners of a hythergraph mean a more extreme climate. Montreal's climate (located near the middle) is more moderate than Kugluktuk's (located near the lower left corner).

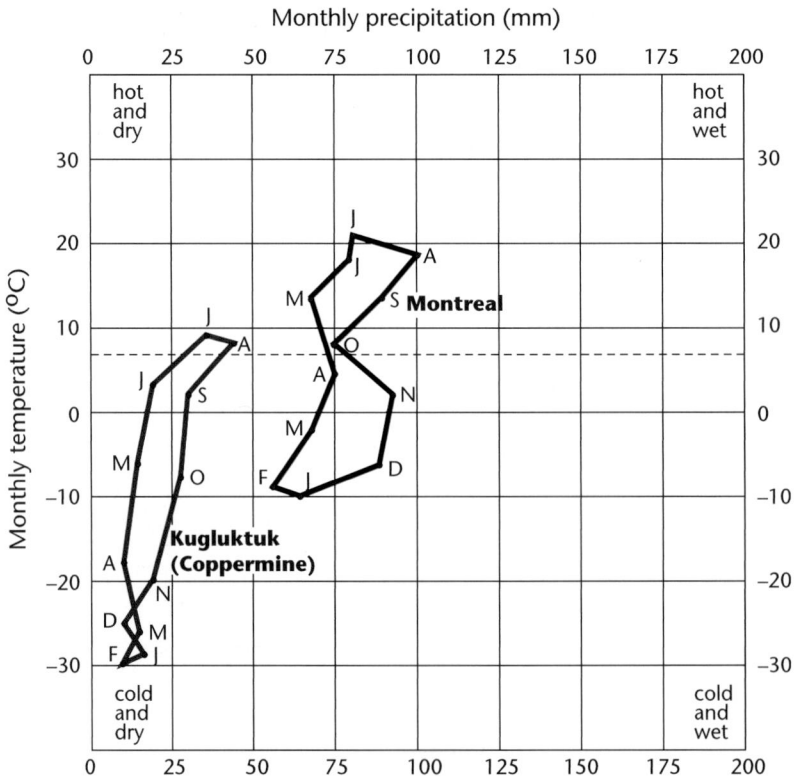

CHECK IT OVER

4. When people ask what the weather is supposed to be like, what two pieces of information are they looking for?

5. a) Using the climate data in Figure 4.3, construct either a climate graph for Toronto, a circular graph for Vancouver, or a hythergraph that shows both locations.

   b) Which type of graph do you think would be easier to make? Why?

6. a) Describe the pattern of precipitation for St. John's, Newfoundland and Labrador, shown in Figure 4.2(a).

   b) Describe the pattern of precipitation for Winnipeg, Manitoba, shown in Figure 4.2(b).

   c) When might a circular graph like Figure 4.2(b) be a better way to show climate data than a climate graph like Figure 4.2(a)?

7. a) Draw a box in your notebook and write in it the words found in the four corners of the hythergraph in Figure 4.2(c). Using Figures 4.1(a) to (c), estimate and plot the climate for Victoria, Iqaluit, Toronto, and St. John's.

   b) Which of these cities has the most extreme climate? Which has the least extreme?

FIGURE 4.3

Climate Data for Toronto, Ontario, and Vancouver, British Columbia
Point out three differences between the climates of Toronto and Vancouver.

Toronto	J	F	M	A	M	J	J	A	S	O	N	D
Daily Max. Temp. (°C)	−3	−2	4	12	18	24	27	26	21	14	7	0
Daily Min. Temp. (°C)	−11	−11	−5	1	6	11	14	13	9	4	−1	−7
Daily Mean Temp. (°C)	−7	−6	−1	6	12	17	21	20	15	9	3	−4
Precipitation (mm)	46	46	57	64	66	69	77	84	74	63	70	66
Measurable Prec. (days)	14	12	13	12	11	11	10	11	10	12	13	15

Vancouver	J	F	M	A	M	J	J	A	S	O	N	D
Daily Max. Temp. (°C)	6	8	10	13	16	19	22	22	18	14	9	6
Daily Min. Temp. (°C)	0	1	3	5	8	11	13	13	10	6	3	1
Daily Mean Temp. (°C)	3	5	6	9	12	15	17	17	14	10	6	4
Precipitation (mm)	150	124	109	75	62	46	36	38	64	115	170	179
Measurable Prec. (days)	19	16	16	13	12	10	7	7	9	15	19	21

FIGURE 4.4

Winter Weather
Most North Americans have adapted to the climate in their region.

Between 1933 and 1937, the Prairies received only 60 percent of its normal rainfall. Thousands of cattle starved and crops dried up. More than 250 000 people across the region left to seek better lives elsewhere.

GEOCAREERS

Meteorologist

Chris Scott became interested in weather when a hailstorm destroyed his family's crops in 1983. This inspired Chris to study Atmospheric Science and Atmospheric Chemistry at York University. He then became a meteorologist. A **meteorologist** investigates the natural forces that shape our weather and climate. Chris collected data for Environment Canada before he started reporting the forecast for The Weather Network.

FIGURE 4.5

Chris Scott of The Weather Network
Chris uses technology (computers, radar, satellites) to discover how natural processes and human activities affect our atmosphere. He can then warn others of severe weather.

Factors That Influence Climate

Six factors influence climate. You can easily remember them by using the acronym (a word formed by the first letters of several words) LOWERN.

Latitude
Ocean currents
Wind and air masses
Elevation
Relief
Nearness to water

Global Climate Factors

Latitude, ocean currents, and wind and air masses are all examples of global factors that influence climate. These are forces that work all around the world.

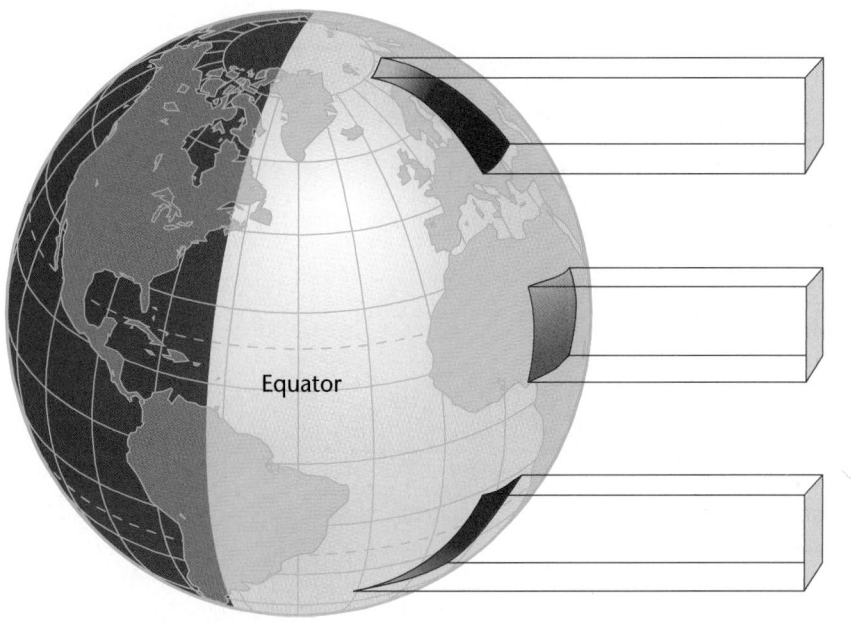

Equal amount of solar energy

Equator

FIGURE 4.6

How Latitude Influences Temperature
Latitude is the distance a place is located from the equator. The closer you are to the equator (0°), the hotter it is. As you move away from the equator toward the north and south poles (90°), temperatures are cooler. This is because the earth's rounded surface causes the sun's energy to be spread out over larger areas.

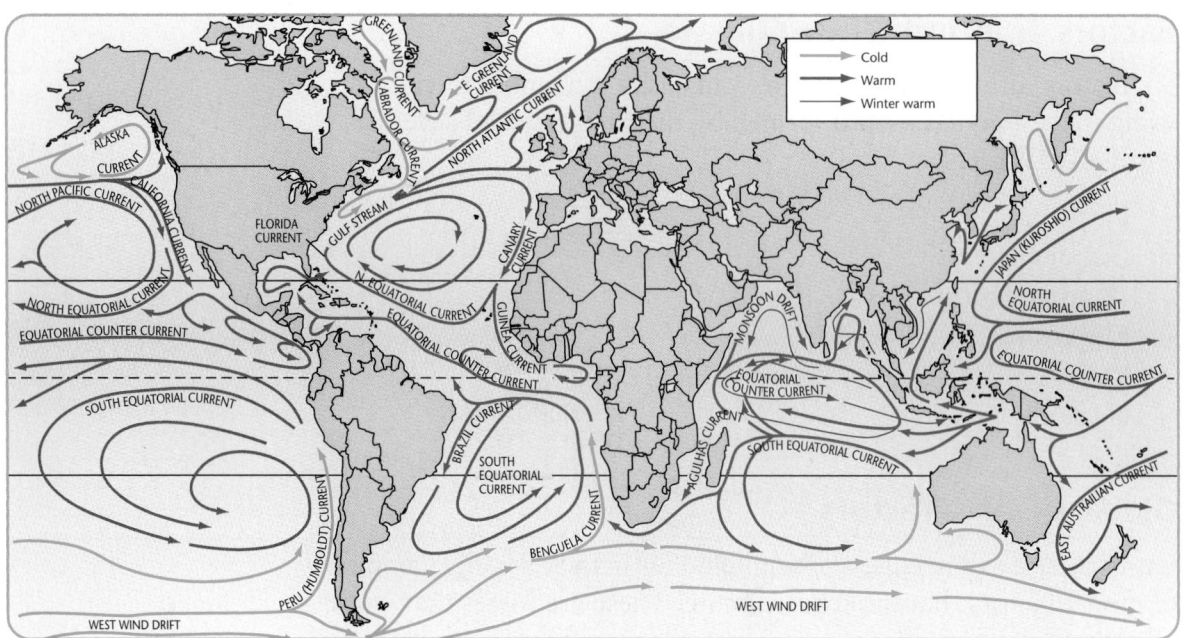

▲ **FIGURE 4.7**

Ocean Currents of the World
Ocean water travels in paths called *currents*. Some currents are warm and others are cold. Warm ocean currents raise the temperature of the nearby land. Cold currents lower the temperature.

Air Mass	Conditions	Temperature
Continental Arctic	very cold, dry	−40°C
Maritime Polar	cool, moist	4°C
Continental Tropical	warm, dry	24°C
Maritime Tropical	warm, moist	24°C

▲ **FIGURE 4.8**

Air Masses in North America
An **air mass** is a large volume of air. Air masses move over an area of land and bring weather conditions with them.

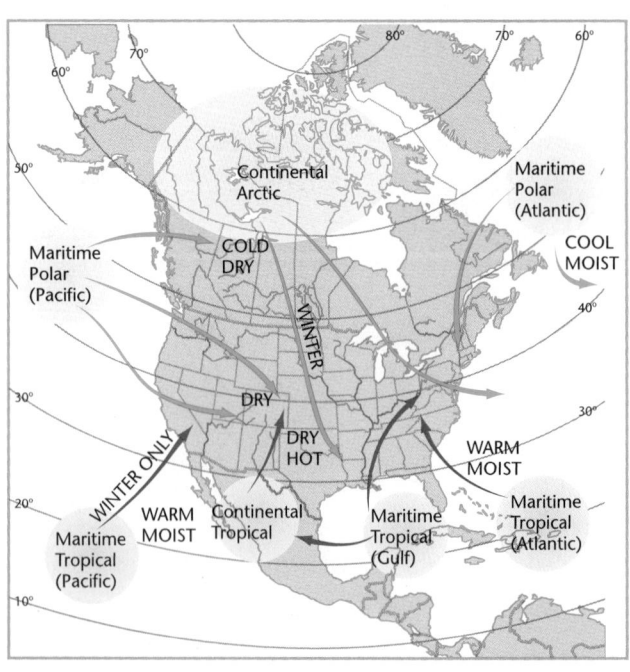

FIGURE 4.9 ▶

The Origin and Movement of Air Masses in North America
The origin of air masses determines their conditions and temperature. The type of weather condition depends on how warm or cold and dry or moist the air mass is. For example, if an air mass forms over a cold area, it brings cold, dry weather to a region. In Canada, winds tend to move weather from west to east. These winds are known as "westerlies."

Ice Storm, 1998

In January of 1998, an unusual freezing rainstorm devastated eastern Ontario, western Quebec, and New Brunswick. It left over 4 million people freezing in the dark. The weight of the ice brought down millions of trees and thousands of kilometres of power lines and telephone cables. There were at least 25 deaths, many from hypothermia (low body temperature caused by exposure to cold). The ice storm affected more people than any other weather event in Canadian history. The storm cost was over $5 billion. That made it Canada's most expensive natural disaster ever!

 CHECK IT OVER

8. Explain why temperatures are colder near the poles than at the equator.

9. Using an atlas, list five places found at the same latitude as Toronto. Research each climate. How do these climates compare to one another?

10. List the ocean currents that influence Canada's climate the most.

11. Why would someone prefer to surf off the coast of Florida than the coast of Peru?

12. Determine which direction winds usually blow between 10° and 30°, both north and south of the equator, and between 30°N and 60°N.

13. In which direction does the wind blow across Canada?

Local Climate Factors

Elevation (height above the earth's surface), relief (difference in the height of an area of the earth's surface), and nearness to water are examples of local factors that influence climate. These are forces within the region that affect climate.

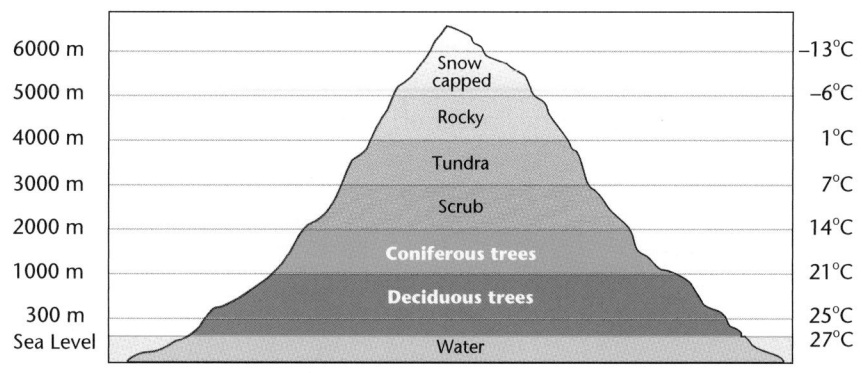

FIGURE 4.10

The Effect of Elevation and Altitude on Climate Mountains influence climate because the higher up you go, the colder the climate is. In dry air the temperature decreases at a rate of 1°C for every 100 m of altitude, in moist air at a rate of 0.6°C for every 100 m of altitude.

FIGURE 4.11

The Effects of Mountains on Climate

Moist air condenses (becomes liquid) as it rises up the mountainside. This causes **relief precipitation.** The **rain shadow** on the **leeward** side (the side away from the wind) receives little rain. The **windward** side of a mountain (the side facing the wind) receives a lot of rain.

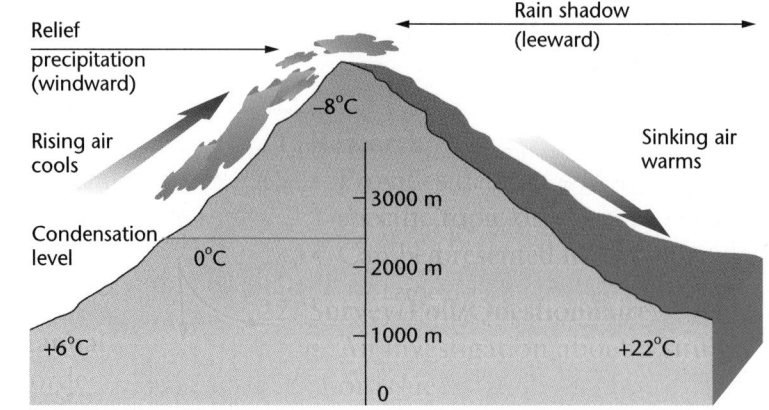

Relief precipitation (windward)

Rain shadow (leeward)

Rising air cools

Sinking air warms

−8°C

Condensation level

3000 m

2000 m

1000 m

0°C

0

+6°C

+22°C

FIGURE 4.12

Surface Temperatures on the Great Lakes

Bodies of water are a source of moisture. Winds carry the moisture over land. This makes the climate there moister. The colder deep water and warmer surface water mix to make the land climate cooler in the summer and warmer in the winter. This means bodies of water make the climate of the land more moderate.

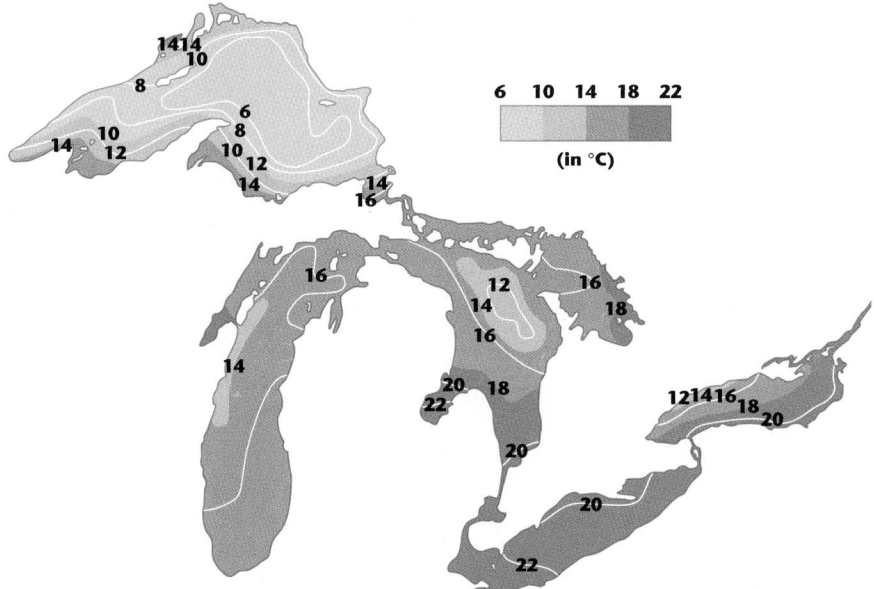

6 10 14 18 22

(in °C)

CHECK IT OVER

14. Suppose the temperature is 28°C in a city at sea level. What would the temperature be at 300 m above sea level? at 1000 m? (Assume that the air is dry.)

15. In which parts of Canada would altitude be the main factor influencing climate?

16. a) Why does condensation occur on the windward side of a mountain?

   b) Why is there little precipitation on the leeward side of a mountain?

17. Using Figure 4.12, list the Great Lakes in order by average temperature, from warmest to coolest.

Climate Change: Human Impacts

Over time, human beings can influence climate change. Cars and factories emit a large number of gases. These gases get trapped in the atmosphere and warm the planet. They have the dangerous ability to heat the earth at a rate never seen before. A warmer globe can lead to an increase in severe weather, such as hurricanes, tornadoes, flooding, and droughts.

CHECK IT OVER

18. Should human impacts on the climate be considered a global climate factor or a local climate factor? Explain your idea.

THINK IT OVER

Knowledge and Understanding

1. Suppose your grandparents were about to retire and wanted to know which part of Canada has the best climate. What area of Canada would you recommend? Give three reasons for your choice.

2. Which of the six climate factors most influence the southern parts of Alberta and Saskatchewan?

3. Choose two of the six climate factors discussed in this chapter. Create a diagram to show how the two climate factors work together to influence the climate of a place.

Thinking and Communication

4. a) Outline 5 to 10 aspects of our lifestyles that affect climate.

   b) Describe how the climate might change over the next 100 years due to human influence.

5. A region's climate affects human activities. Discuss the types of industries and recreational activities common in places with a seasonal climate (like Canada) versus places with a hot tropical climate (like Jamaica).

6. Look at the graphs in Figure 4.2. Explain why these three types of graphs are useful for showing climate information.

Chapter 5 Plants and Soils

Key Words

natural vegetation

soils

bedrock

Prairie

Tundra

topsoil

permafrost

active layer

utilidors

In this chapter you will learn to

◢ identify patterns and differences in Canada's natural systems

◢ describe selected features of natural systems

◢ use different types of maps to understand geographic information

Introduction

Compare the two photographs on this page. Both pictures show scenes in Canada.

FIGURE 5.1

Scenes in Canada
What forces might create such different conditions across the country?

These two photographs show that Canada has a wide range of natural systems. The picture on the left shows a scene along the coast of British Columbia, on Vancouver Island. The picture on the right was taken in Labrador on the Labrador Sea. Each scene is the result of all the different natural systems at work in that place. These natural systems include

- rocks and minerals
- the forces working on the earth's surface, including erosion
- the climate conditions
- plant growth systems
- soil

This chapter will focus on **natural vegetation** and **soils**. *Natural vegetation* means plants and growing conditions that are native to an area and have not been changed by humans. *Soils* are the materials that sit on top of the **bedrock** and allow plants to grow. Soils provide plants with food, water, and a stable location.

This chapter will look at

- the factors that create natural vegetation patterns
- the factors that shape soil patterns
- permafrost as a unique soil condition

CHECK IT OVER

1. Compare the two pictures in Figure 5.1 and write down five words that come to mind when you see each picture.

2. Describe the vegetation in your area. Rate how natural the vegetation is on a scale of 0 (not natural) to 5 (very natural). Give a reason for each rating.

Types of Natural Vegetation

The types of plants in an area will remain the same if people don't interfere with them. This occurs because the plant species reach a balance with the environment. The plants are getting everything they need from their environment.

An important natural vegetation in Canada is trees. In Figure 5.2, you can see that the Coniferous Forest region sweeps across much of Canada. Two other regions also contain trees: the Temperate Rain Forest region of the Pacific coast and the Deciduous Forest region of southeastern Canada.

There are two other types of natural vegetation in Canada:

- In the dry southern parts of Alberta, Saskatchewan, and Manitoba, the main vegetation is grass. We refer to this area as the **Prairie** region.

- In the North, a cold climate means that trees do not grow well. Instead, hardy, low-lying plants, such as mosses, lichens, grasses, and shrubs, are the common vegetation. This is known as the Tundra region.

Natural vegetation is shaped by the systems that operate in it. For example, the amount of moisture and the amount of heat that a place receives affect vegetation growth. Moisture (precipitation) and heat (temperature) are the two most important factors that affect vegetation. Other factors also affect vegetation growth, as Figure 5.4 shows.

Many parts of Canada no longer have completely natural vegetation. Humans have removed unwanted species, introduced new plant varieties, and changed the environment to suit our needs. For instance, we have paved over a field or built a shopping centre. Natural species have had to adapt to these changes or die. Most of the vegetation that we find today includes plant varieties shaped by human activities, except in the most remote areas of Canada.

FIGURE 5.2

Natural Vegetation Regions of North America
What is the name of the region where you live?

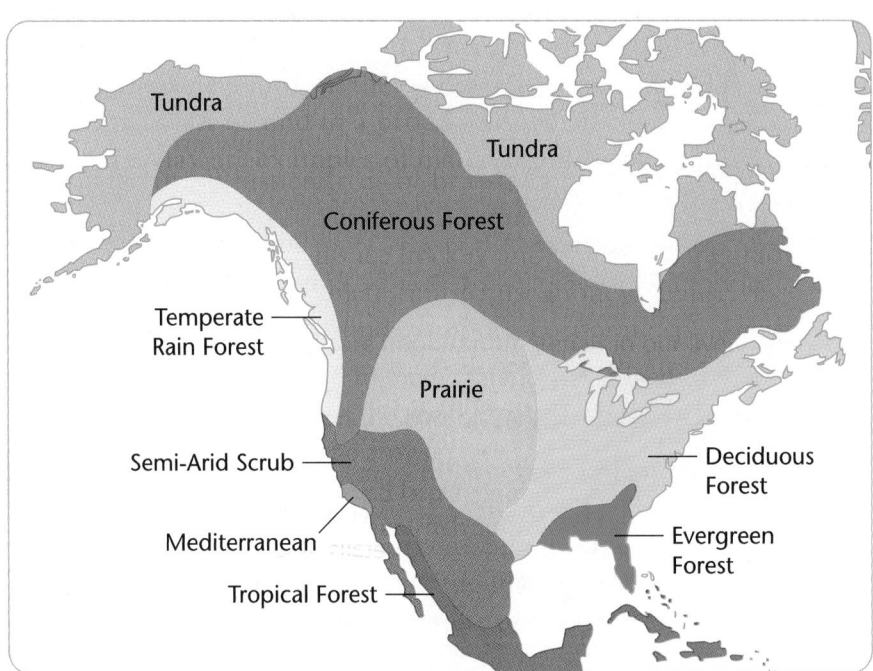

FIGURE 5.3

Tree Species by Forest Region
Growing conditions result in different types of forests. Which forests produce hardwood trees? Why?

Coniferous Forest	Temperate Rain Forest	Deciduous Forest
jack pine	Douglas fir	maple
spruce	cedar	walnut
tamarack	hemlock	oak
fir	Sitka spruce	hickory
white birch	pine	beech

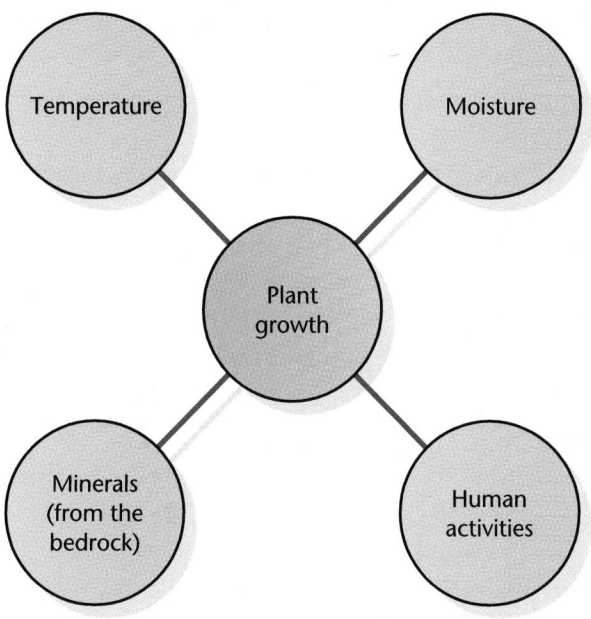

FIGURE 5.4

Factors That Affect Plant Growth
Which factor do you think is most important in Nunavut?

Literacy Strategy

Reading ideas webs
When reading an ideas web (e.g., Figure 5.4 or 5.8), look at the centre to identify the topic. Then follow the lines from the centre to the outside bubbles. These bubbles contain more ideas related to the topic.

LITERACY SKILL

Making Observations About Visual Information

In a subject like Geography, much of the information you work with comes from visual sources. These sources include

- maps
- graphs
- diagrams
- pictures
- statistical tables
- charts
- flow diagrams
- organizational charts

It is not enough just to glance at these visual sources. You need to study them to see all the patterns and details. It is a good idea to develop the habit of making at least three observations about a visual. An observation is when you notice something about the data, such as a pattern or a connection. A pattern is information that is repeated.

When you first start making observations, they might be simpler and more obvious, such as

- highest
- least frequent
- largest

However, as you practise, you will find it easier to see other patterns and relationships. These patterns and relationships might show

- increasing or decreasing trends
- individuals that do not fit general patterns
- connections among the different parts
- geographic distributions

3. Based on your experience, describe the differences between coniferous and deciduous forests.

4. Explain why trees grow across most of Canada, but not in the Tundra region.

5. What might be one impact of global warming on Canada's forests? (Global warming refers to climate change that is occurring because of gases humans have released into the atmosphere.)

6. Give two ways in which humans have affected the natural vegetation in your area.

Soil Patterns

Without soil, much of life on earth could not exist. Soil is a mixture of particles that have come from worn-down rocks, living and dead plants and animals, water, and air.

Soils that have thick "A" layers are best for agriculture (See Figure 5.5). This kind of soil is called topsoil and is usually dark brown. Its richness comes from the organic material (made of living organisms, such as plant or vegetable remains) that builds up from the remains of plants and animals. These remains provide humus,

FIGURE 5.5

Typical Soil Profile
A soil profile shows the layers that you would see if you dug down through the soil. A typical soil has five layers. What is soil made up of?

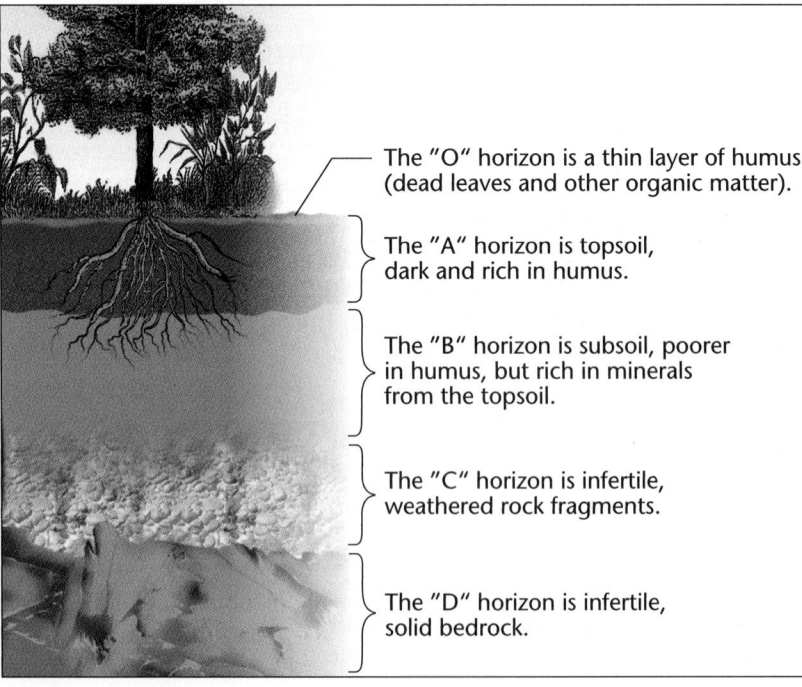

The "O" horizon is a thin layer of humus (dead leaves and other organic matter).

The "A" horizon is topsoil, dark and rich in humus.

The "B" horizon is subsoil, poorer in humus, but rich in minerals from the topsoil.

The "C" horizon is infertile, weathered rock fragments.

The "D" horizon is infertile, solid bedrock.

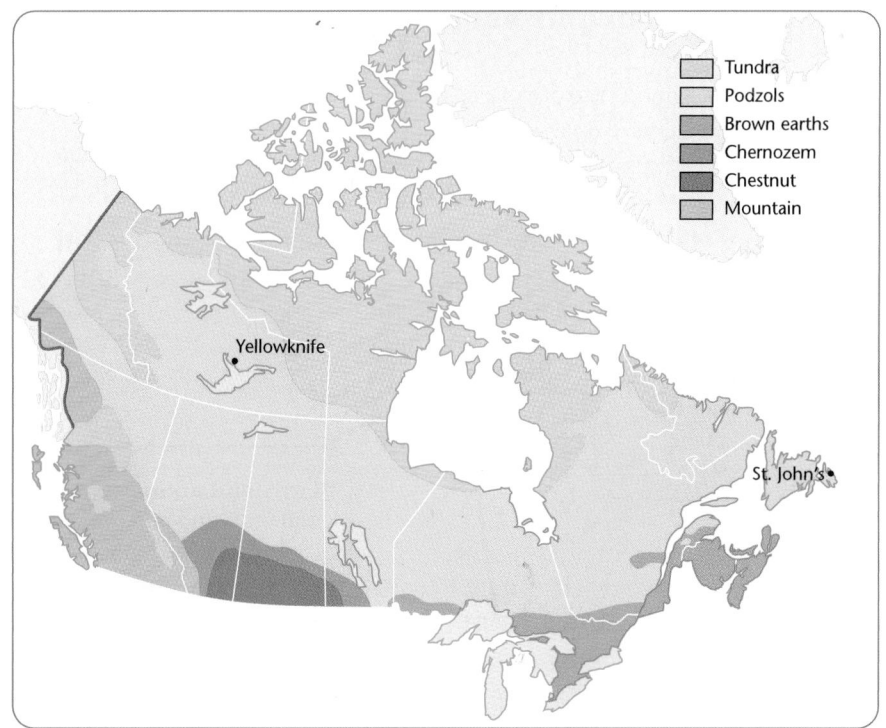

FIGURE 5.6

Soil Types in Canada
Are the soil types found in Yellowknife, Northwest Territories, and St. John's, Newfoundland and Labrador, different? Why or why not?

	Soil Type	Chief Natural Vegetation	Major Land Uses
	Tundra	tundra	largely unused
	Podzols	coniferous forest (boreal)	forestry, livestock farming where appropriate
	Brown earths	deciduous or mixed forests	livestock farming, vegetables, field crops, potatoes
	Chernozem	tall grasslands	grains, field crops
	Chestnut	short grasslands	wheat
	Mountain	wide variation due to relief	forestry and agriculture where conditions permit

FIGURE 5.7

Characteristics of Soil Types in Canada
Which soil types are best for agriculture? Explain your reasons.

FAST *Fact*

Some of the best soils in Canada for agriculture are under grasslands. Lots of organic material is added to the soil each year, and there is so little rainfall in these regions that the good minerals don't get washed away.

the nutrients that create the organic material. Topsoil layers do not form in high latitudes because there is not enough organic material. The soils there—what there are of them—are thin and infertile.

Humans can easily ruin soils. If farmers overwork soils or allow soil erosion to occur, good soils can quickly lose their nutrients and become useless for farming.

FIGURE 5.8

Factors that affect soil development
Take a walk around where you live and observe the soil. Which factor do you think is most important in your area? Explain your answer.

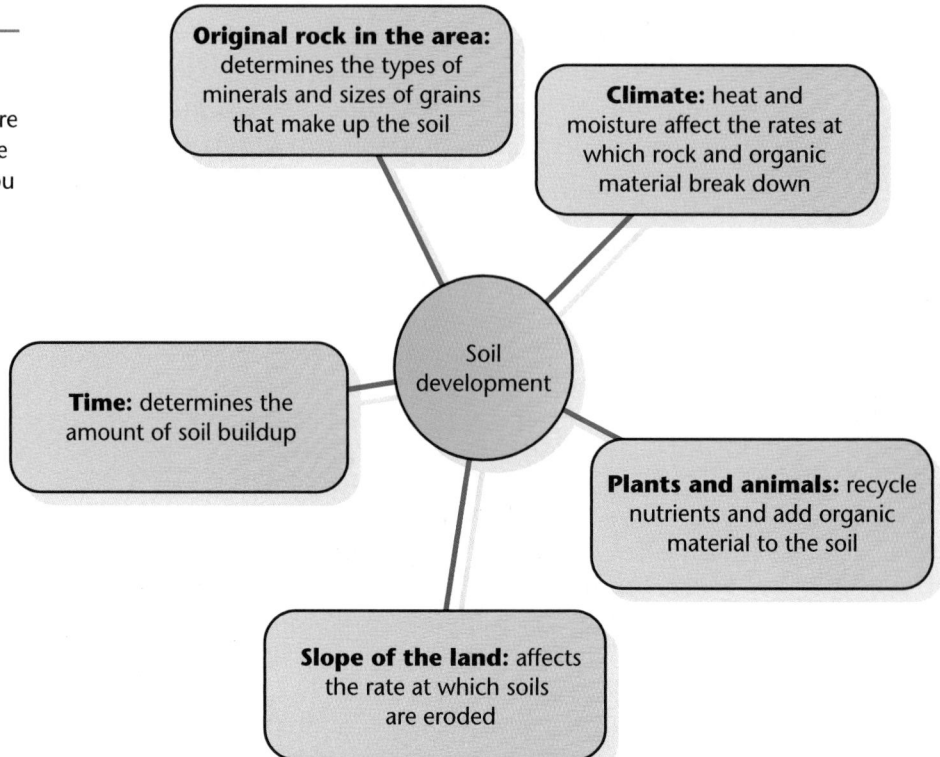

Original rock in the area: determines the types of minerals and sizes of grains that make up the soil

Climate: heat and moisture affect the rates at which rock and organic material break down

Soil development

Time: determines the amount of soil buildup

Plants and animals: recycle nutrients and add organic material to the soil

Slope of the land: affects the rate at which soils are eroded

GEOCAREERS

Landscaper

The job of landscapers is to make a location look pleasing to the eye with grasses, flowers, shrubs, and trees. To do this, landscapers need to understand all the factors that influence vegetation and soils. They use their knowledge to provide the conditions that the plants need for healthy growth. They need to know how to

- create a design and prepare drawings of sites
- prepare the site
- select appropriate plants
- maintain the site as it was designed

Landscapers also need to understand human systems. They need to know how to

- prepare a budget
- work with clients to design the landscape they want
- hire and direct crews
- complete work on schedule

In many cases, landscapers run their own companies.

CASE STUDY

Permafrost

Permafrost is soil or rock that remains frozen all year long. In the Arctic and high on mountains, the ground temperature drops below 0°C during winter. The ground remains frozen even during summer. The rock and soil can be frozen to depths of hundreds of metres.

The very top layer—down to about a metre—does thaw briefly. However, the water in this layer cannot drain away because of the permafrost below it. The top **active layer** remains wet and difficult to travel across. It is a perfect breeding area for mosquitoes.

Roads and communities on permafrost need to be built differently than farther south. Houses cannot be built directly on permafrost. The heat from inside the houses melts the permafrost and the houses gradually sink into the soil. Roads have to be built on thick layers of gravel so they don't collapse into the active layer.

The town of Inuvik, Northwest Territories, is built on permafrost. All the houses are placed on posts. They are connected by **utilidors**. These are above-ground structures that carry heat, power, and water to the homes, and carry sewage away from them. The utilidors are insulated so that the heat from them does not melt the permafrost.

FIGURE 5.9

Utilidors in Inuvik, NWT
How would people in Inuvik heat their homes if they didn't have utilidors?

 CHECK IT OVER

7. Make three observations about the distribution of soil types, using the map in Figure 5.6.

8. Explain why the first sentence under the heading Soil Patterns is a true statement.

9. Farmers and gardeners try to improve the fertility of soils by adding animal manure, compost, or peat moss. How do these materials improve soils?

10. In two sentences, explain how permafrost influences human activities.

THINK IT OVER

Knowledge and Understanding

1. Using the Internet or other sources, find a photo of each of the five vegetation regions in Canada. Make copies of the photos and then write captions in which you identify the characteristics of the vegetation regions.

2. Compare the following maps:
    - Figure 5.6, Soil Types in Canada
    - Figure 5.2, Natural Vegetation Regions of North America

    Write down two observations that you make during your comparison.

3. Copy the following lists of Key Words into your notebook. Fill in a title for each list. At the bottom of each list, explain why you chose the title.

Title: _____	Title: _____	Title: _____
active layer	Prairie	organic material
hundreds of metres	Tundra	bedrock
utilidors	deciduous forest	climate

Thinking and Communication

4. Make up an outline in point form to show the main ideas and their supporting points in this chapter.

5. Make up a diagram or a poem to explain how these topics are connected:
    - landforms
    - climate
    - vegetation
    - soils

6. Make up three questions about vegetation and soils that you would like to know the answers to. Explain why you think these are good questions to ask.

Protecting Canada's Natural Systems

In this chapter you will learn to

◢ *describe issues that affect natural systems in Canada*

◢ see how Canadian natural systems are protected

◢ use different types of maps to interpret geographic information

◢ use Geography terms to talk or write about results of geographic inquiries

Key Words

federal government

provincial governments

national parks

advocate for the environment

Introduction

Look out a window. How much of what you see would you describe as natural? For most Canadians, the answer would be not much. Most Canadians live in places where natural systems have been almost completely changed by human activities. These changes include

- forests that have been cut down so crops can be planted
- rivers that have been dammed to produce hydroelectric power
- animal species that have been driven to the edge of extinction by loss of habitat

Sometimes these changes are planned and seen as positive. For example, we all want enough food to eat, so farming is necessary. However, sometimes changes are unplanned and unwanted. Humans have rarely set out to cause the extinction of species, yet it has happened.

In this chapter we will look at examples of how natural systems are being protected in Canada. We will look at

- methods to protect lands from development
- actions by groups that want to protect the environment

FIGURE 6.1

Isn't Nature Grand?
What is the main
message in this cartoon?

"Isn't nature grand?"

✓ CHECK IT OVER

1. Identify three ways that the natural environment in your area has been changed by human activity.

Protecting Lands and Natural Systems

Governments have important roles in protecting natural systems. In Canada, both the federal government and provincial governments have the power to protect lands and natural systems. The federal government sits in Ottawa, Ontario, and makes decisions that affect the whole country. Provincial governments meet in the capital cities of each province and make decisions that affect only their provinces. For example, at the Manitoba provincial legislature in Winnipeg, elected officials decide on issues that concern the people in Manitoba.

There are two important ways that the federal government can protect nature:

- It can pass laws that declare national parks and other places protected areas, in which some activities such as building or hunting certain animals are forbidden.

- It can pass laws that forbid people from polluting waterways or that require changes in vehicles to reduce air pollution.

All individuals and companies must obey the laws or face legal action.

National parks have been created to preserve natural places for future generations. In Canada, national parks are designed to

- keep natural systems natural
- stop uses or activities that might harm natural systems
- offer spiritual, scientific, educational, and recreational activities for visitors

Park areas are chosen for their scenic value and their tourism potential. Canada's national parks are shown on the map in Figure 6.2. Provincial governments have also created provincial parks. They have the same goals as national parks.

FAST *Fact*

Canada's first national park was Banff National Park, in Alberta. It became a park in 1883. Today there are 46 national parks in Canada.

FIGURE 6.2

National Parks in Canada
How do national parks help to protect natural systems (like drainage and food cycles)?

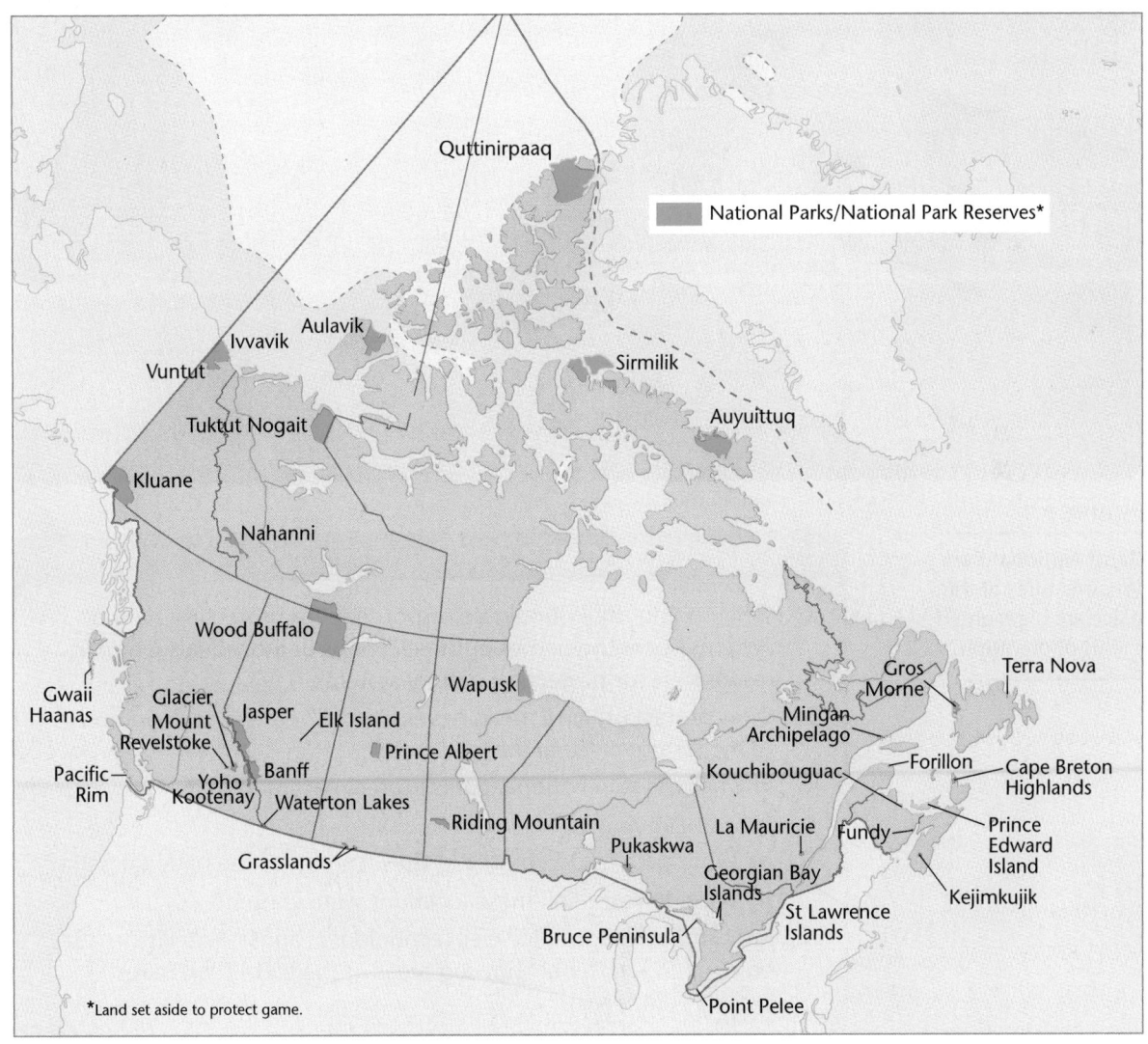

*Land set aside to protect game.

FIGURE 6.3

Banff National Park
What features of this
place are highlighted
in this photograph?

2. Who do you think should be responsible for protecting natural systems? Give the names of three groups or individuals who are responsible for protecting natural systems.

3. Does protecting land mean never using it? Give your definition of the term *protecting the land*.

4. In what ways do national parks protect natural systems?

5. Look at Figure 6.2.
   a) What pattern do you see in the locations of the national parks?
   b) Why do you think these locations were chosen?

6. Are Landsat images (See GeoTechnology: Landsat Satellite Images on page 52) better at showing areas of the earth than maps? Explain your ideas.

LITERACY SKILL

Identifying the Main Idea

To understand what you're reading, you have to identify the main idea. The main idea is the one sentence that captures the point of the article. (The underlined sentence is the main idea in this Literacy Skill box.) This sentence often occurs near the beginning of an article. Other times it may appear partway through an article. You need to read carefully and think about all the information that is presented. Then you can decide what words express the main idea.

The main idea may be followed by supporting ideas. These include examples, additional facts, interesting points, or even a different point of view. They are added by the writer to strengthen the main idea.

Read the article in Figure 6.4. Identify the main idea and supporting ideas.

National Park Asks Visitors to Keep Dogs Under Control

Pacific Rim National Park Reserve of Canada would like to remind visitors that park beaches and day-use areas are meant to be enjoyable for everyone. If you choose to bring along your dog, you must have it on a leash at all times.

There are four reasons for this:
1. There is evidence that dogs running free have a negative impact on shorebirds in the area.
2. The presence of your dog off-leash may upset or bother other park users.
3. Your dog may attract wolves or harass other wildlife such as seals and bears.
4. Under the Canada National Parks Act Domestic Animals Regulations, it is an offence to allow your dog to run free in a National Park.

Respect other visitors to the park. If it is inconvenient for you to keep your dog on a leash, then please consider leaving your dog at home.

Over the course of several days last month, a harbour seal pup was hauled out on Long Beach and carefully looked after by its mother.

After several days it may have been abandoned as a result of harassment by dogs and people (despite warning signage). The seal pup was eventually killed by eagles.

This summer Park Wardens and other park staff will be monitoring the day-use areas and beaches for compliance with the Canada National Parks Act. Fines for failing to keep dogs on-leash begin at $58.

FIGURE 6.4

A Newspaper Article About Tourists' Use of a National Park
Which national park is being discussed in this article?

GEOTECHNOLOGY

Landsat Satellite Images

The Landsat satellite system is a tool that keeps track of natural systems. It was launched in 1972 by NASA. It uses a series of satellites in the earth's orbit to make images of the earth's surface. The satellites do not just record visible light the way a photograph does. Instead, the satellites use sensors to record both visible and non-visible energy, such as energy that is reflected from the ground. This information is beamed down to recording stations.

The satellites orbit 705 km above the earth and make images of places every 32 days. The information from the system is sold to researchers all over the world. The researchers use the information to analyze conditions on the surface of the ground, such as the health of vegetation, locations of forest fires, and changes in ice conditions in the North.

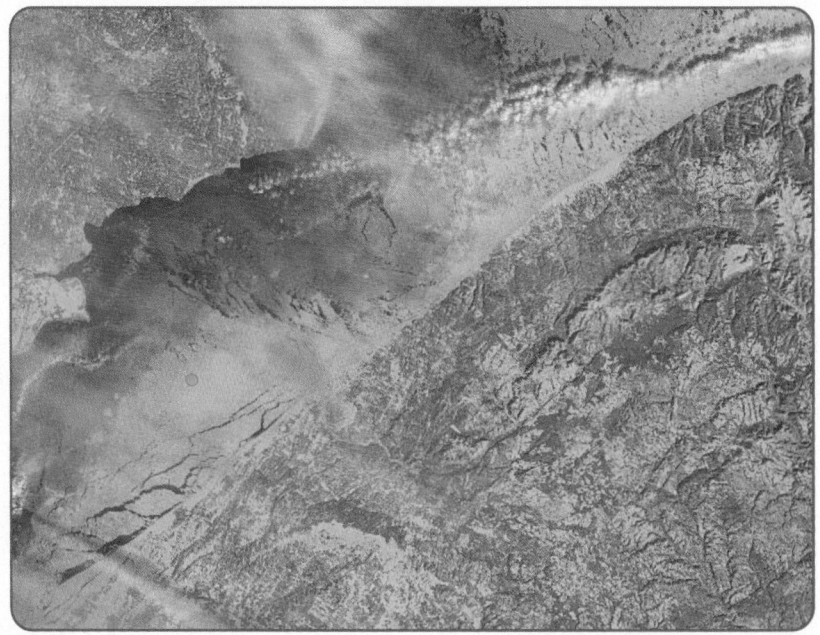

FIGURE 6.5

A Landsat Image of Sea Ice Breakup in the St. Lawrence River
In this satellite image, you can see the large cracks in the sea ice that have appeared as the weather has warmed in the spring. How can images like this be used to protect natural systems?

People Power: Citizen Action

Our modern ways of life have harmed natural systems everywhere—from global climate change, to pollution of waterways, to extinction of species. Sometimes it seems that ruining the environment is simply a part of human life. However, not everyone thinks that way. Some individuals and groups argue that we should do everything we can to protect natural systems. They advocate for the environment. That means they argue in support of protecting the environment. They try to get people in power to change a situation that is damaging the environment.

Advocating for the environment goes beyond recycling and conserving energy. It means that you actively try to bring about change. Greenpeace and World Wildlife Fund are two advocacy groups that have had a great deal of success. These groups do things such as running letter-writing campaigns and pressuring elected officials to change laws.

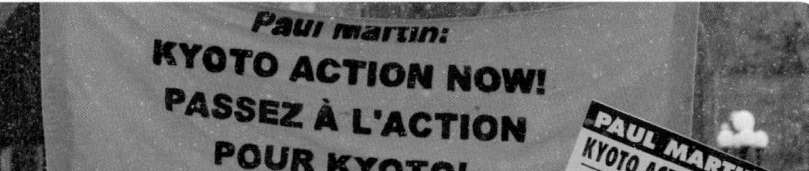

Letter-Writing Campaigns

The most effective letters advocating for the environment should

- be brief
- focus on just one topic or issue
- clearly tell views and positions on the issue
- not be overly emotional
- ask for a reply

FIGURE 6.6

Writing Letters to Decision Makers
Why should you be brief when writing letters advocating for the environment?

FIGURE 6.7

A Greenpeace Protest
What do you think this group hopes will happen as a result of their protest?

The Gully

Off the east coast of Canada is a deep underwater canyon known as "The Gully." It is located just 260 km off Nova Scotia, east of Sable Island. The Gully is deeper and wider than the Grand Canyon.

The steep sides of The Gully force water into giant swirls, similar to twisters in the water. The swirls move upward and carry nutrients towards the surface. Plankton (microscopic plants and animals) feed on the nutrients. The plankton, in turn, are eaten by fish, sea birds, and mammals. This whole area has interesting and unique species that are attracted by the plentiful food.

The Gully is threatened by oil and gas development in the area. Already a number of companies are pumping fuel, with more planned. Many people are upset by this activity. They see the energy developments as harmful to natural systems because of drilling activity, increased shipping, and oil spills.

In 1996, the World Wildlife Fund launched a campaign to have The Gully protected. Their campaign included

- taking part in meetings to discuss energy projects
- paying for scientific research to be done in the area
- working with fishers to check the health of fish populations
- starting a letter-writing campaign to tell government officials about the issues

Faced with increasing pressure from the public, the federal government agreed to protect 7700 km^2 of The Gully.

CHECK IT OVER

7. Three of the following actions could be described as advocating for the environment. Decide which three they are. Give reasons for your choices.
   - putting your litter in a waste container
   - giving a presentation in class about the need to build bluebird houses
   - encouraging your parents to buy an energy-efficient hybrid car
   - always buying products in reusable containers
   - speaking out against a highway that would be built through a nearby forest
   - digging weeds out of your front lawn instead of using pesticides

8. Members of Greenpeace are famous for their dramatic actions on behalf of the environment. Their actions include hanging large banners from bridges and driving their small boats between whales and whale hunters.

   a) What is the purpose of these actions?

   b) In your opinion, do these actions do any good? Explain your opinion.

 THINK IT OVER

Knowledge and Understanding

1. What is the difference between the two terms *protecting natural systems* and *advocating for the environment*?

2. In your opinion, why is it necessary or not necessary for our society to advocate for the environment?

3. Have you, or has someone you know, ever advocated for the environment? What action took place? What were the results? If you don't know someone who has done this, research an action from the media and answer the same questions.

Thinking and Communication

4. Pick one of Canada's national parks and find a Web site that gives you some details about the park. Make notes on the following topics:
   • the name of the park
   • reasons the park was established
   • things that you would see in the park
   • problems that the park is facing

5. Think about one environmental issue in your local area. It could be how garbage is disposed of, or how streams and rivers are becoming polluted. Think about the best way you could advocate for the environment. Plan a campaign to bring about changes that would protect natural systems. Write a point-form outline of your plan.

6. Look again at Figure 6.1. Make up your own cartoon about advocating for the environment. Your cartoon might focus on the dramatic actions of some advocacy groups or on the day-to-day actions of people around you.

PERFORMANCE TASK

Preparing for Natural Disasters

Key Words

natural disasters

hazard

contingency plan

In this performance task you will learn to

◢ *communicate the results of geographic inquiries*

◢ *demonstrate an understanding of Canada's diverse natural and human systems*

Introduction

Sometimes nature is not very friendly to humans. Natural disasters are events that occur when the physical activities of wind, water, or rock damage or destroy human systems. Natural disasters can cause a great amount of damage, including death. One way to deal with natural disasters is to be prepared for them.

Performance Task Assignment

You have just been appointed the natural disasters coordinator for your region and must develop an emergency response plan in the event of a disaster.

Step 1   Do some research to determine a hazard that has affected your area in the past. You may need to use the Internet or other resources provided to you by your teacher.

Step 2   Review the history of the hazard you chose and note ways that it has or could impact your region. Design a worst-case scenario—the worst possible situation—by considering

- time of day that would cause the most chaos
- evacuation/traffic challenges
- possible number of casualties
- secondary problems (fire, looting, etc.)
- other important factors

Step 3 Design a contingency plan to prepare for and react to the hazard in its worst-case scenario. The contingency plan should outline

- ways to evacuate people from the area
- roles that the media, such as television and the Internet, could play
- how to keep services like water supplies and transportation working
- what emergency supplies are needed and where they could be stored
- actions that the fire department, the police, and ambulance workers should take
- what the general population should do

Step 4 Report your findings to the class in the form of a presentation or poster. You must include

- research notes about the history of the hazard in your region
- details of the worst-case scenario
- details of the contingency plan
- pictures of past disasters to support your findings

Step 5 Write and then hand in your worst-case scenario and contingency plan to your teacher for evaluation. Remember to include the sources where you found your information.

FIGURE PT1.1

Damage from an Ice Storm in St. Bruno, Quebec in 1998

FIGURE PT1.2

Damage from a Tornado in Pine Lake, Alberta in 2000

FIGURE PT1.3

A Forest Fire near Peachland, British Columbia in 2003

Unit 2

Human Systems

Overall Expectations

In this unit you will learn to

- identify patterns and differences in Canada's human systems

- describe ways in which renewable, non-renewable, and flow resources are used

- relate lifestyle choices to Canada's economic and environmental well-being

- report on how Canada influences, and is influenced by, its connections to other countries

- identify social and economic changes and explain how they could affect Canadians

- illustrate regional differences using the idea of ecozones

- use the methods and tools of geographic investigation to understand Canada's ecozones

Human systems, such as where people live, depend on the geography of a country. This is a night-time picture of Canada's population.

Chapter 7

The First People in Canada

Key Words

reserves

treaties

land claims

specific land claims

comprehensive land claims

In this chapter you will learn to

⊿ *identify and explain the population distribution of Aboriginal peoples across Canada*

⊿ identify the costs and benefits of recent Aboriginal land claims

⊿ explain the challenges of developing human systems in a territory

Introduction

When your parents and grandparents were in high school, their books on the history of Canada started with the arrival of Christopher Columbus in the New World in 1492. The Aboriginal peoples who had lived here for at least tens of thousands of years were ignored. History was seen as the story of white European settlers, not the story of Aboriginal peoples.

FIGURE 7.1

"Buffalo Herd Grazing" by George Caitlin
What are two things that this painting suggests about First Nations peoples in Canada in the past?

FAST *Fact*

There were more than 1000 Aboriginal nations in North America when the first Europeans arrived. Aboriginal peoples speak over 58 different languages, more languages than there are in Europe.

To understand Canadian human patterns we must start by examining the roles played by Aboriginal peoples. In this chapter we will consider

- the population patterns of Aboriginal peoples
- how land claims are changing the future for Canada's first people
- the difficulties of building human systems in Nunavut

Aboriginal Peoples
This term refers to the people who are descended from the original inhabitants of a place. Many First Nations peoples believe through their traditional stories and creation stories that they have always lived here. Some archeologists believe Canada's original inhabitants arrived in North America about 35 000 years ago. In Canada, Aboriginal peoples are generally divided into three groups.

First Nations
This label refers to all the Aboriginal peoples, except Métis, across Canada who live south of the Arctic coast region. The word *Indian* is only used when referring to the federal Indian Act. The Act defines three categories of First Nations people.

Inuit
These are the people who live in the Arctic region of Canada.

Métis
These are the descendants of European fur traders and explorers who married First Nations people. They settled in the southern Prairie provinces in the nineteenth century.

Status Indian
A person who is registered as an Indian under the Indian Act.

Non-Status Indian
An Indian person who is not registered as an Indian under the Indian Act.

Treaty Indian
A First Nations person who belongs to a First Nation that signed a treaty with the government.

FIGURE 7.2

Terms Used in 2005 to Describe Canada's Aboriginal Peoples
Many of the terms that were used in the past are now seen as offensive to Aboriginal peoples. Why?

CHECK IT OVER

1. Write a list of 5 to 10 ways that Aboriginal peoples contribute to Canada's identity.
2. Does the painting in Figure 7.1 show an outdated view of First Nations peoples? Give two pieces of evidence to prove your opinion.

Aboriginal Population Patterns

In the past, Canada's original inhabitants typically lived in small, relatively isolated groups. Each group had its own ways of life. Aboriginal peoples across Canada had very different ways of life.

FIGURE 7.3

Some Traditional Aboriginal Housing Types
Which dwelling type was probably used in your area?

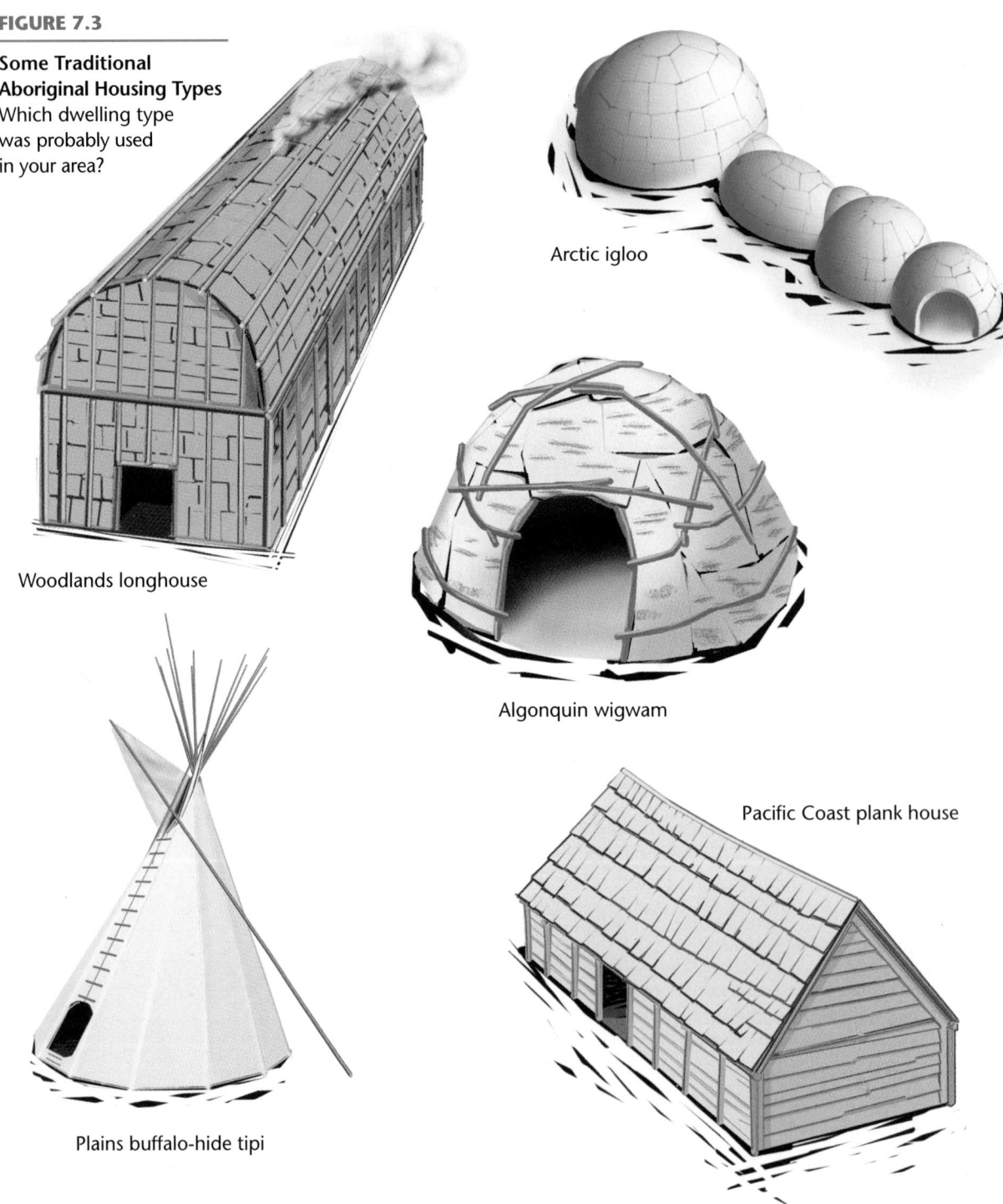

Arctic igloo

Woodlands longhouse

Algonquin wigwam

Plains buffalo-hide tipi

Pacific Coast plank house

Their housing, foods, means of transportation, belief systems, and languages varied depending on the environment in which they lived. Figure 7.3 shows how housing types varied across the continent. People built their homes out of the resources that were available, such as wood, snow, hides, or bark strips.

Contact with Europeans changed many Aboriginal peoples' ways of life. In some cases they welcomed the changes, such as the introduction of iron tools that they could use and trade. However, often the changes were not wanted by Aboriginal peoples. Europeans forced them to learn English or French, to become Christians, and to live on reserves (land that was set aside for their use). We now see that the relationship between Aboriginal peoples and European Canadians for most of our history was racist.

FIGURE 7.4

Aboriginal Populations in the Present (2001) Aboriginal people are those people who on a census reported identifying with at least one Aboriginal group. Multiple origins refers to First Nations people who have ties to two or more Aboriginal groups.

Provinces/Territories	Total Aboriginal Population	First Nations (% of total Aboriginal population)	Métis (% of total Aboriginal population)	Inuit (% of total Aboriginal population)	Multiple Origins (% of total Aboriginal population)
Newfoundland and Labrador	18 775	37.5	29.2	24.2	9.1
Prince Edward Island	1 345	77.0	16.4	1.5	5.1
Nova Scotia	17 010	75.9	18.4	2.0	3.7
New Brunswick	16 990	67.7	25.2	0.9	6.2
Quebec	79 400	64.4	20.0	12.0	3.6
Ontario	188 315	69.9	25.7	0.7	3.7
Manitoba	150 045	60.2	37.8	0.2	1.8
Saskatchewan	130 185	64.3	33.6	0.2	1.9
Alberta	156 225	54.4	42.3	0.7	2.6
British Columbia	170 025	69.6	26.0	0.5	3.9
Yukon Territory	6 540	85.6	8.2	2.1	4.1
Northwest Territories	18 730	56.7	19.1	20.9	3.3
Nunavut	22 720	0.4	0.2	99.3	0.1
Canada	**976 305**	**62.4**	**29.9**	**4.6**	**3.1**

Source: Statistics Canada, from the 2001 Aboriginal census.

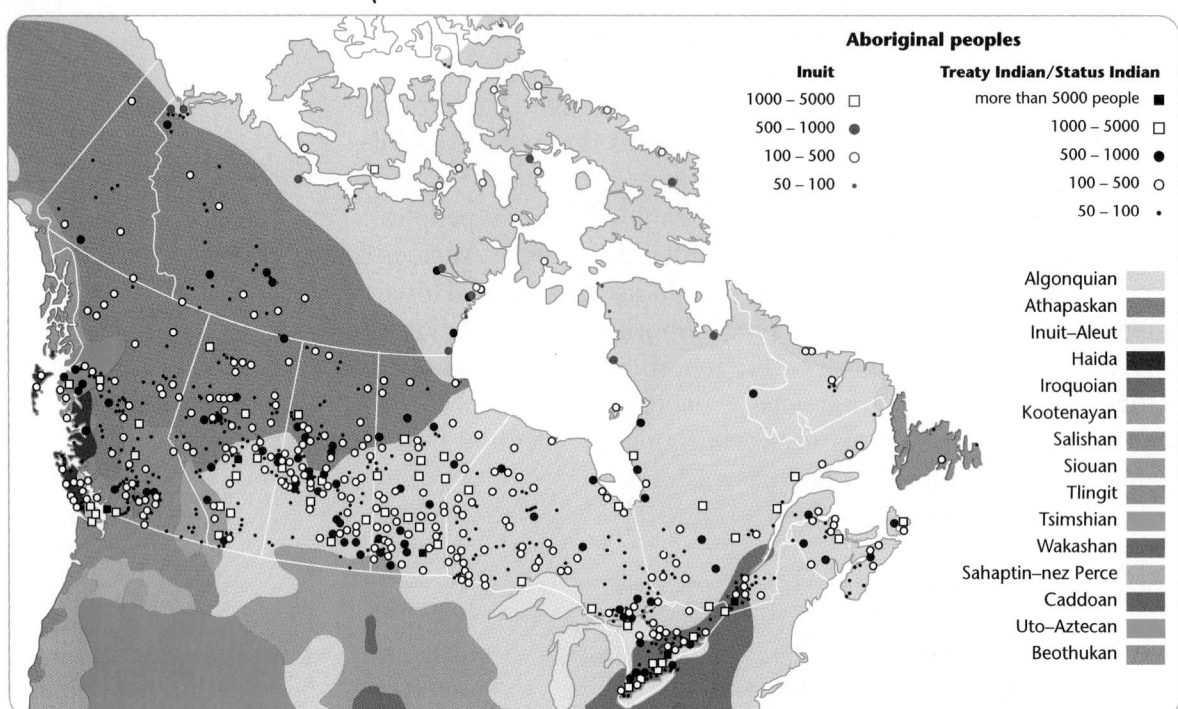

Aboriginal peoples

Inuit
- 1000 – 5000 ▫
- 500 – 1000 ⬤
- 100 – 500 ○
- 50 – 100 ·

Treaty Indian/Status Indian
- more than 5000 people ▪
- 1000 – 5000 ▫
- 500 – 1000 ⬤
- 100 – 500 ○
- 50 – 100 ·

Algonquian
Athapaskan
Inuit–Aleut
Haida
Iroquoian
Kootenayan
Salishan
Siouan
Tlingit
Tsimshian
Wakashan
Sahaptin–nez Perce
Caddoan
Uto–Aztecan
Beothukan

FIGURE 7.5

Aboriginal Language Groups at the Time of European Contact
Each language group consists of many nations with their own distinct language.

FAST Fact

Aboriginal peoples now make up 3.3 percent of the total Canadian population, up from 2.8 percent in 1996.

LITERACY SKILL

Interpreting Statistical Tables

Knowing how to interpret statistical tables is an important skill to have all of your life. Here is a step-by-step strategy:

Step 1: Examine the headings across the top of the table and figure out what the relationships are among them. In Figure 7.4,
- the left column lists the provinces and territories
- the second column from the left gives the total number of Aboriginal peoples in each province
- the next four columns break up the total number of Aboriginal peoples in these provinces and territories into categories. (Note that these figures are percentages of the total numbers in the second column.)

Step 2: Look at the categories in the left column. In Figure 7.4,
- provinces and territories are listed from Eastern to Western Canada and then across the North
- the bottom row gives the total number of Aboriginal peoples in Canada and the percentage of the total Aboriginal population made up by each category

Step 3: Look for patterns and relationships among the data. (For example, most Inuit live in Nunavut.)

CHECK IT OVER

3. Compare the five types of Aboriginal houses shown in Figure 7.3. Make notes using the headings Resources Used, Tools Required, Size of Dwelling, Problems. Research these topics. If you wish, organize your answer as a comparison chart.

4. Consider the map in Figure 7.5 that shows Aboriginal language groups at the time of European contact.

   a) Which provinces and/or territories have large numbers of First Nations people?

   b) Which provinces and/or territories have concentrations of Inuit?

   c) Which provinces have small numbers of Aboriginal peoples?

   d) Which Aboriginal language group is found in your area?

   e) Based on the map, in what ways might the border between Canada and the United States be a problem for Aboriginal peoples?

5. Make three observations about the patterns that you see in Figure 7.4, the statistical table. For example, you might look for the highest values, or the lowest, or places that don't fit the general pattern. When you are finished, compare your observations to those of other students in the class.

Aboriginal Land Claims

As European and other immigrants were settling Canada, governments made treaties with the First Nations peoples who lived on the land. They hoped to avoid the wars and bloodshed that had occurred in the United States as Americans invaded First Nations land. In Canada, many First Nations peoples gave up much of their land. In return, they received reserves, rights to hunt and fish, and annual payments from the government. Figure 7.6 shows the time periods when these treaties were signed.

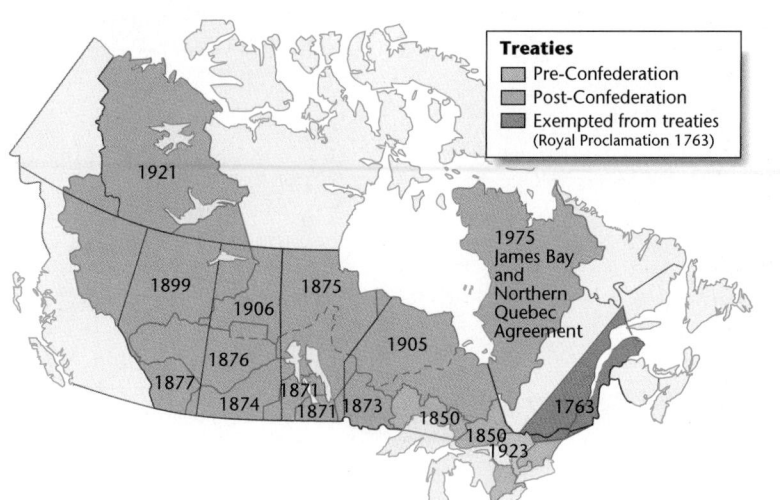

FIGURE 7.6

Treaties Signed With Aboriginal Peoples, 1763–1975
Aboriginal peoples in large areas of Canada did not sign treaties. These are the unshaded areas.

Chapter 7: The First People in Canada   65

By the 1960s, many Aboriginal nations had begun to question whether the governments had fulfilled the treaties their ancestors had signed. They claimed that Canadian governments were not living up to their part of the treaties. For example, they pointed to many cases where the Canadian and provincial governments had sold reserve land or had allowed mining or forestry to take place, without consulting Aboriginal nations or giving them anything in return. They began to demand land claims from governments.

In 1973, the federal government recognized two broad classes of claims: specific land claims and comprehensive land claims.

Specific Land Claims are specific complaints that treaties have not been respected by the government. They are made by Aboriginal groups who signed treaties. These kinds of land claims also cover complaints that the government did not manage First Nations lands properly under the Indian Act. Most important, they argue that when their Elders signed the treaties, they did not intend to give up their ways of life: their language, government, traditional livelihoods, and culture.

Comprehensive Land Claims are based on continuing Aboriginal rights to land and resources, and cover greater areas of land. They are made by Aboriginal groups who did not sign treaties. They argue that governments have allowed their traditional lands to be used by other people without their permission. These claims include land ownership, the right to hunt and fish and trap for furs, and the right to some kind of payment in return when others use their lands.

FIGURE 7.7

Protest in Vancouver About the Slow Progress of Land Claims What do the signs tell you about how these First Nations people feel?

Settling Aboriginal land claims is not easy. Land claim boundaries are hard to map, and the different groups often disagree about them. Some lands covered by broken or forgotten treaties are now being used for farming, mining, forestry, or recreation. In other cases, non-Aboriginal peoples have built homes and communities on land claimed by Aboriginal peoples. Settling land claims takes a great deal of negotiation and time. Between 1973 and 2003, only 15 claims were finalized. About 70 were still being discussed.

CASE STUDY

Treaty Rights to Fish Year Round

In 1993, a man went fishing for eels in Pomquet Harbour, Nova Scotia. The Department of Fisheries and Oceans charged him for fishing without a licence and for fishing when it wasn't eel season. Donald Marshall, Jr., admitted that he had done these things. He fought the charges all the way to the Supreme Court of Canada.

Marshall is a member of the Mi'kmaq First Nation. He argued that, as a member of the Mi'kmaq First Nation, he had a treaty right to fish. A 1760 treaty gave Mi'kmaq and Wolastoqiyik First Nations the right to earn a "moderate living" by fishing and hunting year round. In 1999, Marshall was acquitted by the Supreme Court.

The Supreme Court decision unleashed anger between Aboriginal and non-Aboriginal fishers in the area. The non-Aboriginal fishers felt that all the fish were going to be scooped up by Mi'kmaq fishers. Tensions were so high that the Supreme Court clarified the ruling a few weeks later. They said that the Department of Fisheries and Oceans still had the right to regulate the fishery to conserve the fish. The Aboriginal fishers agreed to honour the government ruling.

GEOTECHNOLOGY

RezMapper

Aboriginal peoples in North America are using GIS (geographic information systems) technologies to gain information and solve problems. Universities have been helping to build databases (collections of information) that focus on Aboriginal reserves. RezMapper is one tool for doing this.

RezMapper provides information on historical patterns of change, identifies current conditions, and builds models to predict the future. Schools can use it to help Aboriginal youth reconnect with their land, history, and traditional language. Aboriginal leaders can use it to plan and develop physical and human systems within their reserves. One important way they can apply it is in helping to prove land claims.

6. Explain why Aboriginal leaders have made land claims against governments in Canada.

7. Make a chart with two columns to show the differences between specific land claims and comprehensive land claims.

8. a) What are two reasons that governments might be reluctant to settle land claims?

   b) Why might some other Canadians not support land claim settlements?

Developing Human Systems in Nunavut

FIGURE 7.8

Celebrations Marking the Beginning of Nunavut, 1999
Nunavut was created because of a land claim.

Nunavut was created by a comprehensive land claim settlement. It became a new territory on April 1, 1999. It covers 2 093 190 km², about a fifth of Canada's land area. Inuktitut is the working language in Nunavut.

Since 1999, the people and government of the territory have been working to build effective human systems. These human systems—like transportation, communication, education, and resource management—are necessary for developing a strong economy. A strong economy will give Inuit the resources they need to protect their unique culture and traditions.

If we focus on transportation in the Arctic, we can see how challenging it is to build human systems here.

FIGURE 7.9

Communities in Nunavut
The territory's 26 000 inhabitants are scattered across 28 small communities. The small map shows where Nunavut is in Canada.

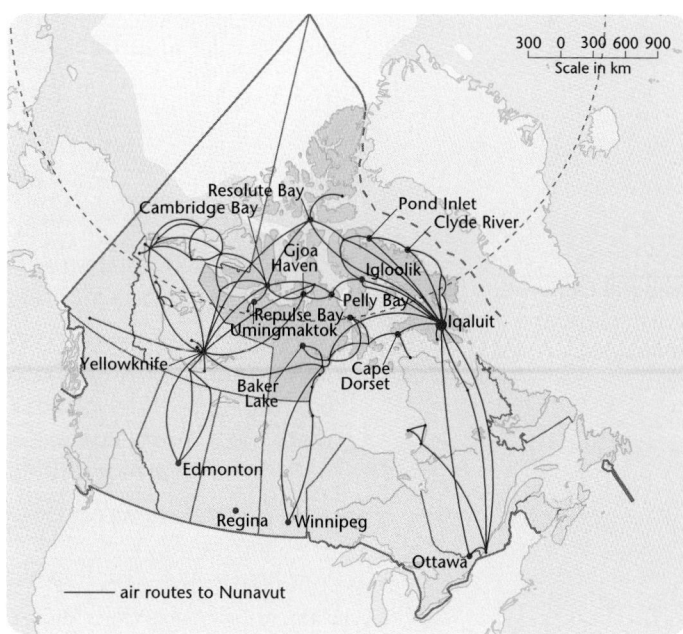

FIGURE 7.10

Air Routes to Nunavut
Air transportation is the best way to get from community to community in Nunavut. Why?

Chapter 7: The First People in Canada **69**

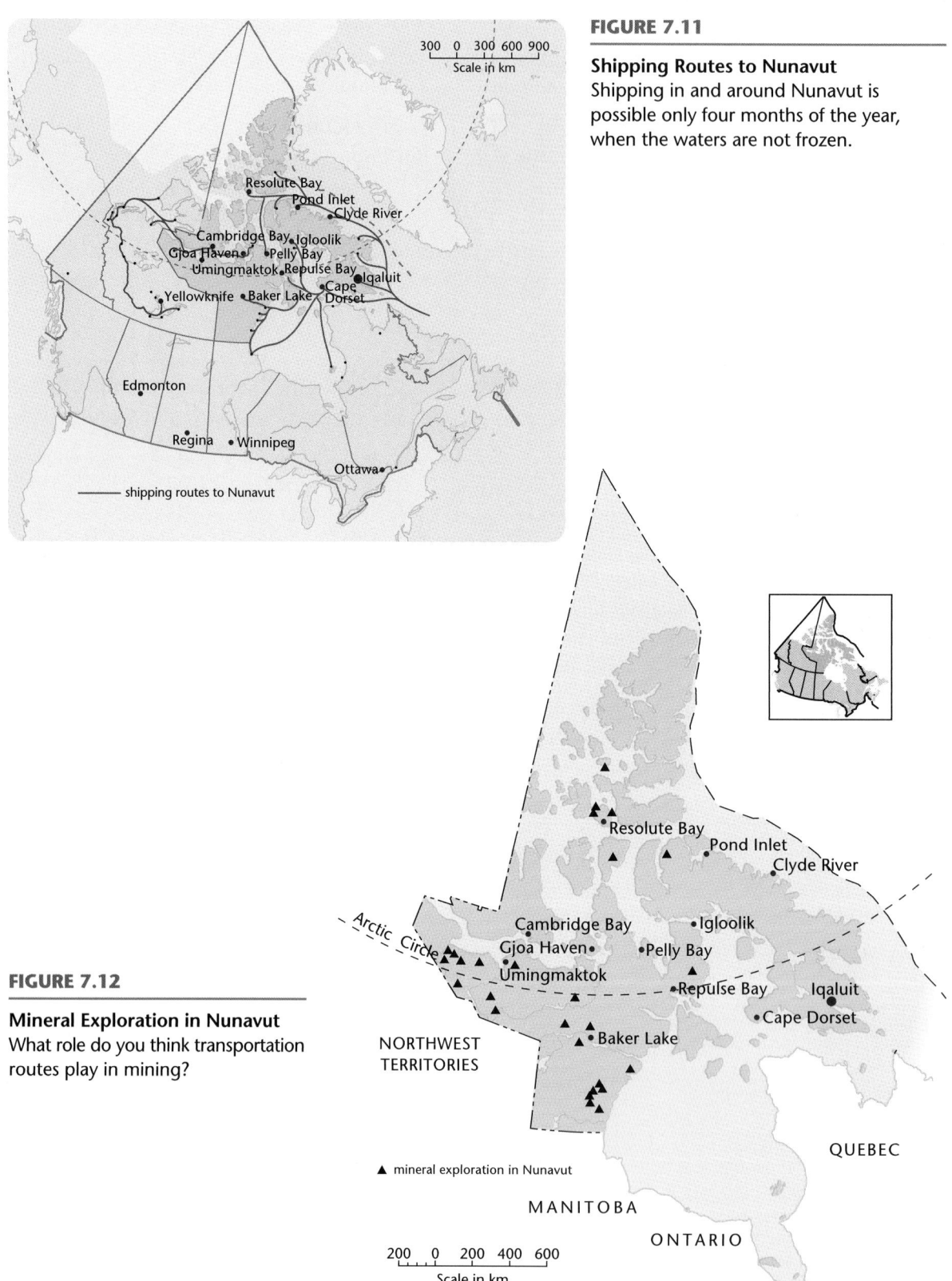

FIGURE 7.11

Shipping Routes to Nunavut
Shipping in and around Nunavut is possible only four months of the year, when the waters are not frozen.

FIGURE 7.12

Mineral Exploration in Nunavut
What role do you think transportation routes play in mining?

CHECK IT OVER

9. Look at the maps in Figures 7.9 to 7.12. For each map, write point-form answers to the following questions. You might organize your answers as a chart.

   a) What is the title of the map?

   b) What is the purpose of the map?

   c) What geographic area is shown on the map?

   d) What is the most important symbol used on the map?

10. Complete a chart, using Figures 7.9 to 7.12. For each map identify patterns and the challenges that these patterns might present in developing human systems in Nunavut. Use the following headings for your chart:

Map Topic	Geographic Patterns	Challenges for Human Systems

11. Create an ideas web or a diagram to show some of the challenges in developing transportation systems in Nunavut.

12. Suppose you were a leader of the Nunavut government. What are three strategies that you would recommend to your government to improve human systems in the territory? Explain your ideas.

THINK IT OVER

Knowledge and Understanding

1. Review the section of the chapter on Aboriginal population patterns. Make up a list of three questions that you would like answers to on the topic of Aboriginal population patterns.

2. **a)** Brainstorm a list of the benefits of Aboriginal land claims. Think about both the benefits to Aboriginal peoples and the benefits to all Canadians.

   b) Brainstorm a list of the challenges facing Aboriginal land claims.

   c) Share your lists with other students and add interesting points to your lists.

   d) What conclusion can you reach when you compare your benefits and challenges lists?

3. What are the differences between specific land claims and comprehensive land claims?

Thinking and Communication

4. Predict what the future holds for human systems, including transportation, for Nunavut. Make a list of human systems. Research information about one topic (other than transportation). Your answer should consider the next 20 years.

5. Use the Internet and other sources to identify five Aboriginal people who have made contributions to Canadian life. Identify some of their contributions.

6. If you were to design a tourism ad for Nunavut, what are three points that you would want to include in your ad? (Hint: Think about the physical and human systems in the region.) Give reasons for your points.

7. Explain how the creation of Nunavut came about, in part, because of Aboriginal population patterns.

Populating Canada

Chapter 8

In this chapter you will learn to

◢ *identify patterns in Canada's human systems*

◢ *report on how Canada influences, and is influenced by, its connections to other countries*

◢ report on how current trends or events affect whether Canada's human systems can sustain themselves

◢ use statistical methods in geographic analysis, observing accepted conventions

Key Words

immigration
emigration
net migration
census
push factors
pull factors
primary sources
secondary sources
census metropolitan area
discrimination

Introduction

The total population of North America and South America is over 890 million people. They are spread out from the Arctic Ocean in the north to the tip of Cape Horn in the south. This population has grown mainly over the past 400 years.

Populations grow for two reasons:

- More people are born than die each year.

- More people arrive than leave each year.

Canada's population has grown over the years mostly for the second reason. People come from all around the globe seeking a better life in Canada.

FIGURE 8.1

A Family Arriving in Canada from Poland in 1905
A hundred years ago, the Canadian government encouraged people from other countries to come to Canada to settle the land.

This chapter will look at how Canada's population grew because people arrived here from other parts of the world. The topics that we will consider are

- immigration patterns
- factors that affect immigration
- destinations within Canada for immigrants

CHECK IT OVER

1. Think about one person you know who lives in Canada but was born in another country. Answer these questions to the best of your ability:

   a) Around what year did the person come to Canada?

   b) Why did the person leave his or her home country to come to Canada?

   c) Where did the person live once he or she arrived here in Canada?

2. Choose one of the children in Figure 8.1. Pretend you are that person. Write a one-paragraph journal entry. In it, identify some emotions that you would be feeling as you and your family arrived in Canada.

Immigration Patterns

Population growth that results from more people arriving than leaving a country can be written in this way:

$$immigration - emigration = net\ migration$$

When people arrive from another country, it is called immigration. When people leave Canada to go to another country, it is called emigration. Both immigration and emigration rates have varied a good deal over Canada's history.

FIGURE 8.2

Immigration to Canada, 1890–1960

This graph shows the number of immigrants (people who come to Canada) from 1890 to 1960. Describe what happens to the line. When does it rise? When does it fall? Research to see what events took place to cause these changes.

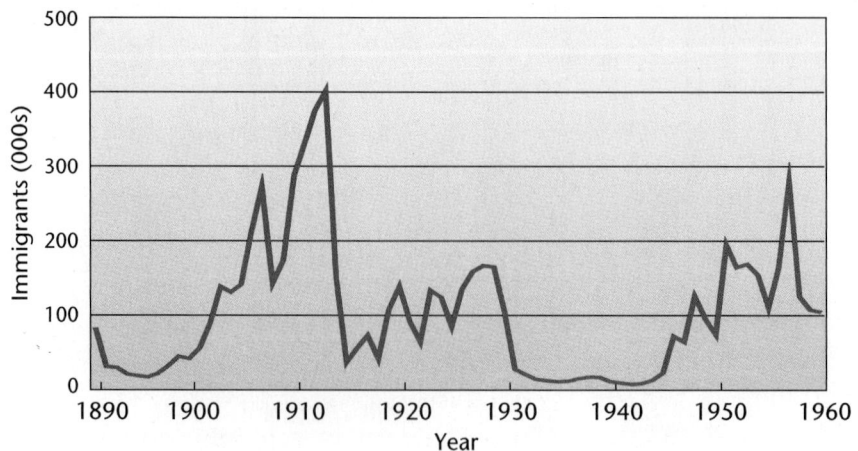

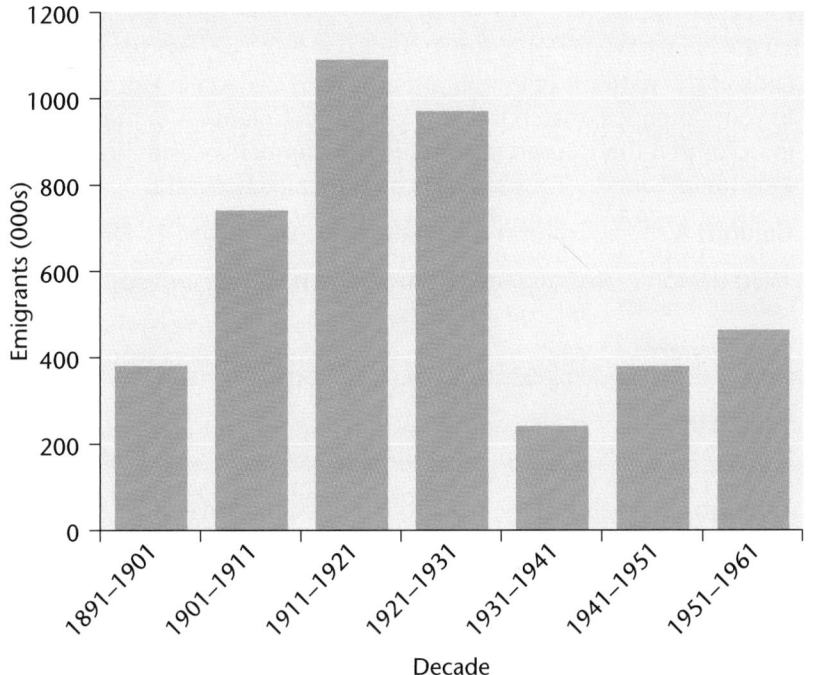

FIGURE 8.3

Emigration From Canada, 1891–1961
Why do you think the number of emigrants (people who leave Canada) changed between 1911 and 1921?

FAST *Fact*

By 2030, the natural increase rate (number of births minus number of deaths) in Canada will be zero. That is because birth rates are falling and, as more of the population ages, death rates are going to rise. At that time, all population growth in this country will occur because of immigration.

Overall, net migration rates (number of immigrants minus number of emigrants) have been rising in Canada, as Figure 8.4 shows. On the other hand, birth rates have been falling since the 1960s. This is because people have chosen to have smaller families. Now most of our population growth comes from immigration, not births.

FIGURE 8.4

Population Growth, 1961–2001
Which rate has changed the most, net migration or natural increase? Why?

Time Period	Total Population Growth (000s)	Natural Increase (000s) (births – deaths)	Net Migration (000s) (immigration – emigration)
1961–1966	1777	1518	259
1966–1971	1553	1090	463
1971–1976	1626	931	695
1976–1981	1470	977	493
1981–1986	1386	987	399
1986–1991	1973	987	986
1991–1996	1820	912	908
1996–2001	1349	616	733

CHECK IT OVER

3. Look at the patterns of immigrant arrivals in Canada in Figure 8.2. In your notebook, match the time periods in Column A to the events in Column B that caused changes in the numbers of immigrants arriving in Canada. They are not correctly matched here.

Column A	Column B
1930–1945	Immigrants from war-torn Europe arrived in large numbers.
1950–1960	Western Canada was open for settlers who took the trans-Canada railway.
1900–1912	The Great Depression and Second World War created global turmoil.

4. Through Canada's history, peaks of immigration have often been followed by peaks of emigration. Here are three reasons why recent immigrants left Canada:

   • Canada's harsh climate and rugged lands

   • unemployment and poor job opportunities

   • loss of culture and family connections

   In a sentence or two, explain how each of these reasons led to higher emigration rates.

5. a) What are the two factors in Figure 8.4 that cause population growth?

   b) What evidence in Figure 8.4 shows that a baby boom (a period of high birth rates) occurred in Canada?

   c) How is Canada's lower birth rate changing the factors that make up population growth?

The share of the Canadian population that immigrants make up has been rising over the past half century. The 2001 census (a count of the population) showed that 18.4 percent of Canadians, or a total of 5.5 million people, were born in another country. About one third of these immigrants arrived in Canada between 1991 and 2001. Following are other facts about immigrants that the census showed.

Origins of Immigrants

Europe had been the source of most immigrants to Canada throughout the twentieth century. However, between 1991 and 2001, most immigrants came from Asia and the Middle East, from countries like China, India, and Sri Lanka. This trend continued in the following years. People from Asia made up 52 percent of arrivals in 2002.

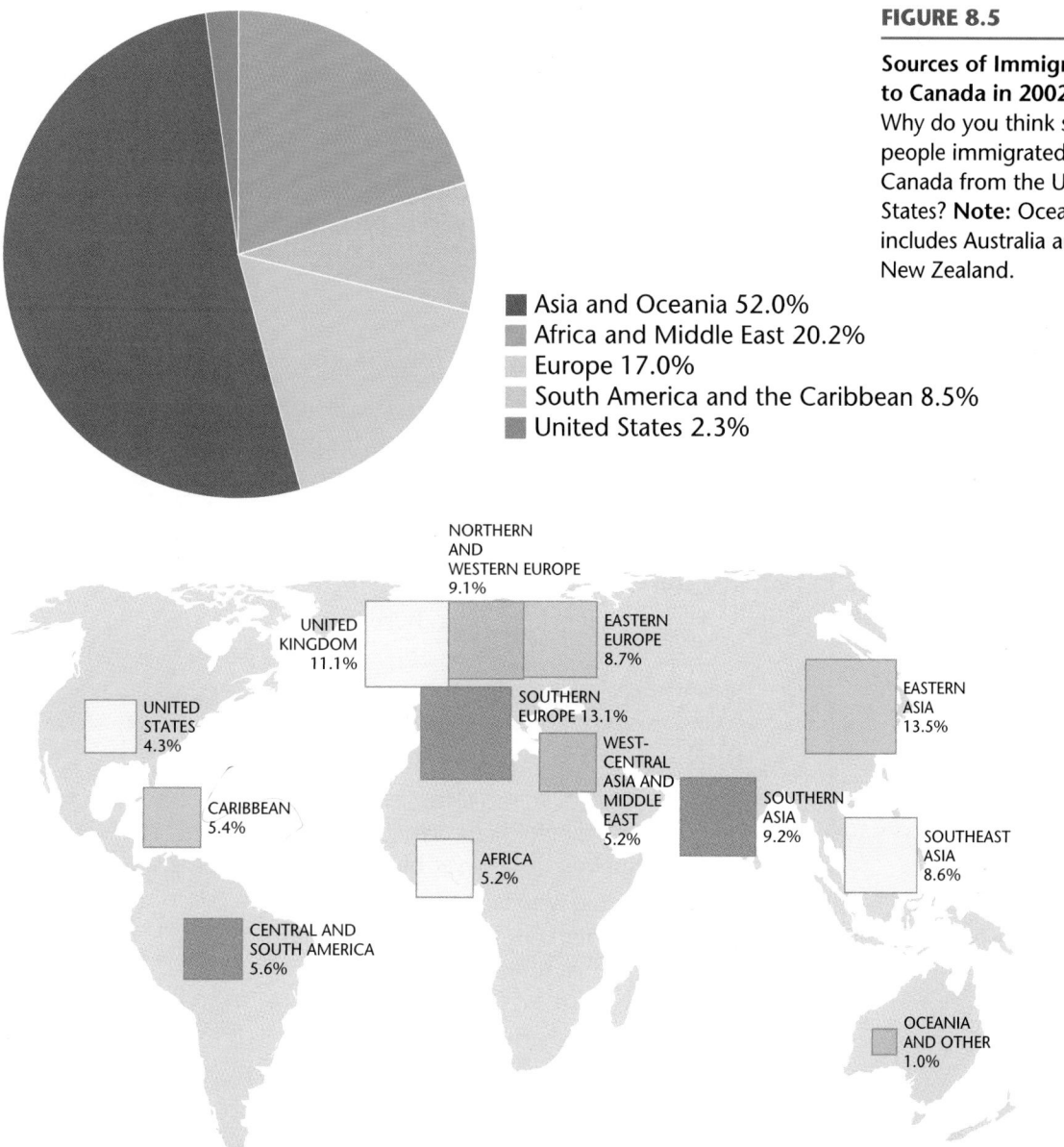

FIGURE 8.5

Sources of Immigrants to Canada in 2002
Why do you think so few people immigrated to Canada from the United States? **Note:** Oceania includes Australia and New Zealand.

■ Asia and Oceania 52.0%
■ Africa and Middle East 20.2%
■ Europe 17.0%
■ South America and the Caribbean 8.5%
■ United States 2.3%

NORTHERN
AND
WESTERN EUROPE
9.1%

UNITED
KINGDOM
11.1%

EASTERN
EUROPE
8.7%

UNITED
STATES
4.3%

SOUTHERN
EUROPE 13.1%

EASTERN
ASIA
13.5%

WEST-
CENTRAL
ASIA AND
MIDDLE
EAST
5.2%

CARIBBEAN
5.4%

SOUTHERN
ASIA
9.2%

SOUTHEAST
ASIA
8.6%

AFRICA
5.2%

CENTRAL AND
SOUTH AMERICA
5.6%

OCEANIA
AND OTHER
1.0%

FIGURE 8.6

Immigrant Population by Place of Birth, 2001
A smaller size box means fewer immigrants from that country lived in Canada in 2001. How might this picture change over the next 20 years or so?

Language and Religion

The 2001 census reported that 60 percent of new arrivals to Canada did not speak English or French at home. One third of all recent immigrants speak Cantonese, a Chinese dialect. New immigrants also practise religions that were not a large part of Canadian society in the past. New arrivals to Canada are more likely to report themselves as Muslims, Hindus, Sikhs, or Buddhists. In the past, Christians, Jews, and people with Aboriginal spiritual beliefs made up most of the population.

Age and Education

On average, recent immigrants are younger and better educated than the Canadian-born population. Two thirds of these people are between 25 and 64 years of age, as compared to 52 percent of all Canadians born in this country. Forty-one percent of immigrants have attended university. This compares to about 30 percent of Canadians born in this country.

Employment

Immigrants make up 20 percent of all workers in Canada. Between 1991 and 2001, immigrants made up 70 percent of the total number of new workers who were added to the labour force in Canada. But the 2001 census showed a disturbing picture. Most immigrants earn less than Canadian-born workers and find it hard to get jobs. For example, even after they have been in Canada for 10 years, male immigrants earn an average of only 80 percent of the wages of Canadian-born workers. Unemployment rates for immigrants are higher than for workers born here.

 GEOCAREERS

Settlement Counsellor

Immigrants to Canada often face very confusing situations. Think about buying groceries if you have never been in a large grocery store:
- How do you find items among all the aisles?
- How do you figure out the price you have to pay?
- Who do you ask for help?

Settlement counsellors help immigrants. They greet them once they have arrived and help them to find housing, which is their biggest concern. Over the next weeks or months, settlement counsellors coach new arrivals in such areas as
- how to budget for housing
- how to get health care
- how to use transportation
- how to find the food they need
- how to handle legal issues

Settlement counsellors usually speak two or more languages and have good geographic knowledge, including an understanding of people and places. Often they are immigrants to Canada themselves. They understand the pressures and problems faced by new arrivals. They also have a good general knowledge of the Canadian system and how it works. Settlement counsellors have college or university educations in fields like social work or counselling.

CHECK IT OVER

6. Write one sentence for each of the following sections in this chapter, stating the main idea that was discussed:
   - Origins of Immigrants
   - Language and Religion
   - Age and Education
   - Employment

7. Explain why the birthplaces of immigrants arriving in 2002, shown in Figure 8.5, are quite different from the birthplaces of the immigrants living in Canada in 2001, shown in Figure 8.6.

8. Why do you think immigrants are usually younger than the Canadian population?

9. Suggest three reasons why immigrant workers have lower wages on average, even though they tend to be better educated than Canadian-born workers.

10. Think of a person you know who might make a good settlement counsellor. Give three of that person's qualities that suit that person to the position.

Factors That Affect Immigration

Immigration rates to Canada are affected by events both here and around the world. We can break these events and conditions into two categories: push factors and pull factors.

Push Factors
These are the reasons people leave and go to another country to live.

Pull Factors
Once they have chosen to leave their home country, people need to decide where to go. Pull factors are the reasons that people go to Canada.

◄ War and violence
In countries like Sudan, in Africa, citizens fear for their lives because of the civil war.

◄ Lack of freedoms
In some countries, like China, people risk their lives if they speak out against the government.

▲ Poverty
Poverty and the hardships that come from not having enough food, clothing, and shelter encourage people to leave their home countries.

PUSH FACTORS

FACTORS THAT AFFECT IMMIGRATION

PULL FACTORS

▲ Peace and security
Canadians are guaranteed the right to express their opinions under our Constitution.

▲ Government policies
Government policies, such as the policy of celebrating our multicultural heritage, have encouraged immigration.

◄ Jobs and opportunities
Education and training help Canadians build prosperous lives and futures.

FIGURE 8.7

Factors That Affect Immigration
Many people around the world want the way of life we have here. This encourages them to immigrate to Canada.

LITERACY SKILL

Seeing the Difference Between Primary and Secondary Sources of Information

Information that we use about the world can come from either **primary sources** or **secondary sources**. When you research, the value of your information is affected by the sources that you use.

Here are some characteristics of each type of source:

Primary Sources

- first-hand, eyewitness accounts
- reflect the witnesses' personal viewpoints or biases
- reflect the attitudes and biases of the time the event occurred
- examples: letters, literary works, minutes of meetings, original research studies

Secondary Sources

- interpret, analyze, or explain things that have happened in the past
- created after the time period being discussed
- reflect the attitudes of the time in which the secondary source was written
- examples: reviews of authors' work, analyses of original documents, summaries of research studies

CHECK IT OVER

11. a) Think up one more push factor and one more pull factor that could be added to Figure 8.7.

   b) Describe or draw pictures to illustrate the two factors you just identified.

12. Explain how push and pull factors make Canada a popular choice for immigrants from around the world.

13. People who have immigrated to Canada and people born in Canada sometimes leave the country to live somewhere else. Many go to the United States or to Europe. Identify three push factors that might encourage people to leave this country.

Destinations for Immigrants to Canada

Once people from other countries have been admitted to Canada, they must choose where they will live. New immigrants make those decisions after thinking over a number of factors. Some of these factors are

- to be close to family and friends already here
- to be close to where other members of their cultural group have already settled
- to be where jobs are most plentiful
- to have access to education and training centres

Immigrants don't settle in all parts of Canada. Immigrants are more likely to go to Ontario, Quebec, and British Columbia. Figure 8.8 shows where immigrants to Canada settled in 2002.

FIGURE 8.8

Destinations of Immigrants to Canada, 2002
Which region of Canada attracts the fewest number of immigrants? Which region attracts the greatest number?

Destination	Number of Immigrants
Newfoundland and Labrador	405
Prince Edward Island	110
Nova Scotia	1 419
New Brunswick	710
Quebec	37 627
Ontario	133 641
Manitoba	4 621
Saskatchewan	1 665
Alberta	14 729
British Columbia	34 000
Yukon Territory	49
Northwest Territories	61
Nunavut	12
Canada	**229 049**

Immigrants also choose to live in the largest cities. More than 90 percent of people who came to Canada in the 1990s settled in large cities like Toronto and Montreal. (Almost 65 percent of all Canadians live in these huge cities.) Few immigrants make their way to smaller cities and towns.

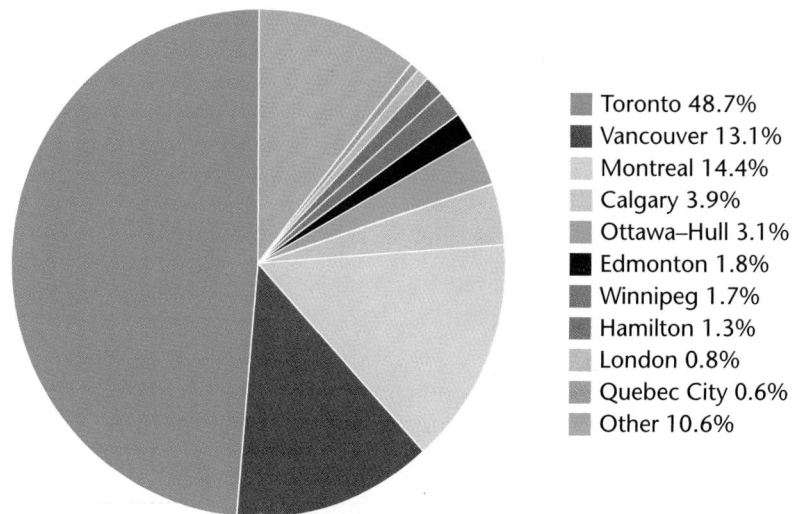

Toronto 48.7%
Vancouver 13.1%
Montreal 14.4%
Calgary 3.9%
Ottawa–Hull 3.1%
Edmonton 1.8%
Winnipeg 1.7%
Hamilton 1.3%
London 0.8%
Quebec City 0.6%
Other 10.6%

FIGURE 8.9

Top Ten CMA Destinations for Immigrants, 2002
Census metropolitan areas (CMAs) are large cities plus their surrounding communities. Why might the Toronto CMA attract so many immigrants?

Region of Birth	Place of Residence (% of immigrants)			
	Toronto	Vancouver	Montreal	Rest of Canada
East Asia	22.0	49.7	9.9	13.2
Southeast Asia and Pacific	10.9	14.6	9.1	13.4
South and Central Asia	26.4	16.2	15.1	13.0
Western Asia and Middle East	2.9	0.9	12.9	5.1
Africa	4.8	2.4	7.4	5.2
Eastern Europe	13.2	6.8	11.3	18.0
Western Europe	3.8	1.8	11.2	9.1
United Kingdom	1.8	2.4	0.8	6.4
Latin America	2.8	2.6	9.3	6.5
Caribbean	9.8	0.4	10.6	3.0
United States	1.5	2.1	2.4	7.0
Total	**100.0**	**100.0**	**100.0**	**100.0**

FIGURE 8.10

Recent Immigrant Population in Canadian Cities, 2001
What is the largest region of birth for immigrants to Toronto? Vancouver? Montreal? the rest of Canada?

FIGURE 8.11

A Classroom in the Toronto Area
How might large numbers of immigrants in a school system create opportunities? How might they create problems?

Finding supporting ideas
To find supporting ideas in a text, look for linking words such as *for example, in addition to, interestingly enough, in contrast to.*

CASE STUDY

Discrimination in Canada

Most Canadians view the flow of immigrants to Canada as a good thing. Some people have a different view. They see the increasing numbers of "outsiders" from Asia and the Middle East as a burden, even as a threat. They distrust people who look different from themselves.

This distrust has resulted in **discrimination** against immigrants. Discrimination means that people are treated unfairly. This unfair treatment might show up when immigrants

- apply for jobs
- look for housing
- attend school systems
- deal with police

For example, a study of policing in Kingston, Ontario, in 2005 found that people of colour were three times more likely to be stopped by traffic officers than white people. In another report, over one third of people of colour reported being victims of discrimination.

The *Canadian Charter of Rights and Freedoms* protects Canadians from discrimination. Laws stop the unfair treatment of people and promote tolerance and trust. Over the next several decades, discrimination based on race and ethnic group should decline.

8

CHECK IT OVER

14. Identify the main idea and at least two supporting ideas in the section of the chapter called Destinations for Immigrants to Canada.

15. Figure 8.8 shows that the three territories and four Atlantic provinces do not attract many immigrants.

   a) What are three factors that might discourage immigrants from going to those places?

   b) What could those regions do to attract more immigrants?

16. Study Figure 8.10. What are two ways that the immigration patterns for Canada's largest cities are the same? What are two ways that they are different?

17. What three pull factors might attract immigrants to Toronto?

THINK IT OVER

Knowledge and Understanding

1. Give three examples of ways that the physical environment of Canada might affect where immigrants choose to live.

2. Create a word web to show how the following terms are connected: *immigration, emigration, net migration, push factors, pull factors.*

Thinking and Communication

3. Identify one skill in statistical analysis that you used in this chapter.

4. a) Use three primary sources of information to find words that describe the problems recent immigrants faced when they came to Canada (e.g., *challenging, frustrating*). Your sources could be interviews with immigrants, stories about immigrants in magazines or newspapers, journal entries, and so on.

   b) Write down the name of one secondary source of information on the same topic.

5. Create an outline of a presentation titled "Using Statistics to Understand Immigration Patterns." Include five important ideas that you have learned from the tables and graphs in this chapter.

6. Have you ever witnessed discrimination? Have you ever been the victim of discrimination? Describe how you felt about it in one paragraph.

7. Make up a poster to show ways in which recent immigration patterns are changing Canadian society.

Chapter 9

People Patterns

In this chapter you will learn to

⊿ *describe issues that affect human systems in Canada*

⊿ *identify and explain how the population is spread across Canada*

⊿ identify what urban, suburban, fringe, and rural environments are made up of

⊿ report on how national trends affect Canada's human systems

Key Words

population distribution

rural

urban

rural-to-urban migration

suburban

fringe

demographers

rural depopulation

median age

Introduction

Suppose there was a politician who liked to shake people's hands. She thought that if she shook every Canadian's hand, she would have a better chance of getting reelected. Her election workers arranged to have every Canadian file past her at a rate of one person per second. How long would it take to shake every Canadian's hand if the country has a population of 32 805 000 (as it did in July 2005)?

She could shake 60 hands per minute, 3600 hands per hour, or 86 400 hands per day. To shake every Canadian's hand would take one full year plus an extra 15 days or so! If a politician in India tried the same thing, that person would be shaking hands for over 34 years. Chinese people would file past a politician for over 41 years!

FIGURE 9.1

The Population of Canada, 1981–2026
What was the population around the year you were born?

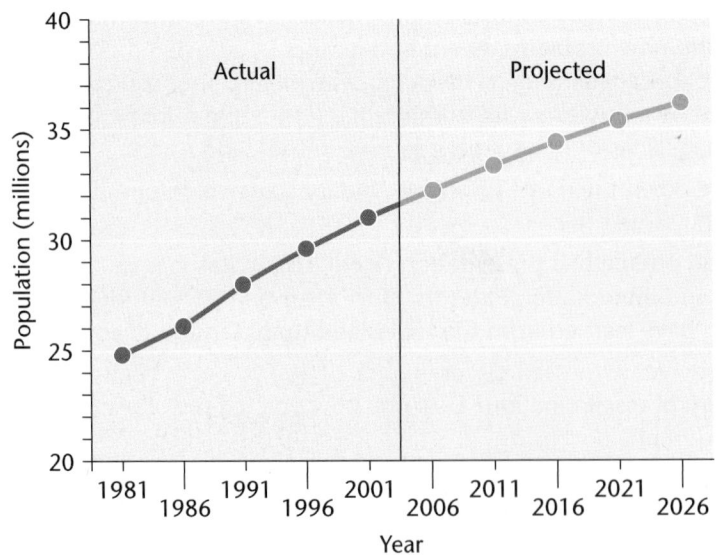

Even with recent growth, Canada does not have a very large population compared to some other countries. We rank thirty-sixth in the world, a good deal smaller than India and China, but larger than many other countries.

Population size is just one of the characteristics to think about when you look at population patterns. In this chapter, we will look at these characteristics:

- population distribution (the number of people who live in a place)
- rural-to-urban migration
- an aging population

CHECK IT OVER

1. Brainstorm a list of seven terms that you would expect to find in a chapter dealing with population patterns. Then scan through this chapter to see if the words are here. Check your spelling of the words. Add three new words from the chapter to your list.

2. Why might politicians and government officials want to know how many people are in a country? Give two reasons.

Population Distribution

Look at the map in Figure 9.2. This is the view of Canada that you would see if you flew over the country on a clear night. The lights of the towns and cities would show up as bright spots, while places with few people would be dark. This map shows how people are spread out across the land area of Canada. This is called the population distribution.

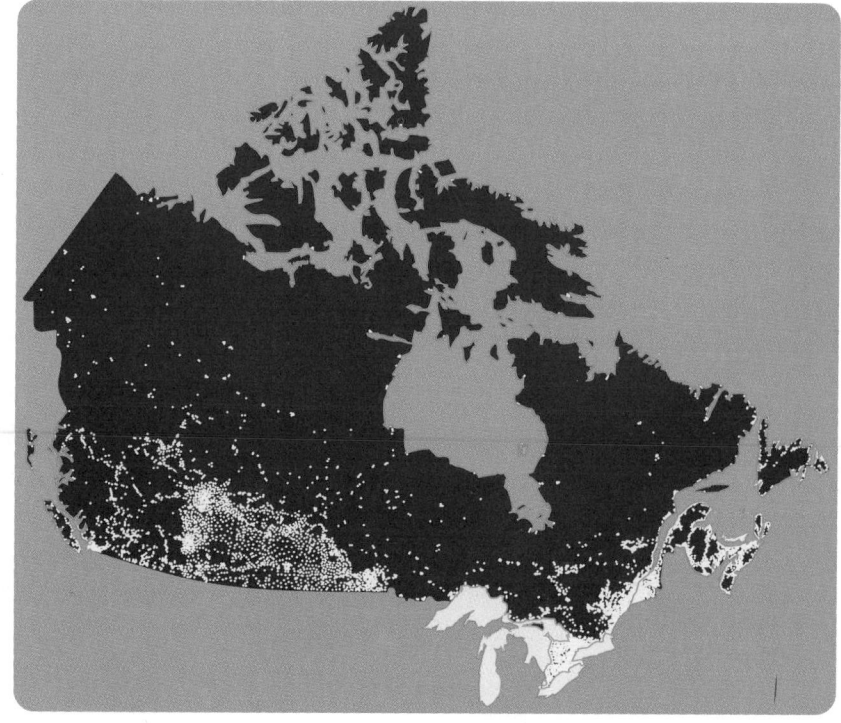

FIGURE 9.2

A Night View of Canada
One of the first things that people notice about Canada's population distribution is how close most people live to our southern border. Where are you located on this map?

Canadians are not evenly spread across the land. Figure 9.3 shows some words geographers use to describe how people are spread out across the land.

FIGURE 9.3

Population Distribution Words
Look at Figure 9.2 and suggest one more distribution word that could be added to this list.

clustered	describes areas where many people live close to each other
sparse	describes land where a few people are spread over a large area
evenly distributed	describes areas where people are spread over the land equally
linear	describes land where people are arranged along a line

FIGURE 9.4

Factors that Affect Population Distribution
Which one of these factors do you think most influences the population distribution where you live?

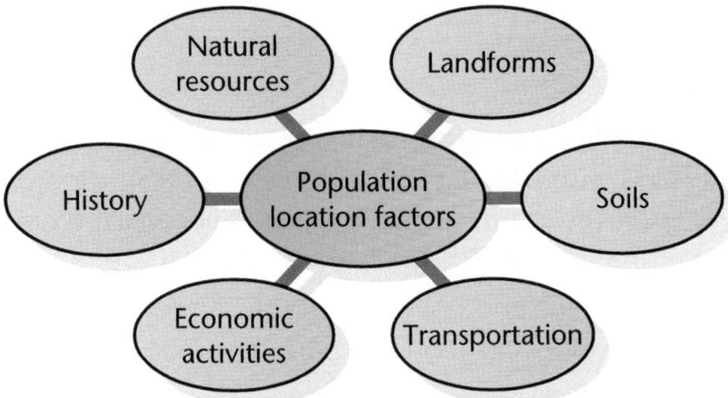

Population location factors: Natural resources, Landforms, History, Soils, Economic activities, Transportation

FIGURE 9.5

Populations of Provinces and Territories
Which province had the largest change in population from 1991 to 2005?

Province/Territory	1991 (000s)	2005 (000s)	Change 1991–2005 (000s)
Newfoundland and Labrador	580	516	−64
Prince Edward Island	130	138	8
Nova Scotia	915	938	23
New Brunswick	746	752	6
Quebec	7 065	7 598	533
Ontario	10 428	12 541	2 113
Manitoba	1 110	1 178	68
Saskatchewan	1 003	994	−9
Alberta	2 593	3 257	664
British Columbia	3 373	4 254	881
Yukon Territory	29	31	2
Northwest Territories	39	43	4
Nunavut	22	30	8

3. Explain why a night view of Canada, as in Figure 9.2, is a good way to show population distribution.

4. Create small sketches to show the population distribution patterns that are described in Figure 9.3. Give the distribution patterns you have sketched different names from those in Figure 9.3.

5. a) What words would you use to describe the population distribution of people in your classroom?

   b) Think about three other places in your school and describe the population distribution at a certain time of day, for example, the cafeteria at lunchtime.

6. Think about the community where you live. Rank the six factors in Figure 9.4 by most important to your community to least important. Explain why you ranked the factors this way.

7. Study the statistical table in Figure 9.5. Make three observations about Canada's population distribution. Your observations could be about individual provinces or territories, about regional patterns, or about Canada as a whole.

Rural-to-Urban Migration

If you had visited Canada 100 years ago, you would have quickly noticed that most Canadians lived in the countryside. They worked on farms, cleared forests for timber, and fished the oceans. Canada was a rural nation at that time.

However, change was taking place. More and more people moved to cities to find jobs in the fast-growing industries. Canada soon became an urban nation, and most of the population lived in towns and cities. This movement of people from rural parts to urban parts is called rural-to-urban migration.

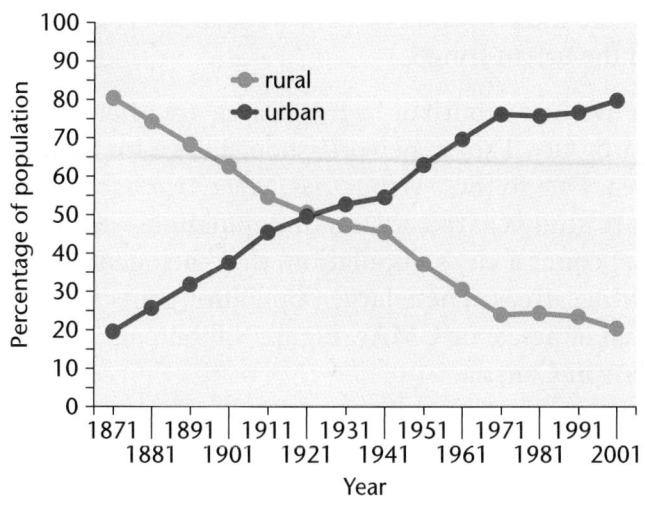

Literacy Strategy

Reading line graphs
A line graph shows changes that occur over time. The y-axis (vertical) shows intervals of change and the x-axis (horizontal) shows intervals of time. To answer questions using line graphs, you must identify whether you are being asked to find time or change.

FIGURE 9.6

Urban and Rural Populations of Canada, 1871–2001
What was the first year that more than half of Canadians lived in cities? What year did more than three quarters of Canadians live in the country?

CHECK IT OVER

8. Sometimes people left the rural parts of Canada because they were "pushed" out by negative factors, such as a decrease in the number of farms. Sometimes people left the rural parts because they were "pulled" toward the cities by positive factors, such as good jobs. Suggest push and pull factors for rural-to-urban migration. Make a two-column chart with these headings:

Factors That Push People Out of Rural Areas	Factors That Pull People to Urban Areas

9. a) Refer to Figure 9.6. When was rural-to-urban migration slowest in Canada?

   b) When did rural-to-urban migration reverse?

   c) Why do you think that Canada will never have everyone living in cities?

10. Make up a diagram to show the differences in the terms *rural*, *urban*, and *rural-to-urban migration*.

Cities grew larger because of rural-to-urban migration. They spread beyond their boundaries and spilled into nearby rural areas. These areas started to have some characteristics of urban places, like many homes and roadways. They also still had some characteristics of rural places, including land used for farming or other rural activities. Geographers describe these areas on the edges of cities this way:

- Areas that are mostly urban but have some rural characteristics are called suburban.

- Areas that are mostly rural but have some urban characteristics are called the urban fringe.

People who live in a suburban or fringe area are often strongly linked to the nearby city. They may work, shop, and go for health care in the urban area. Due to these strong ties, when demographers (whose job it is to study characteristics of populations, including counting people) count a city's population, they include the suburban and fringe areas. These large population units are called census metropolitan areas, or CMAs. Figure 9.9 on page 92 shows the largest CMAs in Canada.

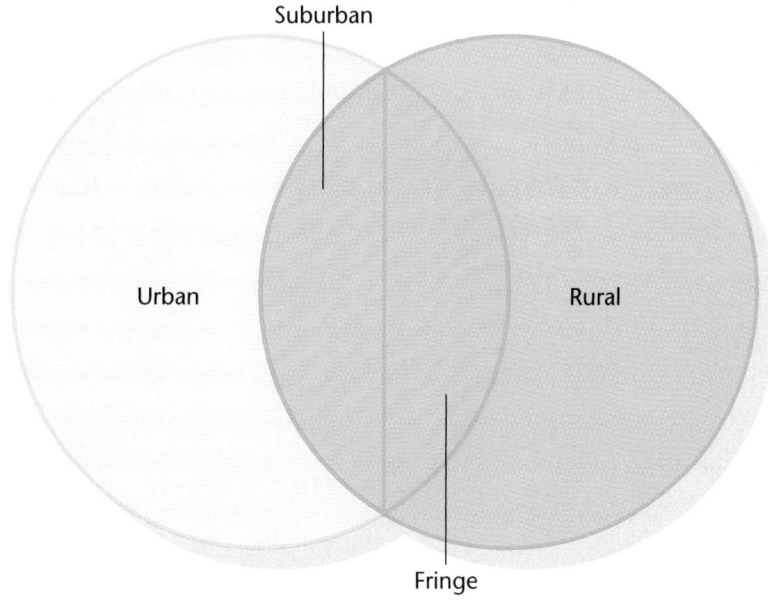

Suburban

Urban

Rural

Fringe

FIGURE 9.7

Urban and Rural Environments
Which of these words best describes where your home is?

LITERACY SKILL

Venn Diagrams

Venn diagrams are charts that show how categories of information are related. Each category is shown as a whole circle. Overlapping circles are used to show the areas where the categories are the same.

Figure 9.8 is an example of a Venn diagram. It shows us that there are a number of rich countries in the world and a larger number of poor countries. Some countries have features that we would find in rich countries and features that we would find in poor countries. We would put these countries in the overlapping part of the chart. Venn diagrams can be drawn with two or more circles and can have different amounts of overlap.

FIGURE 9.8

An Example of a Venn Diagram
The circles of a Venn diagram do not have to be the same size. Why would you use different-sized circles in a Venn diagram?

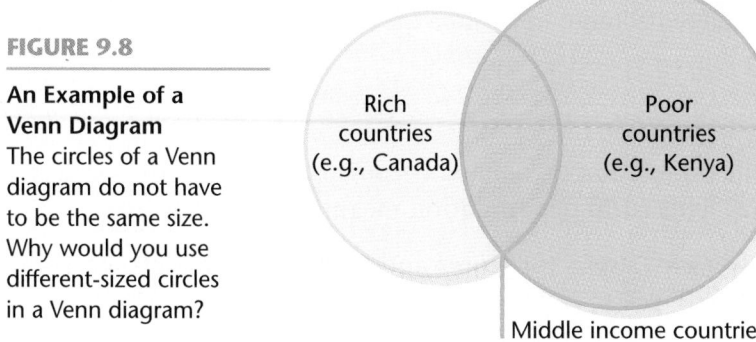

Rich countries (e.g., Canada)

Poor countries (e.g., Kenya)

Middle income countries (e.g., Mexico)

Census Metropolitan Area	1951		2004	
	Population (000s)	% of Canada's Population	Population (000s)	% of Canada's Population
Toronto	1117.5	8.0	5203.6	16.3
Montreal	1395.4	10.0	3606.7	11.3
Vancouver	530.7	3.8	2160.0	6.8
Ottawa–Hull	281.9	2.0	1142.7	3.6
Edmonton	173.1	1.2	1001.6	3.1
Calgary	139.1	1.0	1037.1	3.2
Quebec	274.8	2.0	710.7	2.2
Winnipeg	354.1	2.5	702.4	2.2
Hamilton	259.7	1.9	710.3	2.2

FIGURE 9.9

Populations of Canada's Largest Urban Areas, 1951 and 2004
Which was the largest urban area in 1951? Which was the largest urban area in 2004?

FAST *Fact*

Between 1996 and 2001, Calgary, Alberta grew 15 percent. It grew faster than all other CMAs.

CHECK IT OVER

11. How did suburban areas result from rural-to-urban migration?

12. Choose the best definition for the word *urban* from the options below. Write an explanation of your choice.

    a) the process by which an area becomes urban

    b) the places outside towns and cities

    c) a large number of people, economic activities, and buildings within a small geographic area

13. Look at the statistics for Toronto in Figure 9.9. Explain how Toronto increased in population by almost five times, but only doubled its percentage of Canada's population.

14. a) Make up three questions about the patterns you see in Figure 9.9. For example, one question could be "What factors might have caused Toronto to become the largest urban area in Canada?"

    b) Answer your three questions.

As the population of Canada became more urban, the rural areas struggled. This rural depopulation meant that there were

- fewer customers for stores and business in small towns and villages

- fewer people to give financial support to churches and community groups

- fewer taxpayers to fund hospitals, road maintenance, schools, and so on

Many of the rural parts of the country could not survive when people moved to the cities.

FIGURE 9.10

Rural Depopulation in Gimli, Manitoba
This photograph shows the effects of rural depopulation. Why have people left rural areas?

CASE STUDY

Doctor Shortages in Rural Areas

Many people who live in small towns and rural areas cannot find family doctors. The number of doctors outside of large cities has decreased by over 15 percent since 1994. At the same time, the populations in these areas have increased by 4 percent. By 2010, there will be a shortfall of 1337 doctors in rural parts of Ontario alone. This situation is predicted to get worse right through to 2021. At that point, the doctor shortage should begin to improve.

Why is there a shortage of doctors? Several factors have caused this shortage:

- Doctors, like many of the population, are getting older and are retiring.

- More medical students are choosing to specialize. This means they have to work in large hospitals in big cities.

- To cut costs, governments have reduced enrollments in medical schools.

- Canadian doctors are moving to the United States. For every 19 Canadian medical graduates who go to the U.S., only one American doctor moves north.

In recent years, some provinces have boosted the number of spaces in medical schools and have made it easier for foreign doctors to work in Canada. Critics say that these efforts are "too little, too late." They predict that the doctor shortage is going to get worse.

15. Name three results of fewer and fewer people living in rural parts of Canada.

16. Suppose you are a doctor in Canada who has just graduated. Would you move to a rural area to practise medicine? Explain your ideas.

An Aging Population

Canadians are getting older, statistically speaking. In 1921, the median age of Canadians was 23.9 years. In other words, half of the population was older than this age and half was younger. The median age was 37.9 years in 2003 and is expected to be over 40 years by 2036.

You could look at this trend another way by looking at the percentage of the population that is over 65 years of age. In 2004, senior citizens made up just over 13 percent of the population. This figure will increase to 16 percent by 2016 and to 23 percent by 2041.

This increasing average age has been called "the greying of Canada."

FIGURE 9.11

Reasons for Canada's Aging Population
Why might some Canadians be concerned about the aging of Canada's population?

The condition:	longer life expectancies	lower fertility rates	the baby boom
is produced by:	improved nutrition, health care, and hygiene	family planning and lifestyle choice, careers for women	high post-Second World War birth rate (1947–1965)
which results in:	more older people in society	fewer younger people in society	median age has increased, meaning more older people
and leads to:		a greying Canada	

17. Find two pieces of evidence from this chapter that show the Canadian population is getting older.

18. What are two ways that living in an older society may affect you personally?

19. Use the ideas in Figure 9.11 to write a short paragraph on why Canada's population is getting older.

FIGURE 9.12

Active Canadian Senior Citizens
What challenges might there be because of a rise in the number of seniors in a society? What opportunities might there be?

Year	% under 5	% 5–19	% 20–44	% 45–64	% over 65
1941	9.14	28.39	37.19	18.61	6.67
1951	12.29	25.60	36.63	17.74	7.75
1961	12.37	29.44	33.19	17.37	7.63
1971	8.42	30.97	33.87	18.66	8.09
1981	7.32	24.70	39.14	19.13	9.70
1991	6.99	20.42	41.33	19.66	11.61
1996	6.65	20.60	39.03	21.49	12.23
2001	6.04	19.85	37.97	23.50	12.64
2006	5.71	19.05	35.88	26.29	13.03
2011	5.59	18.12	34.14	28.09	14.04
2016	5.53	17.42	32.27	30.60	15.88

FIGURE 9.13

Age Structure of Canada's Population, 1941–2016
How can you tell from this table that a baby boom took place in Canada?

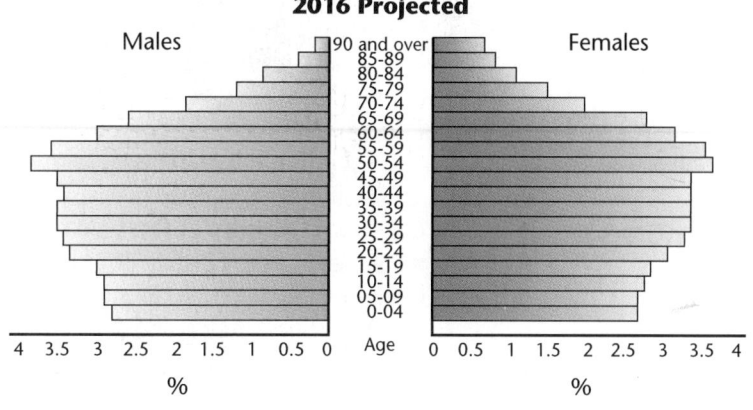

2016 Projected

Males — Females

FIGURE 9.14

Canada's Projected Population, 2016
Which age group is largest? What does that tell you about Canada's population?

FAST *Fact*

An average Canadian over 65 years of age uses three times the amount of health care of an average Canadian under that age.

Many people are worried about the financial costs of a greying population. There are several reasons for their concern:

- Senior citizens will no longer contribute to both private pension plans and the Canada Pension Plan.
- A huge number of retired workers will be making withdrawals from pension plans at the same time.
- Senior citizens use health care and social services more than other age groups, so these costs will rise.

More seniors mean that there will be more people relying on fewer workers to pay for their benefits.

The aging population also provides opportunities. Older Canadians are consumers. Their changing needs create new markets. For example, travel companies are targeting seniors. They offer packages that meet the needs and interests of older travellers. The fashion industry has also responded. They are making clothing for mature tastes and sizes. The greatest growth in services for seniors is in health care. More and more Canadian businesses, like those listed above, are targeting the needs of Canada's aging population.

 GEOTECHNOLOGY

Statistics Canada

We are bombarded every day with statistics, such as

- the number of people without jobs
- the amount spent by tourists
- crime rates

Much of this information comes from Statistics Canada. This agency collects statistics about the whole of Canada plus the provinces and territories.

Statistics Canada conducts a census every five years to gather statistical information. Households must fill out census forms and give information about race, education, employment, and so on. The agency also uses about 350 other surveys to collect information on all aspects of life in Canada. This includes information about businesses, travel patterns, and spending habits.

Researchers and businesses can get this information by downloading data from Statistics Canada's Web site. They can also get it from print resources in many public libraries. Anyone can access the Web site. Click free resources, such as Canadian Statistics or Community Profiles. More specific data can be purchased from Statistics Canada.

9

CHECK IT OVER

20. Write down words or phrases that you think might summarize how the following Canadians think about the aging population:

    a) an elementary school teacher

    b) a nurse

    c) a car insurance salesperson

21. Think about your plans for the future. What are two ways that you might think of the greying of Canada as an opportunity?

22. You are studying population trends such as the greying of a population. Describe three consequences of collecting data that are not accurate.

THINK IT OVER

Knowledge and Understanding

1. Choose three of the terms in the list of key words at the beginning of this chapter. Create a diagram to show how the terms are connected.

2. Make up a chart to identify two problems and two opportunities that Canada's population distribution creates for us.

3. Make up an ideas web to show some of the factors that have caused the rural-to-urban migration in Canada.

4. Explain why a study of Canada's aging population should be included in a chapter titled "People Patterns."

Thinking and Communication

5. Suppose you are an adviser to the prime minister. You are asked to write a report titled "The Greatest Population Challenge Facing Canadians." Using ideas from this chapter, give your opinion of what the greatest challenge is and make three points to back up your opinion.

6. What are three things that you think the governments in Canada could do to help Canadians deal with the greying of the population?

7. Create a poster to show several ways that the changing population patterns of Canada will affect physical systems, for example, the effect on water use if more people are living in cities.

A Nation of Cities

In this chapter you will learn to

◢ *identify patterns and differences in Canada's human systems*

◢ describe characteristics of urban systems

◢ identify characteristics of urban, suburban, fringe, and rural environments

◢ use appropriate statistical methods in geographic analysis

Key Words

technological change

central business district

metropolitan areas

urban functions

land use

Introduction

We are a population of city dwellers—at least, most of us are. We saw in Chapter 9 that movement of people from rural areas to urban areas has been an important trend in Canada. Now, four out of five Canadians live in large towns and cities.

People often have mixed feelings about cities. While most jobs in Canada are centred in cities, most crimes occur in cities. It is a case of taking the bad with the good.

In this chapter we will focus on what goes on in cities. We will discuss the following topics:

• how cities change over time

• how land is used in cities

• urban poverty

jobs entertainment

educational opportunities *excitement*

anonymity **services**

crime crowded streets

no one cares

high prices for housing **no privacy**

few parking spaces

FIGURE 10.1

Views About Living in Cities
What is your personal view of living in large cities?

 CHECK IT OVER

1. Which point of view in Figure 10.1 do you think is closest to your own opinion of cities? Give reasons for your answer.

2. Brainstorm with a partner to make up two lists, one showing the good things that cities contribute to our society, and one showing the bad things.

Changing Urban Places

Canada has changed in many ways over the years. For example, we started out by gathering the natural resources of the lands and seas to provide for ourselves. Then we began manufacturing goods. Now most Canadians provide services to others. (You will learn more about these ideas in the coming chapters). As our ways of earning a living changed, the places where we lived also changed.

Cities have been growing over the past century or so. They have grown in two directions, upward (higher buildings) and outward (spreading out at the edges). This growth has allowed more people to live within cities. A key element of this growth has been technological change. The ways in which we build cities has changed, as Figure 10.2 shows.

FIGURE 10.2

Impacts of Technological Change on Cities
What changes have allowed cities to grow outwards?

Technological Innovations	Impacts on Cities, People, and the Environment
1. Improvements in public transit, such as subways and light rapid transit lines, increase the speed of people moving within cities.	People are able to move farther away from their places of employment, often the centre of the cities, encouraging growth along the transit lines.
2. Expressways are constructed to move automobiles rapidly from outside the cities to the centres of the cities and to industrial areas within the cities.	Along the expressway routes, suburbs grow quickly, expanding the outer edges of the cities.
3. Use of reinforced concrete and steel in the construction of large buildings means that they can be built much higher than before.	Cities expand upward with the construction of skyscrapers in the central areas of the cities.
4. The infrastructure of cities—such as sewers, water lines, and power grids—are updated and expanded to meet the greater demands of urban dwellers.	Population densities rise as more people are able to be accommodated within the city and its suburbs.

FIGURE 10.3

A View of Edmonton, Alberta
What evidence shows that the city has been growing?

FIGURE 10.4

Populations of Canada's Largest Cities
Which province does not have a city large enough to be a census metropolitan area?

FAST Fact

Census metropolitan areas (CMAs) are metropolitan areas of at least 100 000 people. They also include the people who live in nearby areas who are closely tied to the large cities. These people may work, shop, and go for health care in the metropolitan area.

Census Metropolitan Area	Population in 1996	Population in 2004	Land Area (km²)
Abbotsford, BC	136 500	160 100	626
Calgary, AB	821 600	1 037 100	5083
Chicoutimi/Saguenay, QC	160 500	154 200	1754
Edmonton, AB	862 600	1 001 600	9419
Halifax, NS	343 000	379 800	5496
Hamilton, ON	624 400	710 300	1372
Kingston, ON	144 500	156 500	1907
Kitchener, ON	382 900	450 100	837
London, ON	416 500	459 700	2333
Montreal, QC	3 326 400	3 606 700	4047
Oshawa, ON	268 800	332 000	903
Ottawa-Hull, ON-QC	998 700	1 142 700	5218
Quebec, QC	671 900	710 700	3154
Regina, SK	193 700	198 600	3408
St. Catharines-Niagara, ON	372 400	394 900	1406
St. John's, NL	174 100	179 900	805
Saint John, NB	125 700	126 500	3360
Saskatoon, SK	219 100	234 000	5192
Sherbrooke, QC	149 600	162 300	1108
Sudbury, ON	165 600	161 100	3536
Thunder Bay, ON	126 600	127 100	2548
Toronto, ON	4 263 800	5 203 600	5903
Trois Rivières, QC	140 000	141 200	881
Vancouver, BC	1 831 700	2 160 000	2876
Victoria, BC	304 300	330 200	695
Windsor, ON	286 800	330 900	1023
Winnipeg, MB	667 100	702 400	4151

10

LITERACY SKILL

Reading Photographs

Reading a photograph is a lot like reading a newspaper article. You need to read carefully to find out the topic, pick out the main idea, and note supporting ideas. You then need to think about the significance of the ideas you have just read.

With photographs, you look for the same things. It is often helpful to look at the different parts of a photograph. Look at

- the foreground: the area closest to the camera
- the background: the area farthest from the camera
- the middle ground: the details between the foreground and background

FIGURE 10.5

A Part of a City Where Poverty Is Found
What would you identify as the main idea in this photograph?

FIGURE 10.6

Growth Around a City
When cities expand outward, they often take over useful farmland. What are some other problems that go with the growth of cities?

In Canada's early days, most people wanted to live near the centre of cities, where they could find shops and businesses that provided jobs. This area was called the central business district (CBD). As cities grew, people who could afford to commute left the crowded central part of the city and moved to new homes on the edges of the city. This trend has continued throughout the past 100 years.

Cities that become very large are called metropolitan areas. Jobs are increasingly being created at the edges of metropolitan areas, in the suburbs. This causes more growth to take place at the fringes of the cities. Cities then expand outwards into the rural areas.

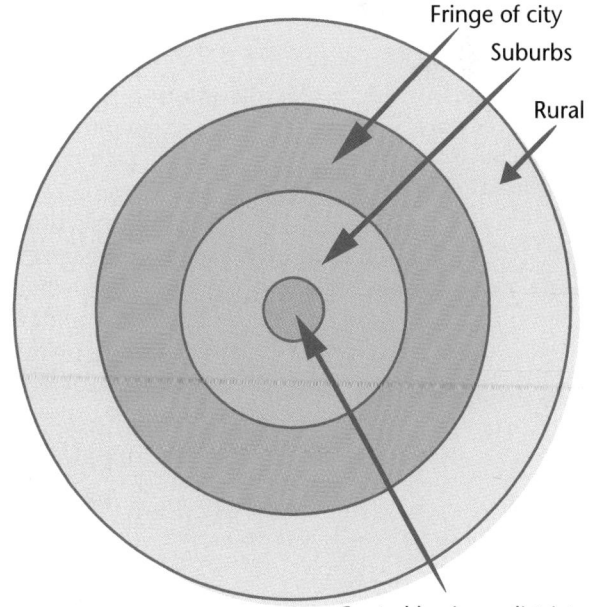

Fringe of city
Suburbs
Rural
Central business district

3. Give one example to show how economic change, technological change, and urban change work together to change how cities look.

4. Use Figure 10.4 to answer these questions:
   a) Which census metropolitan area (CMA) has the largest population?
   b) Which CMA has the smallest population?
   c) Which CMA has the largest area?
   d) Which CMA has the smallest area?

5. Explain why cities expand outward as their population grows.

6. Suggest two reasons why companies may want to locate their businesses at the fringes of cities rather than in the central business district.

The Geography of Cities

Urban functions are economic activities that go on in towns and cities. A convenience store is an example of an urban function. The store provides employment while meeting the needs of the people. Urban functions can be grouped into two categories: basic and non-basic. Figure 10.7 explains these two types. Most communities have some of each type of urban function. The larger the urban area, the more functions it has.

FIGURE 10.7

Basic and Non-Basic Urban Functions
Into which category would you put a convenience store?

	Basic Activities	Non-Basic Activities
Explanation	These economic activities produce goods and services to be sold outside the community. They are called *town-forming activities*, because without these activities, the urban area would have no reason to exist.	These economic activities produce goods and services that will be used within the community. They are called *town-serving activities*. Non-basic activities do not bring money into the urban area. They just circulate money that is already there.
Examples	mine or mill, manufacturing plant, large tourist park, bank headquarters	auto repair shop, video store, movie theatre, local bank branch

CHECK IT OVER

7. Make a list of 10 urban functions that you have used in the past several weeks. Organize your list into functions that are basic and non-basic to your location.

8. Health care is one kind of urban function. The health care offered in different urban areas depends on their size:
   - **Metropolitan area:** several hospitals, specialty clinics such as for cancer treatment
   - **City:** one large hospital, some clinics
   - **Town:** one small hospital or clinic
   - **Village:** doctors' office
   - **Hamlet:** no health care services

   Research automobile services and recreation facilities. Then complete the same type of list for those functions.

The lands that the urban functions sit on are the land uses of the urban area.

Most urban functions rely on customers coming to them. That means many urban functions need to be in locations where people can easily get to them, such as major roadways or intersections. That is why you often see stores and services grouped together as malls or plazas at busy corners. If the owners of commercial businesses do not choose locations that customers can reach easily, they will not be successful. So, owners often pay high rents to get the best possible locations. On the other hand, owners of factories may choose to locate in out-of-the-way areas. They do not need customers to find them, so they have no reason to pay high rents.

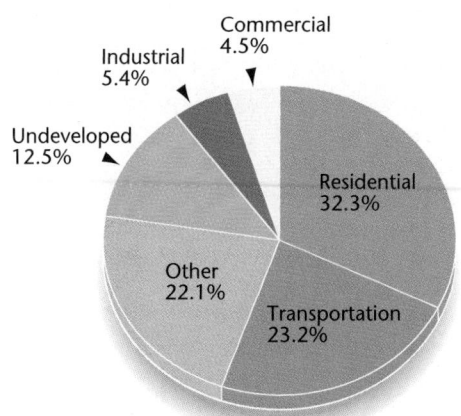

Commercial 4.5%
Industrial 5.4%
Undeveloped 12.5%
Residential 32.3%
Other 22.1%
Transportation 23.2%

FIGURE 10.8

Land Uses in a Typical Urban Area
Name one land use that would fit into the category of "Other."

FIGURE 10.9

Types of Land Uses in Urban Areas
Give an example of each of these land uses in your local area.

Land use	Purposes	Subdivisions of land uses
Residential	Where people live	Single-family homes Multi-family homes (townhouses and duplexes) Apartments and condos
Industrial	Factories and industries	Light industrial uses, often located in industrial parks (areas set aside for use of businesses) Heavy industry, such as steel mills or auto assembly plants
Commercial	Places that sell goods and services	Single shops, such as corner stores CBD (central business district) locations Strip plazas, usually along major streets Shopping malls
Transportation	Land used to provide facilities to move goods and people	Roadways Railways and their stations Airports Harbour and port facilities
Other	To meet the various other needs of people in urban areas	Public administration uses, such as city hall and libraries Recreational areas Institutions, including religious places and schools Health care facilities

FIGURE 10.10

Toronto's Harbour Area
What types of land uses are shown in this aerial photograph?

Toronto's Waterfront

Toronto's waterfront on Lake Ontario is going through a great deal of change. In the past, land uses were usually tied to transportation. This area had

- docks and berths for loading and unloading ships' cargoes
- railway stations, train repair facilities, and tracks for passenger and cargo traffic
- large multi-lane roadways used by commuters

The skyline was a row of huge industries, warehouses, and shipyards. In recent years, however, railway and shipping activities have become much less important because many companies prefer using truck and air transportation.

The City of Toronto is working hard to change this area. The old land uses are being removed or changed into something more modern. For example, a large warehouse building was renovated and is now the home of exclusive shops and expensive condominiums called Queen's Quay. An area that was once filled with distilleries for making alcohol is now a vibrant arts and theatre district: the Distillery District. Parks, residences, offices, and shops are also going to be developed on that land.

Toronto's waterfront is an interesting case of changing land uses to respond to changing times.

 GEOCAREERS

Urban Planner

Urban planners try to answer the question, what kind of community do people want? Their goal is to help design safe, healthy urban environments. They design places that meet our social, economic, and physical needs. They are constantly thinking ahead. For example, they figure out how much traffic a city will have in the future. Planners need geographic skills such as mapping, researching, and communicating.

Planners focus on how to develop and use land, how to use resources, and what facilities and services people need. They decide where to put green spaces, and how to put schools in neighbourhoods where they are needed most and hospitals in the centres of cities. They also decide where sewage and drainage systems should go. Politicians often use urban planners to help them make decisions on how best to use urban land. Urban planners usually have a university degree in subjects like geography, environmental studies, or economics.

CHECK IT OVER

9. Describe the land uses around your school. What is the main land use?

10. Explain why stores will pay high rents to be at busy intersections but homeowners will usually not pay these expensive rents.

11. a) Describe the types of land uses that are being developed on Toronto's waterfront. Refer to Figure 10.10.

   b) Why might these land uses be considered "better" than what was there before?

Urban Poverty

Poverty is largely an urban problem. In Canada, 7 out of 10 low-income families live in cities with populations of 100 000 or more. Overall, 17.7 percent of people in CMAs have low incomes.

While people in smaller cities with low incomes may be spread throughout the whole city, in larger communities they are often concentrated in areas near the central business district. These areas have the oldest buildings with the least expensive rents. Owners of these buildings have often divided them into small rental apartments that quickly become run-down.

Most people who rent in run-down parts of cities have few other options. People with more money are able to move out to better neighbourhoods. Low-income people struggle to get out of the poverty cycle that keeps them poor.

FAST *Fact*

In Canada, the poor are often recent immigrants, female single parents and their children, senior citizens, and First Nations peoples.

FIGURE 10.11

The Poverty Cycle
What should people try to do to break out of the poverty cycle?

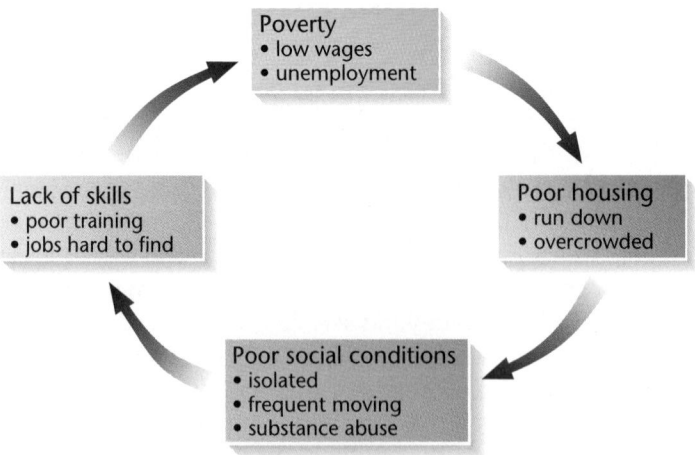

CHECK IT OVER

12. Explain why people who have low incomes tend to live in the central or older parts of cities.

13. Suppose you were the mayor of a large city. What are two actions that you might take to try to reduce the number of people living on low incomes?

14. The number of people living on low incomes in Montreal, Quebec, is more than double the number in the city of Oshawa, Ontario. What are some factors that could influence poverty rates in the cities of Canada?

 THINK IT OVER

Knowledge and Understanding

1. Find pictures to illustrate the different types of residential land uses that are found in cities. Look in magazines that are about cities. See Figure 10.9 to get some ideas of residential types of housing.

2. Construct a bar graph with the title Number of CMAs by Province. Use the information in Figure 10.4. When you are finished, make three observations about your graph.

Thinking and Communication

3. In Canada, cities have grown outwards as people have bought homes at the edges of the cities. Make a comparison chart. Compare what it is like living in the centre of a large city to what it is like living at the outside edge.

4. Find out about the history of population growth in your community or in one near you. Some questions to try to answer are
   • When was the community founded?
   • When did it grow most quickly?
   • Has the population ever decreased? When?
   • What problems is it experiencing because of population growth?

5. Do some research to find out more about one important problem of large cities. Some problems you might consider are waste disposal, crime, racism, traffic congestion, and homelessness. Prepare a one-page report, a poster display, or a Web site to show your findings.

Making Things: Patterns of Industry in Canada

In this chapter you will learn to

◢ *relate current lifestyle choices of Canadians to Canada's economic structure*

◢ find the best place to locate an industry in Canada

◢ predict the impact of selected technological changes on the future quality of life for Canadians

Introduction

Over the years, changes have taken place in the industries that make up Canada's economy. Compare the graphs for the three years shown in Figure 11.1 and then think about the following questions:

- What has been the trend for each category over the years?

- Which category has changed the most?

- What conditions might bring about such remarkable change in economic categories?

FIGURE 11.1

Percent of the Work Force in Economic Categories
What is your overall reaction to the patterns in this graph?

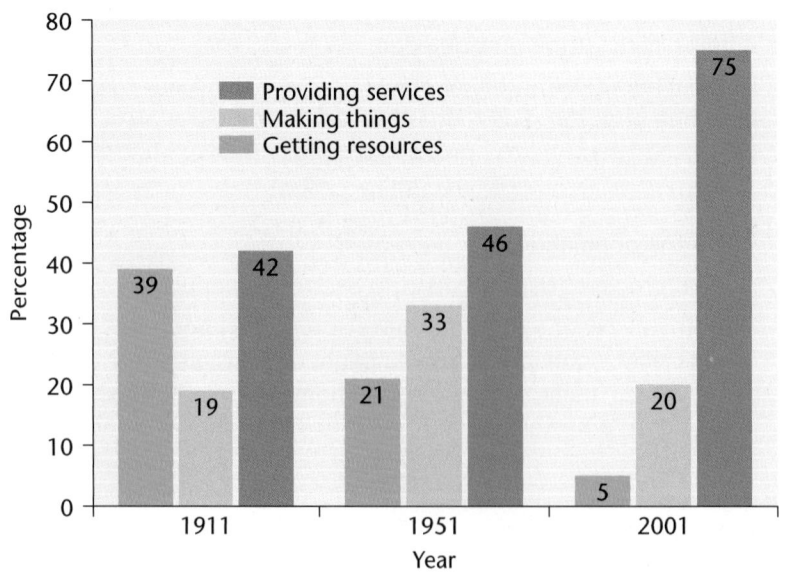

Figure 11.1 tells us that Canada's economy has shifted in some dramatic ways over the past century. In this chapter we will look at

- how Canada's economic structure has changed
- changes in secondary industries
- the impacts of technological change

Changing Economies

Canada's economic structure has changed over the decades. Economic structure is the way all the economic activities in a country are organized. These activities can be divided into three broad categories:

- primary industries
- secondary industries
- tertiary industries

Primary, *secondary*, and *tertiary* mean "first, second, and third." The strength of each of these categories determines the economic structure of the economy. In Figure 11.1,

- "Getting Resources" refers to primary industries
- "Making Things" refers to secondary industries
- "Providing Services" refers to tertiary industries

At first, Canada's economy focused on using and developing natural resources (primary industries). However, our economy did not remain based on resources. The Industrial Revolution began in Europe at the end of the 1700s and soon spread to North America. This was a time when great technological change took place, such as the use of the steam engine to power trains and other machines.

By the second half of the 1800s, manufacturing (secondary industries) was an important part of this country's economy. Throughout the twentieth century, businesses were created to offer services (tertiary industries, such as banking) to the growing Canadian population. The economy now includes all three sectors: primary, secondary, and tertiary.

FAST Fact

The term *industries* is a general term that refers to the parts of an economy. It does not mean a single factory or store.

FIGURE 11.2

Categories of Industries
Look at the examples for secondary industries. What other kinds of goods does Canada manufacture?

	Primary Industries	Secondary Industries	Tertiary Industries
Definition	This set of industries takes natural resources from the environment and makes them into semi-finished products.	Secondary industries take the semi-finished products from primary industries and make them into finished products that consumers can use.	This set of industries provides services to businesses and consumers to help them enjoy a better quality of life.
Key Word	extraction	manufacturing	services
Example	The steel industry takes (extracts) iron ore from the ground and processes it into steel. The steel is sold as long rolls, beams, or tubes.	The automotive industries take the steel and other products and make (manufacture) them into cars.	When people buy cars, they need services such as insurance, banking, fuel, and repairs.
Types of Industries	mining, forestry, farming, fishing, fur trapping	manufacturing, construction	transportation, communication, finance, insurance, personal services (e.g., hairdressing)

FIGURE 11.3

Factors That Affect Economic Structure
In what ways might education and training affect how an economy is organized?

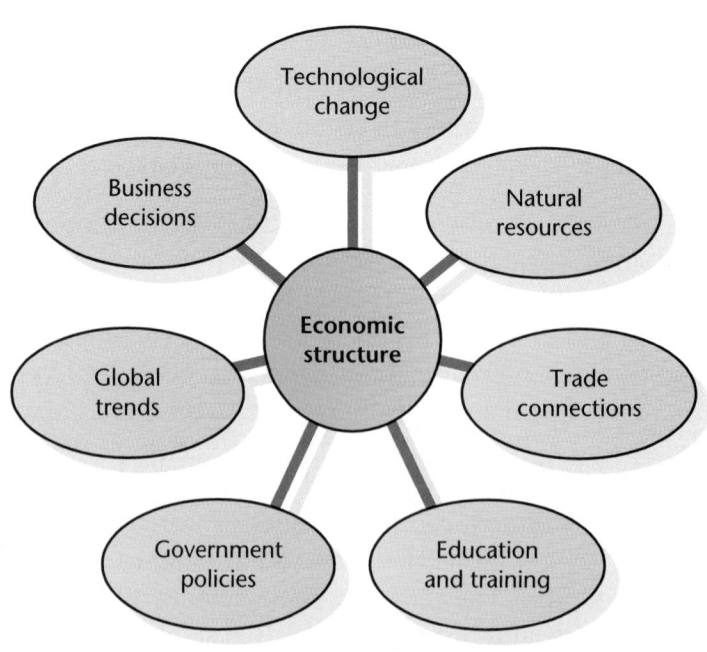

LITERACY SKILL

Creating Categories

Creating categories is often a helpful way to analyze information about a problem or topic. In this chapter we have broken all economic activities into the categories of primary, secondary, and tertiary industries. You can then pick out trends, patterns, or connections in the categories.

Here are some other ways that categories are used in geographic studies:

- Countries are often grouped by income or levels of development. This is helpful because rich countries have different characteristics from poor countries.

- People's opinions on issues are often categorized. For example, on the topic of Aboriginal land claims, the different views fall into a range between people who favour settling land claims and people who are completely against doing this.

- Canada's trading partners can be categorized: those that are already important trading partners, those that we would like to see become more important, and countries that we choose not to have strong trade ties with.

Breaking information into categories will help you when you are studying a subject.

CHECK IT OVER

3. Create a diagram that shows how primary, secondary, and tertiary industries rely on one another. Focus on one product in your diagram, such as a skateboard or a fast-food item.

4. What might be two ways that the changing economic structure would affect towns and cities?

5. Look at Figure 11.1.

   a) List five skills of workers that would have been valued by employers in 1911.

   b) List five skills of workers that would have been valued by employers in 2001.

   c) In what ways might the different skills demanded by employers affect the education and training of workers? Give one example.

6. Give one example to show how technological change can affect the economic structure.

Secondary Industries in Canada

Most secondary industries in Canada are located in southern Ontario and southern Quebec. This strip of Canada from Windsor, Ontario, to Quebec City, Quebec, is called our industrial heartland. Ontario alone accounts for 53 percent of Canada's secondary industries. In addition, 14 of the country's top 20 manufacturing cities are in Ontario. Quebec produces 23 percent of all manufacturing in Canada.

FIGURE 11.4

Value of Manufacturing by Province, 2000 and 2004 (billions of dollars) Nova Scotia and New Brunswick have similar economies. Why do you think the value of New Brunswick's manufacturing was higher than Nova Scotia's in 2004?

	2000	2004
Alberta	44.4	53.0
British Columbia	40.7	42.3
Manitoba	11.4	12.5
New Brunswick	10.9	14.1
Newfoundland and Labrador	2.5	3.1
Nova Scotia	8.3	9.3
Ontario	297.7	310.3
Prince Edward Island	1.1	1.4
Quebec	136.9	137.7
Saskatchewan	7.1	9.6
The Territories	0.3	0.1
Canada	**561.3**	**593.4**

Location Factors for Manufacturing

Why are manufacturing industries so concentrated in one part of Canada? It often has to do with history, such as the conditions that existed as manufacturing was growing in this country. (For example, this area of Canada had the most people at that time.) Here are four other reasons that manufacturing is such a large industry in Ontario and Quebec:

Locations of markets: Most of our trade is with just one country: the United States. For example, car parts are shipped southward out of plants near Windsor. Meat products travel from packing plants in the Kitchener–Waterloo region to the huge cities of the eastern United States. Wood construction materials from Vancouver Island are used for building in California. Shipping costs to the U.S. are lower for Canadian businesses located close to the Canada–U.S. border.

Access to raw materials: Manufacturers need a reliable supply of raw materials, such as minerals, wood, energy, and farm products. Many of these materials can be found in great amounts in Ontario and Quebec.

Labour supply: Workers with manufacturing skills are found in southern Ontario and Quebec. This is because these workers are trained in the many colleges, apprenticeship programs, and universities in this region.

Transportation: Raw materials and finished products have to move easily to and from manufacturing plants. The Great Lakes and the St. Lawrence River provide good ports. Ontario and Quebec have airports that allow products and people to move quickly. They also have rail and road links to move goods across the border.

FIGURE 11.5

Trucks on a Major Highway Near Toronto
What is one advantage in using truck transportation in manufacturing?

FIGURE 11.6

Canada's Leading Industries (percentage of Canadian manufacturing)
What manufactured products might fit into the "All Other" category?

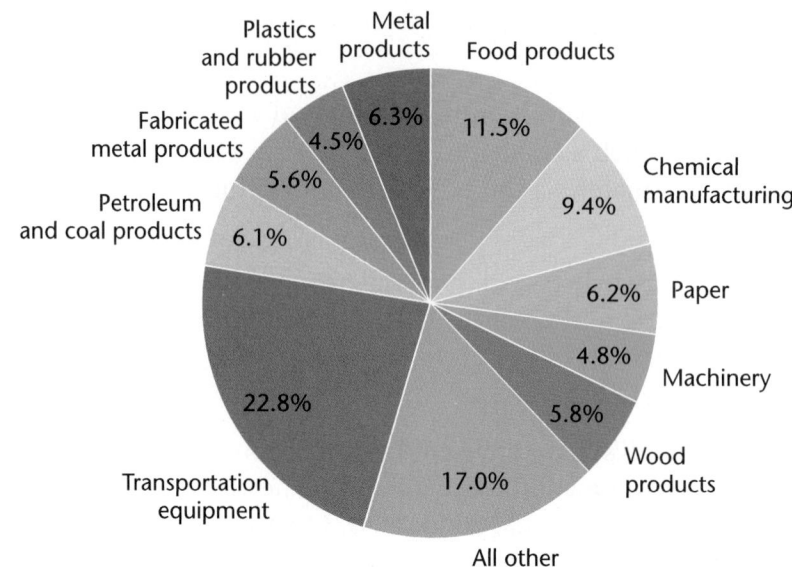

- Plastics and rubber products — 4.5%
- Metal products — 6.3%
- Food products — 11.5%
- Chemical manufacturing — 9.4%
- Fabricated metal products — 5.6%
- Paper — 6.2%
- Petroleum and coal products — 6.1%
- Machinery — 4.8%
- Wood products — 5.8%
- All other — 17.0%
- Transportation equipment — 22.8%

Unfortunately, communities that are not in the industrial heartland find it very difficult to develop secondary industries. They simply cannot provide the location factors that businesses need. As a result, workers often leave these places and move to locations where there are more jobs.

 GEOCAREERS

Real Estate Sales

Real estate salespeople provide a vital link between people and corporations who have property they want to sell and those who wish to buy. Real estate salespeople

- find properties that owners want to sell
- work with owners to set prices and advertise their properties
- show potential buyers the properties that are available
- draw up sales agreements

Most real estate sales people work on a commission basis. (They are paid a fee only when they sell a property.) The more properties they sell, the more money they make.

A secondary school diploma is needed to work in real estate sales. You will also need to take a training course and get a licence in the province in which you are working.

A good knowledge of geographic patterns (e.g., transportation routes) and issues (e.g., crime rates) is helpful for real estate salespeople. In addition, you will need excellent communication and planning skills.

CASE STUDY

Canadian Automobile Industry

The auto industry is this country's largest manufacturing industry. It employs over 530 000 workers, or about one in seven Canadian workers. The auto industry includes both making parts for trucks, buses, and cars and assembling these parts into finished vehicles.

The "Big Three" car companies of Ford, General Motors, and Daimler Chrysler are the leaders in auto production. In recent years, foreign manufacturers—like Honda, Suzuki, and Toyota—have become important players in Canada. This shows how the auto industry is tied to the **globalization** of the economy. Businesses locate wherever they can make strong profits.

Parts and assembly plants are mainly concentrated in southern Ontario and Quebec. This is largely because the U.S. auto industry began in Michigan and spread over the border into Canada. The industry continues to be strong in Ontario and Quebec because of the other location factors mentioned above.

FAST Fact

Canadians must be doing something right. In 2005, General Motors announced the largest ever investment in the Canadian auto industry: over $2.5 billion. Also, Toyota Motor Corporation unveiled its plans for a manufacturing plant in Woodstock, Ontario, that will produce 100 000 cars by 2008.

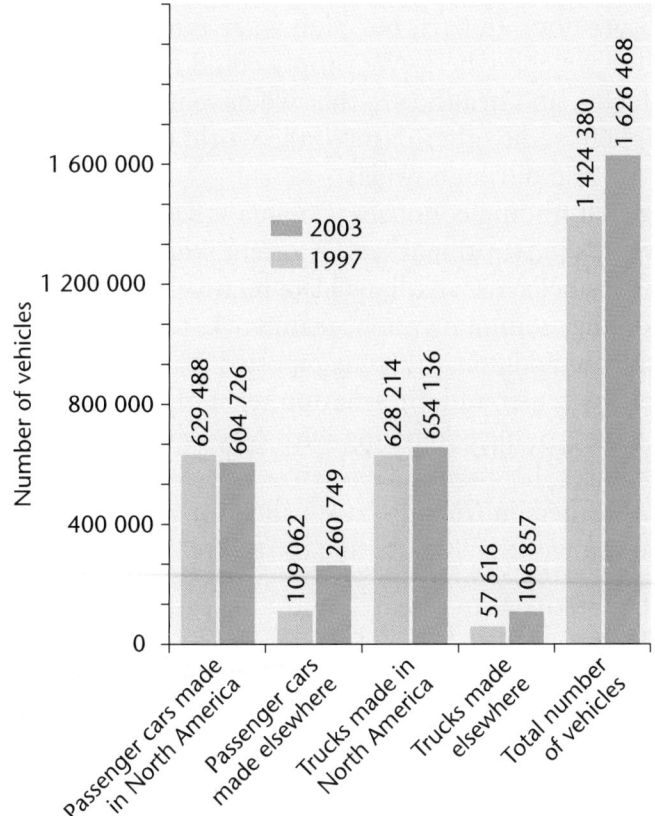

FIGURE 11.7

New Vehicle Sales in Canada, 1997 and 2003
What problem does this graph suggest?

7. Ask your teacher for an outline map of Canada. Highlight the location of the industrial heartland.

8. Besides Ontario and Quebec, what other provinces have a significant amount of manufacturing? Refer to Figure 11.4.

9. Decide how well your own community rates on the four location factors for manufacturing. Use a scale from 1 (not well) to 10 (very well). When you are finished, share your ideas with a classmate and discuss any differences in ratings. How can your community improve its ratings?

Can We Compete?

One of the concerns about Canadian manufacturing is our ability to succeed in a global setting. Globalization means that we must compete for business with companies from all around the world.

Wage rates in many countries are much lower than in Canada. As a result, it costs more to make goods in Canada than in countries with lower wage rates. For example, in China, wages average $3 per hour. In part, our high wage rates are tied to the quality of life we enjoy here. We simply could not afford the homes, vehicles, and health care that we have if our wages were lower. People in some other parts of the world do not enjoy our quality of life and our high wages.

Among rich trading countries, Canada is seen as having low competitiveness in world markets. A recent study showed that these countries believe Canadians have relatively weak skills—in problem solving, communication, teamwork, technical skills, and literacy skills. In addition, the study reported that we are seen as having weak computer and information technology skills. As a result, we have trouble competing with other major nations like the United States, Japan, and Germany.

Business leaders in Canada have called for a change of thinking. Among the changes they would like to see are

- more investment in research and the development of new products
- an emphasis on skills in the labour force
- improved business management skills
- bolder attitudes on the part of business leaders and government

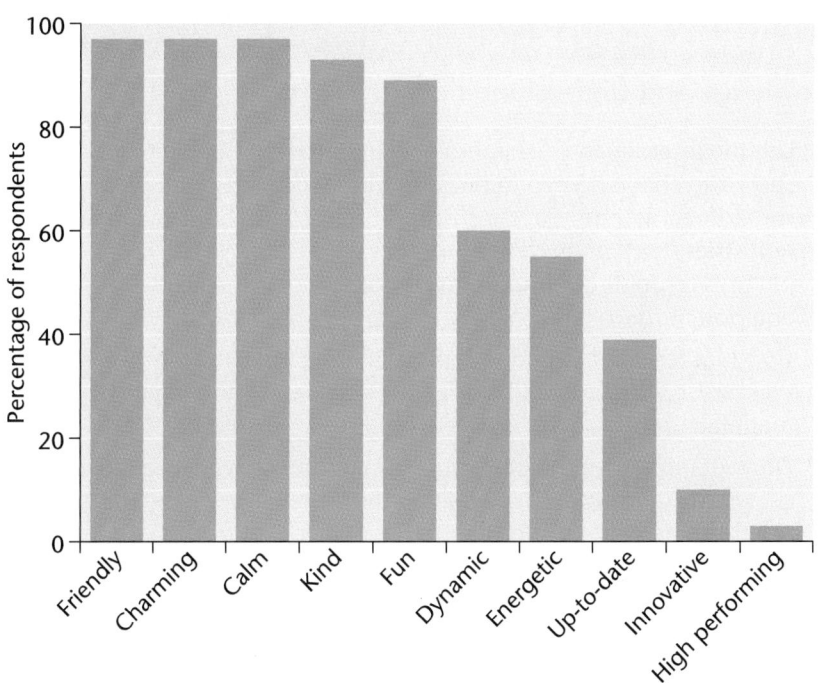

FIGURE 11.8

Perceptions of Canadians by Americans
This survey shows what Americans think of Canadians' business competitiveness. Do you think this view is a problem?

Canadians used to think that doing a good job would guarantee success as a manufacturing nation. Greater competition from all around the world means that we have to get "lean and mean"—that is, cut costs as much as possible We need to change quickly, or be left on the sidelines.

CHECK IT OVER

10. What are two ways that lower wages in other countries reduce Canada's competitiveness?

11. What might be some of the consequences of not being able to compete on a global scale?

12. Suggest two ways that Canada could improve our competitiveness around the world.

THINK IT OVER

Knowledge and Understanding

1. Use the Internet and classroom resources to find three pictures that show the changing economic structure of Canada. One picture should be about primary industries, the second about secondary industries, and the third about tertiary industries. Label your pictures to point out important details (such as the kind of equipment used).

2. Conduct research to find out about the secondary industries in your area. Make a list of some of the companies and what they manufacture.

3. Do you agree with the perceptions Americans have of Canadians shown in Figure 11.8? Why do you think they have these attitudes? Are these perceptions good or bad for Canadian manufacturing?

Thinking and Communication

4. Predict the impact of technological changes on the future of Canada. Identify two examples of technological changes that have recently had, or will have, important impacts. Give reasons for your ideas.

5. Suppose you were a company official responsible for choosing where to locate your next manufacturing plant. Choose one of these products: inexpensive jewellery, high-end video electronics, or frozen food products.

   a) Make up a list of location characteristics that you feel are necessary for your company to be successful.

   b) Using classroom and Internet resources, identify three suitable locations in Canada.

Harvesting Our Natural Resources

In this chapter you will learn to

⊿ *describe ways in which renewable, non-renewable, and flow resources are used*

⊿ identify some techniques used to remove resources

⊿ describe how regional differences affect the economic sustainability of communities

⊿ predict the impact of selected technological changes on the future quality of life for Canadians

Introduction

In 2002, Canada's beef industry put almost $8 billion into the economy. That year about one quarter of all Canada's income from farms came from the beef industry. These are cattle that end up on our dinner plates or in fast-food restaurants. Then disaster struck!

On May 20, 2003, it was revealed that one cow in northern Alberta had tested positive for bovine spongiform encephalopathy, also called mad cow disease. Immediately, over 40 countries closed their borders to all shipments of Canadian live animals and meat products. Canadian beef farmers could not sell their animals anywhere.

The impact on the Canadian economy was huge. The economy lost $5.7 billion in income from beef. About 75 000 jobs disappeared from farms and meatpacking plants. In addition, farmers lost money because they had to continue to feed animals they couldn't sell.

Key Words

resources

mechanization

agriculture

clear-cutting

minerals

resource-based communities

boom-and-bust cycles

river diversions

FIGURE 12.1

Beef Cattle
Mad cow disease can spread between animals, and also to humans who eat meat from infected animals. Why did other countries stop Canadian beef from coming across their borders?

Eventually, the United States and other countries reopened their borders to Canadian beef, but a great deal of damage had been done. Many beef farmers had already left the industry.

The mad cow crisis was a grim reminder that Canada is a resource-based country. Resources, minerals for example, are one of a country's means of building economic wealth. Much of our wealth comes from selling our natural resources. We are dependent on other countries to buy our resources. Natural resources can be grouped into different categories.

FIGURE 12.2

Categories of Natural Resources
Into which of these categories does beef farming fit?

	Renewable Resources	Non-Renewable Resources	Flow Resources
Definition	resources that can replace themselves even after they have been used	resources that are gone once they have been used	resources that are replaced naturally whether or not humans use them
Examples	farm products, forests, fish	minerals, fuels such as oil and gas	running water, wind, ocean currents
Explanation	These resources can renew themselves in a relatively short period of time.	These resources can only be created under certain conditions, usually over a long time (thousands of years)	These resources exist because of natural systems and natural processes.

In this chapter we will look at some of the issues that are part of the primary industries (see Chapter 11, pages 109–110). We will focus on

- renewable natural resources
- non-renewable natural resources
- flow natural resources

CHECK IT OVER

1. Why should Canadians who are not beef farmers be concerned about mad cow disease?
2. What are three natural resources that you have used today?

Renewable Natural Resources

Farming the land and harvesting (process of gathering the forest resources) the forests are two industries based on renewable natural resources. In this section of the chapter we will consider some issues of renewable natural resources.

Mechanization of Farming

All natural resource industries have seen a great deal of technological change over the past several decades. Mechanization is one of the most important changes. Mechanization occurs when machines take over jobs that used to be done by humans or by animals. Farming—also called agriculture—is a resource industry that clearly shows the changes caused by mechanization. We can see this in how land is ploughed, crops are harvested, cows are milked, and animal wastes are disposed of.

FIGURE 12.3

A corn harvester on a Farm Near Forest Grove, Ontario
How was this job done before corn harvesters were used?

Farms have become mechanized for three reasons:

- machines make workers' jobs easier
- the work can be done faster
- farmers can expand their farms because they can do more work

Mechanization also has negative consequences. One is that many farm workers lose their jobs.

FIGURE 12.4

Results of the Mechanization of Farming
Identify three consequences of mechanization from this diagram.

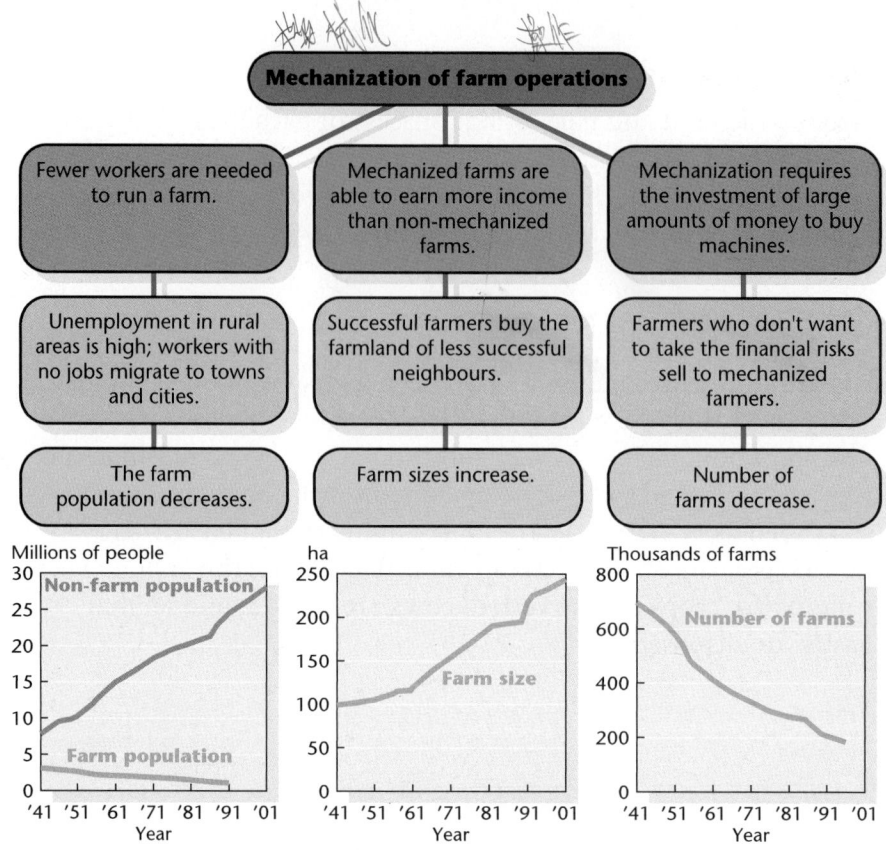

Even when farms are highly mechanized, farmers have to protect their most important resource—the land. This means working it in ways (e.g., crop rotation) so the soil remains fertile. Overuse or improper use can destroy this renewable resource and weaken our food supply and economic health.

Clear-Cutting of Forests

Mechanization in the forest industry means that forests can be cut down much faster than in the past. This has encouraged a cutting method known as clear-cutting. In clear-cutting, all the trees within an area are cut down, even trees that are too small to be used. The land is left barren. This method is used because machinery operates most efficiently if there are no trees left in the way. Another method of cutting is selective cutting, taking only mature trees.

Clear-cutting is a controversial topic. Many people do not think it should be done. They argue that when a whole forest is removed

- soils are washed away
- wildlife lose their habitat
- the cultures of the Aboriginal peoples living in those regions are threatened

FIGURE 12.5

A Clear-Cut Forest
What is your reaction to this scene?

Logging companies, on the other hand, point out that

- clear-cutting is the most profitable way to harvest forests
- the habitat replaces itself over time
- the loggers take care to protect streams and rivers from damage
- new trees are often planted

 LITERACY SKILL

Organizing Evidence That Supports and Opposes Arguments

When you argue about a controversial topic, it is helpful to know the evidence that is for and against the topic. You can use a chart with two columns to help you organize this evidence. Each column lists the different points. Evidence that supports an argument goes in one column. Evidence that opposes it goes in the other column.

Evidence That Supports an Argument	Evidence That Opposes an Argument

Use a two-column organizing chart to record points that support and oppose this statement: Clear-cutting is a good way to harvest forests.

See Figure 14.8 in Chapter 14 to see an example of how this chart can be used.

Literacy Strategy

Note-making
When you are asked to make point-form notes, you need to

- know the purpose for the note-making
- read the text through once
- think about the main idea(s)
- record the idea(s) in your own words

Forest Technician

Forest technicians are part of forest management teams. Their duties include
- doing field surveys about the amount and quality of trees
- preparing management and harvest plans
- planning forest roads
- supervising forest-cutting operations
- supervising replanting

Forest technicians receive their training in two- or three-year college programs.

Geography is good preparation for this career because it teaches
- how forests need to be managed
- how resources are important to our quality of life
- the different viewpoints people have about the harvesting of resources
- how to use GIS technology to manage geographic data

 CHECK IT OVER

3. Give three examples of how a farmer's life would have changed after he or she started using machines.
4. Explain why mechanization led to larger farms.
5. How are mechanization and clear-cutting of forests related?

Non-Renewable Natural Resources

Minerals are important non-renewable natural resources. Minerals are natural substances with crystal-like structures. Humans use minerals to

- make things (e.g., iron to produce steel)
- carry electricity and water (e.g., copper wires and pipes)
- improve our food supplies (e.g., potash fertilizer)
- have convenient forms of energy (e.g., oil)

	Metallic	Nonmetallic	Structural	Fossil Fuels
Description	have a shiny appearance; good conductors of heat and electricity	have a dull appearance; break apart easily	used in construction; a subgroup of nonmetallic minerals	used for a wide variety of products, including energy and plastics
Examples	gold, copper, iron, diamonds	salt, potash, asbestos	sand, gravel, limestone, gypsum	petroleum, natural gas, coal
Formation	usually found in rocks that have cooled from molten rock	usually found in sedimentary rocks	found in sedimentary rocks	formed from the remains of plants and animals buried underground

FIGURE 12.6

Types of Minerals
From each of these four categories, give one example of a mineral that you use daily.

Resource-Based Communities

Minerals are scattered in deposits across Canada. Mines are often in hard-to-reach places. Communities are built near the mines to house the workers and their families. Often, the mines are the only real sources of employment in the area. Such communities are called resource-based communities.

Resource-based communities often experience boom-and-bust cycles. When a mine starts up, jobs, economic opportunities, and wealth are created: this is a boom time. Figure 12.7 shows the boom that is occurring now around Yellowknife, Northwest Territories, because of diamond mining. However, most mineral deposits eventually run out. Then the jobs are gone and people have to move away: that is the bust time. Mining communities often face an uncertain future because they are not sustainable. This means they do not have what they need to continue to exist.

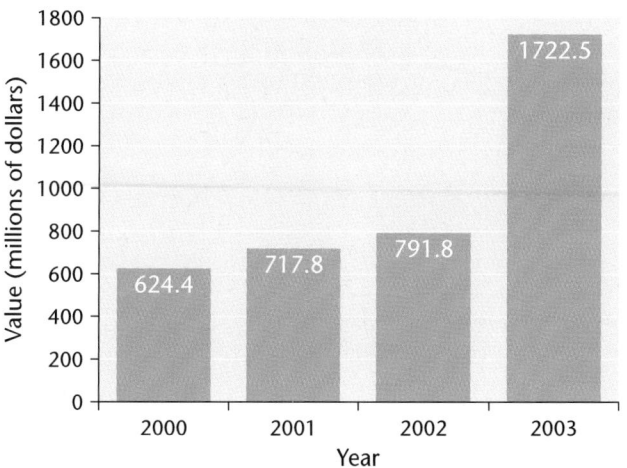

FIGURE 12.7

Value of Diamond Mining in Northwest Territories, 2000–2003
Estimate the increase in value between 2000 and 2003.

FIGURE 12.8

Mining of Metallic and Nonmetallic Minerals by Province, 2003
Which province/territory has the greatest value?

Province/Territory	Value (millions of dollars)
Newfoundland and Labrador	932.9
Prince Edward Island	—
Nova Scotia	65.8
New Brunswick	437.4
Quebec	1901.5
Ontario	4455.0
Manitoba	780.5
Saskatchewan	108.4
Alberta	324.4
British Columbia	1508.0
Yukon Territory	36.4
Northwest Territories	1772.8
Nunavut	29.9

FIGURE 12.9

Factors Affecting the Sustainability of Mining Communities
Explain why the size of a mineral deposit may affect how long a mining community can exist.

FAST *Fact*

The closure of its coal mine in 2000 badly hurt the town of Tumbler Ridge, B.C. However, the town's residents didn't simply let it die. Instead they began to promote the town as a retirement community, with health care facilities, shopping, parks, and nice homes.

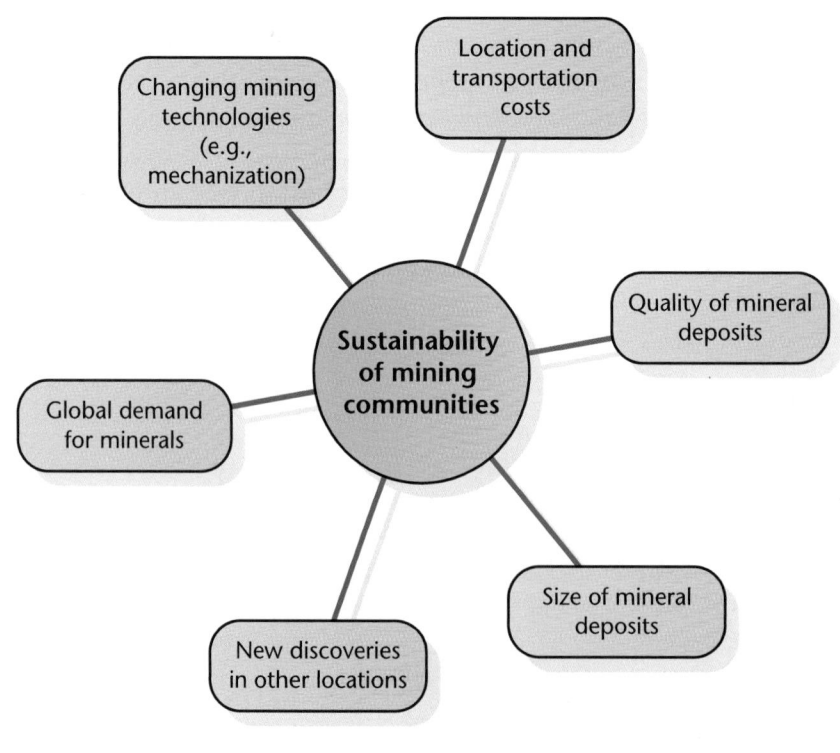

CHECK IT OVER

6. Make up a definition for the term *resource-based communities*.
7. What actions could a resource-based community take to make itself more sustainable?
8. The sustainability of a mining community is often influenced by conditions that the community cannot control. Prove this statement, using at least six points.

Flow Natural Resources

Flow resources are natural resources that renew themselves naturally; for example, rivers and wind. Most flow resources are also renewable natural resources. For example, wind is a flow resource that we can use without using it up. Flow resources, including wind and water resources, are produced by natural systems and processes.

Water Resources

Water is essential for life. Canada is rich in fresh water. We take this resource for granted. We treat water as though it will never run out. As a result, we have one of the highest rates of water use per person in the world. We need water for

- personal use (e.g., for showers or flushing toilets)
- industrial use (e.g., to produce food, make goods, and generate electricity)

FAST *Fact*

On average, each Canadian uses 390 L of water per day. That equals about four bathtubs of water. Toilet flushing uses about 40 percent of this water.

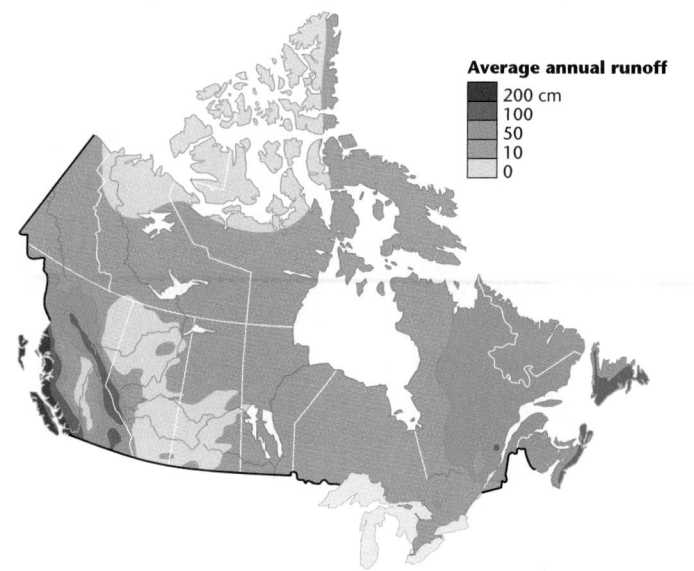

Average annual runoff
- 200 cm
- 100
- 50
- 10
- 0

FIGURE 12.10

Runoff From Rivers in Canada
Runoff is water on the land's surface that has not soaked into the soil. It comes from snow and rainfall. This water runs off land to rivers and streams. Canadians take much of their water from rivers and lakes. Runoff affects the amount of water that is available for use.

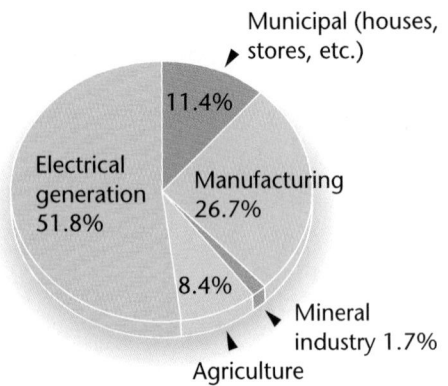

Municipal (houses, stores, etc.) 11.4%

Electrical generation 51.8%

Manufacturing 26.7%

8.4%

Mineral industry 1.7%

Agriculture

FIGURE 12.11

Water Use in Canada
What sector uses the greatest amount of water?

Conflicts occur over how to use our water resources. Some uses simply do not work well together. For example, the Fraser River of British Columbia could be used for generating hydroelectricity, but that would cause problems for salmon swimming upstream to spawn. The Great Lakes provide huge supplies of fresh water, but cities around the lakes have polluted the water.

CASE STUDY

The Bow River Diversion Project

The Bow River, in Alberta, was diverted to provide water to irrigate crops. Its course was changed because this part of the country is dry, and a stable water supply is important for farming. A new diversion plan for the Bow River will open up another 8000 ha for irrigation. This will create a reservoir—a container that stores water. The reservoir created by the diversion can be used by local towns for their water supply, recreation, and transportation.

A number of Canadian rivers have gone through **river diversions**. River valleys have been dammed to cause the water to flow in another direction, or to create large reservoirs. Diversions give economic benefits, including

- stopping downstream flooding
- generating hydroelectric power
- allowing crops to be irrigated in dry parts of the country
- industrial development, such as processing aluminum

In some cases, the water in a diversion stays within the drainage basin. In other cases, the water is diverted to a different river system.

Many people oppose river diversions. Water moving from one river system to another can carry unwanted species and spread diseases. Plants and animals around the rivers are affected because of the changes in natural stream flow and flooding. Aboriginal communities can lose their traditional lands and hunting areas because of reservoirs. Planners need to understand that when water is removed upstream, it cannot be used downstream in the river system.

CHECK IT OVER

9. Name three flow resources and explain why they can be considered flow resources.

10. a) Which parts of Canada have the greatest amount of water runoff?

    b) Compare population distribution (see Chapter 9, pages 87–88) and water availability in Canada. What is one conclusion you can draw from this comparison?

11. What are three reasons that some people are opposed to river diversions?

THINK IT OVER

Knowledge and Understanding

1. Here are 10 terms that are related to primary industries and harvesting natural resources. Group the terms into three categories. Give each category a heading.

diversions	global demand
boom-and-bust cycles	clear-cutting
nonmetallic	wind
runoff	agriculture
increased farm size	forest technician

2. Explain why mining activity often causes boom-and-bust cycles.

3. Write three endings to this sentence: Flow resources are important because….

Thinking and Communication

4. Make a list of the types of farms found in your region. What are the main products of these farms?

5. Imagine that you are a TV news reporter watching the opening of a new irrigation diversion project. Identify for your viewers three good points and three problems with the project.

6. Search on the Internet and in newspapers to identify some water issues in Canada. Describe the problems as well as the different points of view on the problems.

Chapter 13

Enjoying a Good Life: Service Industries

Key Words

services

quaternary industries

retail trade sector

infrastructure

telecommute

knowledge workers

discretionary
   spending

In this chapter you will learn to

- relate current lifestyle choices of Canadians to the sustainability of Canada's economic structure
- determine the best place to locate a service industry
- report on how current trends or events affect Canada's economy
- predict the impact of technological changes on Canadians' future quality of life
- identify job, career, or volunteer opportunities that require geographic knowledge and skills

Introduction

Look at the jobs being done in these three photographs.

FIGURE 13.1

Canadian Workers
These workers are a hairstylist, a fast-food server, and a transit driver. What characteristic do the jobs have in common?

These workers are all performing services for others. As you saw in Chapter 11, people who provide services are part of the tertiary industries. In this chapter we will explore some of the patterns and issues of tertiary industries. We will look at

- retail sales
- transportation and communication services
- business and personal services

CHECK IT OVER

1. What services have you used in the past few days?
2. List the names of five people you know who work in service industries. What jobs do they do?

Tertiary and Quaternary Industries

About three quarters of Canadians work in the tertiary industries. This means that they provide services to businesses and other people. The tertiary industries include a wide variety of services.

Types of Services in the Tertiary Industries	
selling goods in a store	loading trucks
publishing books	working in a call centre
selling real estate	repairing computers
teaching swimming	teaching in a daycare centre
working as a camp counsellor	cleaning up parks and recreation areas

FIGURE 13.2

Some Services in the Tertiary Industries
What service jobs are you interested in doing?

In fact, the range of jobs in the tertiary industries is so large that some people question whether the category has any value anymore. For example, specialized surgeons and the prime minister are included in the same category as people who cut hair or sell you the latest DVDs. In recent years, another category has been added to Canada's economic structure: the quaternary industries. *Quaternary* means fourth. This category includes people who provide services but whose main job is to make important decisions, such as doctors, accountants, lawyers, bankers, and elected officials.

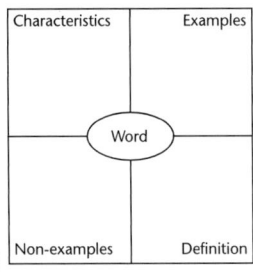
Retail Sales

The retail trade sector employs over 258 000 workers in Canada. These are the people who work in places like convenience stores, shopping malls, gas stations, and donut shops. Their main job is to help customers spend their money. They do this by

- stocking shelves
- preparing items for customers
- working as cashiers
- providing security
- responding to customers' requests

FIGURE 13.3

A Large Shopping Mall
Many Canadians' first jobs are in retail sales. Why?

One of the challenges of working in retail sales is that wages in this sector are low. In part, this is because many of the jobs require little training or experience. Often students work part-time in retail sales. Many workers in retail sales get few benefits, such as medical plans, that workers in other sectors get.

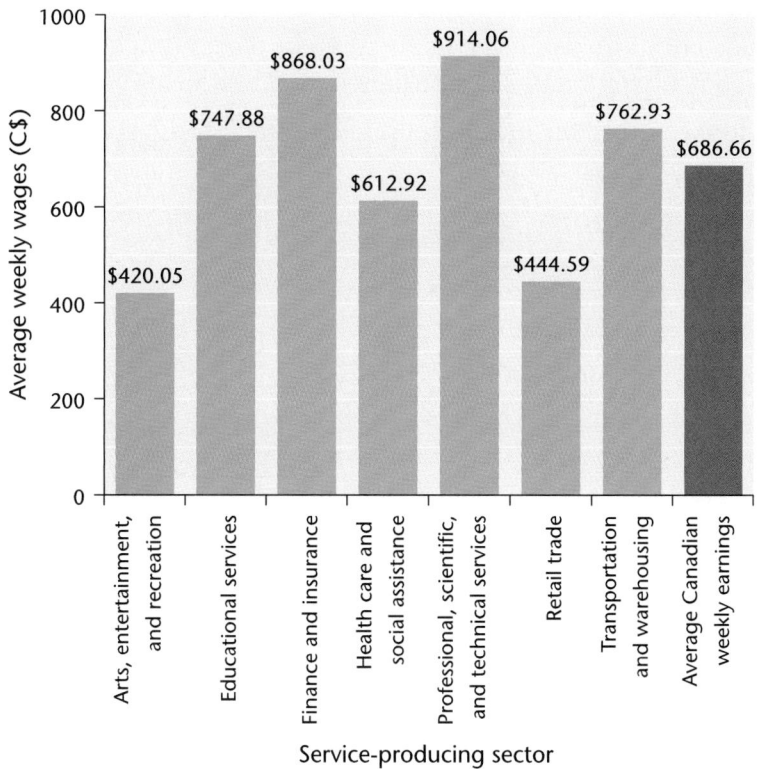

FIGURE 13.4

Average Weekly Earnings for Selected Service Sectors, 2003
How do weekly earnings in the retail sector compare to the Canadian average?

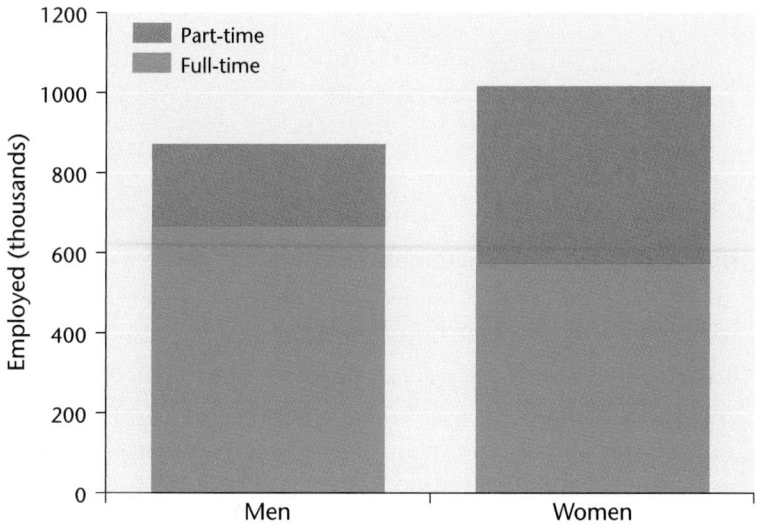

FIGURE 13.5

Employment in Retail Sales, 2003
What is one pattern that you see in the graph?

In retail sales, location is very important. Have you ever walked through a shopping mall and noticed that shoe stores tend to be located near other shoe stores, or that new car dealerships are often close to one another? You might think that it would be a disadvantage for these businesses to be located close to their competition. However, that is not the case. Customers want to compare products when they shop. They will go to locations that offer the best variety and selection. They are also more likely to go to places that are easy to reach. That is why retail sales businesses tend to locate

- close to other businesses selling the same products
- at major intersections
- along busy roadways
- just off expressways

FIGURE 13.6

Factors That Affect the Location of Retail Services
Think about a retail shopping area that you know. What are the most important factors in its location?

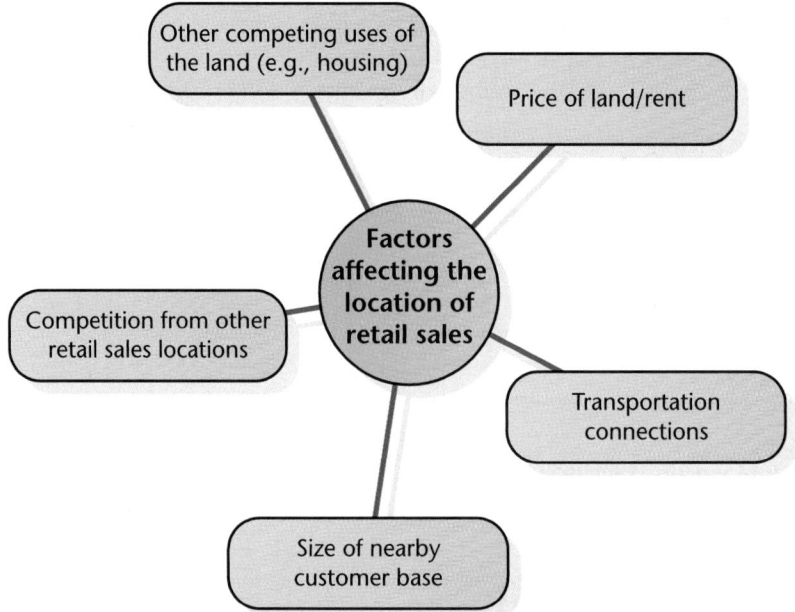

Other competing uses of the land (e.g., housing)

Price of land/rent

Factors affecting the location of retail sales

Competition from other retail sales locations

Transportation connections

Size of nearby customer base

CHECK IT OVER

3. How are tertiary and quaternary industries connected?
4. Give two reasons why earnings in the retail trade sector are low compared with other sectors of the economy.
5. Explain why some stores want to be located near their competitors.
6. Think about where you live. Where would be the best location for a new music store? Identify the location requirements for this retail sales business and then decide which place best meets those needs.

Transportation and Communications

Transportation and communications are part of Canada's infrastructure. Infrastructure refers to the basic services that support all economic activities. Without these services, the economy could not function. Energy supplies and waste disposal are two other infrastructure services.

Transportation

Transportation moves goods and people around. The type of transportation used depends on what is best suited to the cargo.

	Advantages	Disadvantages
Air Transport	• fastest form of travel over long distances • best for moving perishable goods (e.g., human organs, oysters) • useful for moving passengers	• expensive • can't handle large or heavy cargoes • requires convenient airports and terminals
Shipping	• cheapest form for bulk goods (e.g., coal) • useful for moving goods overseas	• requires convenient ports and harbours • many of Canada's waterways are closed for part of the year due to ice
Railways	• cheapest form for moving bulky goods over land (e.g., cars) • rarely affected by weather	• require train tracks to reach destinations • too slow for perishable goods • slow for moving people
Road Transport	• can reach the greatest number of destinations by using road networks • relatively fast for moving goods • useful for moving people	• affected by weather conditions • expensive for moving bulky goods • requires a well-developed road network
Pipelines	• not affected by weather • cheapest way of moving fluid goods (e.g., oil, water)	• require construction of pipelines • not possible to move people this way

FIGURE 13.7

Methods of Moving Goods and People
What would be the best way to move cars made in Japan to Canada?

Literacy Strategy

Finding the best solution
When you are asked to find the best solution, you must identify the criteria you will use to make your final decision. For example, to answer the question asked in Figure 13.7, your criteria can be

• cost
• time
• infrastructure

FIGURE 13.8

The Cockpit of a Commercial Airliner
What kinds of skills do you think pilots need to do their jobs well?

Railways used to be the main form of transportation in Canada. They carried both cargo and passengers to and from large cities and rural areas. However, today air travel and better roads do the same job faster. Railway tracks have been torn up across the country. They now serve only larger communities along main lines.

FIGURE 13.9

Cargo Loaded and Unloaded by Water Transport, 2003 (in tonnes)
Why are Saskatchewan and Alberta not included in this statistical table?

Province/ Territory	Domestic Cargo	International Cargo	Total Cargo
Newfoundland and Labrador	39 767 000	26 822 000	66 589 000
Prince Edward Island	781 000	64 000	845 000
Nova Scotia	5 086 000	37 935 000	43 021 000
New Brunswick	3 570 000	27 199 000	30 769 000
Quebec	27 307 000	79 793 000	107 100 000
Ontario	27 847 000	47 698 000	75 545 000
Manitoba	13 000	615 000	628 000
British Columbia	31 864 000	86 512 000	118 376 000
Northwest Territories	32 000	0	32 000
Nunavut	106 000	0	106 000

Communications

Technological change in communications is affecting how Canadians work and live. The growth of the Internet means that many people can telecommute. They can do their jobs from home—working in their pajamas and slippers if they want—and do not need to go into a central workplace in a big city. They can live anywhere that is connected to the Internet. Many telecommuters choose to live far from large cities, often in smaller towns and cities.

FAST *Fact*

Close to half of Canadian homes have two or more telephone numbers. Only 1.3 percent of households do not have a telephone.

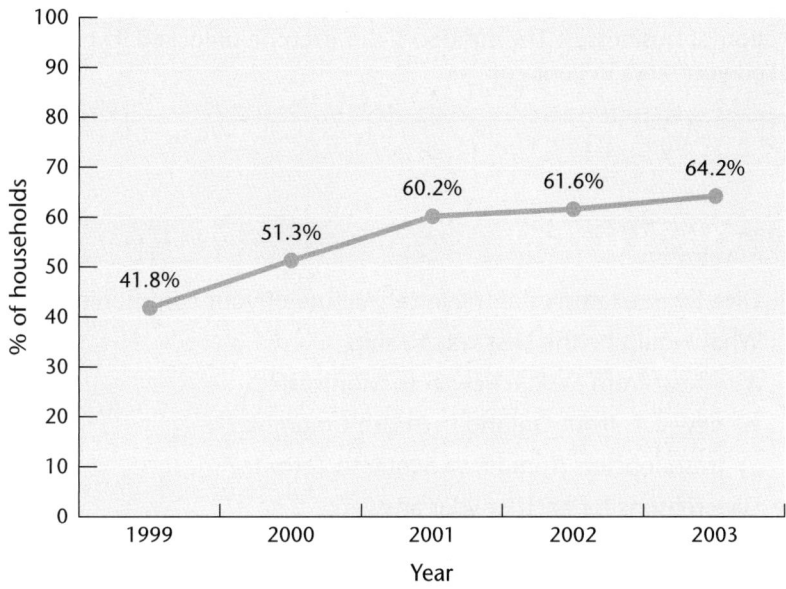

FIGURE 13.10

Percent of Canadians Using the Internet, 1999–2003
In which year did more than half of Canadians have access to the Internet?

CASE STUDY

Knowledge Workers in Canada

Knowledge workers are people who are highly skilled and highly educated. These people have skills and abilities beyond those of most other workers. They work in all sectors of the workforce, but most often in high-tech sectors, like communications and information technologies. About one in four Canadians is considered a knowledge worker.

As Canada's economy grows and changes, knowledge workers will be in even greater demand in such areas as

- management
- research and development
- communications
- education
- health care

OnStar Navigation System

The OnStar system is an option in most General Motors cars and trucks. It combines Global Positioning System (GPS) and cellular phone technologies. When you push the blue OnStar button on the dashboard, the cell phone link connects you to call centres in Oshawa, Ontario, or the United States. The call centre displays the location, vehicle identification number, and the name of the car owner. You can request various services, including roadside assistance, route directions, or the location of businesses. The car doors can even be unlocked if you have locked your keys in your car.

 CHECK IT OVER

7. Give three examples of the infrastructure of your community.
8. What would be the best way to ship
   a) wheat from Saskatchewan to Montreal?
   b) new cars from Ontario to British Columbia?
   c) fresh lobsters from Nova Scotia to Toronto?
   Give reasons for each of your answers.
9. What are two advantages and two disadvantages of telecommuting?
10. See Figure 13.9. List the top three provinces/territories by the amount of goods that pass through their ports. Are you surprised by your findings? Why?

Business and Personal Services

The largest and fastest-growing sector of tertiary industries is business and personal services. Canadians use these services to improve their quality of life. Some examples are

- auto mechanics
- dry-cleaning companies
- real estate agents
- travel agents
- barbers

This sector also includes companies that provide services to other businesses, such as

- office cleaners
- business management services
- advertising agencies
- printing and publishing

FIGURE 13.11

A Travel Agent
Why should a travel agent be included in the category of business and personal services?

The demand for personal services depends on economic conditions. Most of the services we buy are not essential to life: we buy them because we want them, not because we need them. For example, we would probably get along fairly well if all the haircutting places went out of business, if skateboard parks were closed, and if movie theatres were shut. If the economy is bad, we have the option of not spending our money on personal services. Choosing to spend money on things we want rather than things we need is called discretionary spending. In Canada, regions with high rates of unemployment have fewer personal and business services than wealthier places do.

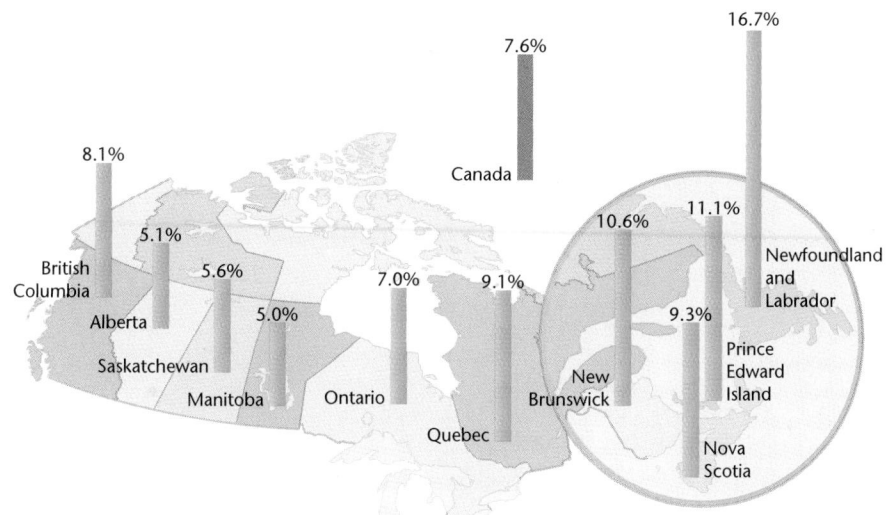

FIGURE 13.12

Unemployment Rates by Province, 2003
Which province has the highest unemployment rate? Which has the lowest?

CHECK IT OVER

11. Give two examples of personal services that you have used recently.
12. Explain why using personal services is considered discretionary spending.
13. Look at the information in Figure 13.12. Make two statements about patterns that the map shows. Use the term *region* in each observation.

THINK IT OVER

Knowledge and Understanding

1. a) Identify two ways that technological change has had an impact on tertiary industries in Canada.

   b) Predict one change that will take place in tertiary industries as a result of technological change.

2. Using information in this chapter, identify two trends that are affecting Canada's economy.

3. Identify three jobs in the tertiary industries that require geographic understanding.

Thinking and Communication

4. Prepare a presentation or a poster to identify the best location in your area for a new sports recreation centre. Begin by identifying five location factors that you think are important for this type of service. Then use the factors to determine the best location in your neighbourhood or community.

5. Suggest two reasons why train travel by passengers has declined.

6. Suppose you are an executive in an advertising firm, which is a business service. A client wants to sell a line of clothing to people in your age group. Make three suggestions to the client for advertising campaigns that will reach people like you.

Challenges for Human Systems

In this chapter you will learn to

◢ identify changes to human systems and explain how they could affect Canadians

◢ describe how regional disparities affect the economic health of communities

◢ report on how current trends affect the sustainability of Canada's human systems

◢ predict the impact of technological changes on the future quality of life for Canadians

◢ use appropriate statistical methods and data in geographic analysis

Key Words

regional disparities

core

periphery

equalization payments

life expectancies

Introduction

You might think that all Canadians should share in the high quality of life that we have in this country. Each Canadian should get the same benefits as every other Canadian. To some extent, this is the case: the laws that protect your rights apply equally to each one of us. For example, no matter where you live in this country, you can't be discriminated against because of your race, gender, or culture.

However, when it comes to economic conditions, equality is not so certain. In the last chapter, you saw that unemployment rates in Newfoundland and Labrador were three times greater than rates in the Prairie provinces and more than twice as high as those in Ontario. This is a sign that economic equality does not exist in Canada. Economic differences between one part of Canada and another are called regional disparities.

In this chapter we will look at two challenges facing Canadians:

• the causes and consequences of regional disparities

• the health care crisis in Canada

FIGURE 14.1

Average Annual Earnings by Full-Time Workers, 2001
Which region of Canada earns above the national average?

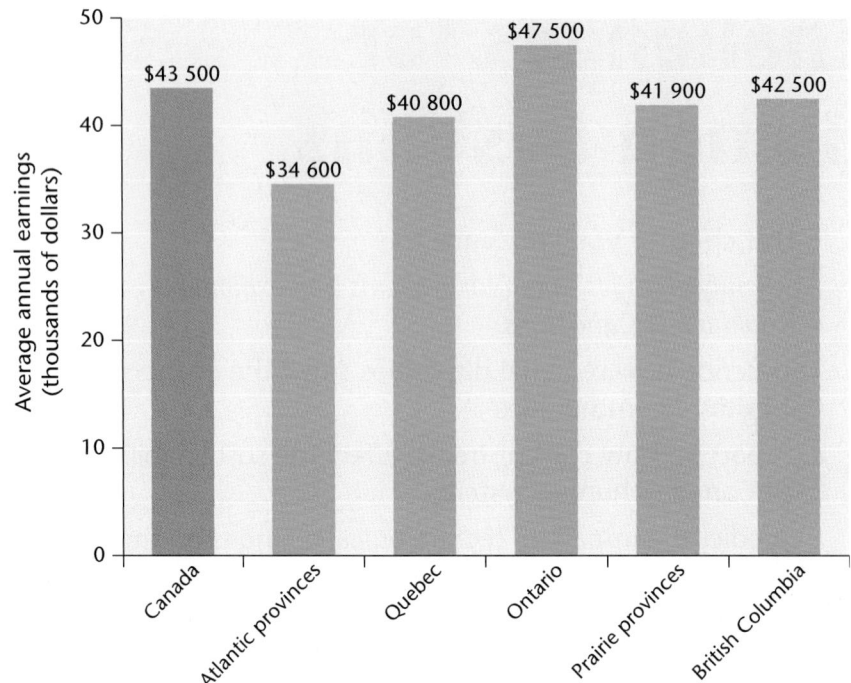

CHECK IT OVER

1. From Figure 14.1, identify the value of the average annual earnings for full-time workers in your region of Canada.

2. Figure 14.1 shows that there is a difference of almost $13 000 between the region with the highest earnings and the region with the lowest. Give one reason why Canadians should be concerned about that difference.

Regional Disparities in Canada

Regional disparities exist when opportunities and incomes are not equal across the country. A young person graduating from high school in Newfoundland and Labrador has much less chance of getting a full-time job paying decent wages than a young graduate in Ontario does. Over a lifetime, people who live in areas with weak economies will not have the same amount of money to spend as other Canadians on food, clothing, housing, education, and so on. They will not have the same opportunities to set up their own businesses or to develop satisfying careers. Regional disparities often cause people to move out of provinces with poor economies.

Province	1995	2000
Newfoundland and Labrador	21.4	18.8
Prince Edward Island	15.2	12.6
Nova Scotia	18.8	16.6
New Brunswick	19.0	15.7
Quebec	23.4	19.1
Ontario	17.7	14.4
Manitoba	20.6	17.5
Saskatchewan	18.3	15.8
Alberta	18.4	13.8
British Columbia	19.6	17.8
Canada	**19.7**	**16.2**

FIGURE 14.2

Percentage of People With Low Incomes, 1995 and 2000
The table shows fewer people with low incomes in 2000 compared with 1995. However, there are still important differences from one region of Canada to another. What was the percentage of people with low incomes in your province in 2000?

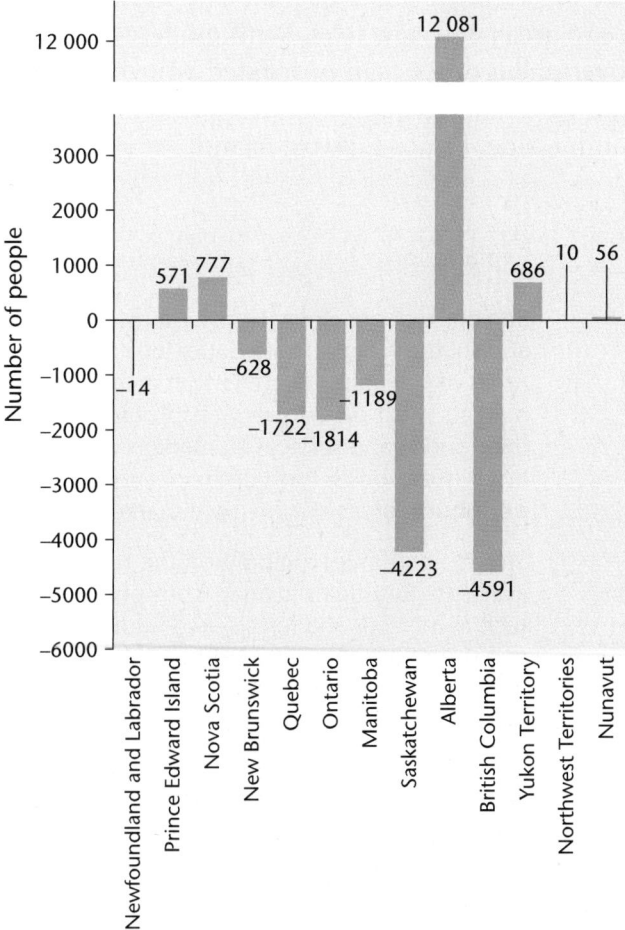

FIGURE 14.3

Net Internal Migration, 2003
Net internal migration is the number of people who move into a province or territory from another part of Canada minus the number of people living in that province or territory who leave to go to another province or territory. Some provinces have a negative net migration. What does this mean?

Chapter 14: Challenges for Human Systems   143

FIGURE 14.4

The Impacts of Negative Net Migration
Why is this flow diagram drawn as a cycle?

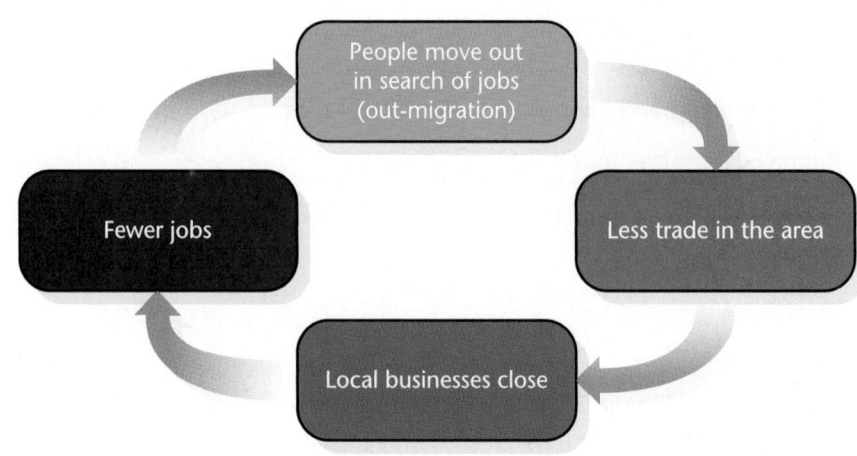

FAST Fact

Between 1996 and 2001, about 42 percent of Canadians moved from one province or territory to another.

Why do regional disparities exist? Geography has a good deal to do with regional disparities. Figure 14.5 identifies three important reasons. In some cases, governments have attempted to reduce regional disparities by targeting the reasons. One strategy, for example, was to move some government services out of Ontario and Quebec to areas with few jobs. With modern communication systems, government offices can be located anywhere. Canada Customs and Revenue Agency, to name one example, has a large office in Summerside, Prince Edward Island.

FIGURE 14.5

Reasons for Regional Disparities
Give one example of how physical resources are not distributed equally in Canada.

Factor	Explanation
Location	Regions that are close to **core** markets such as the U.S. and southern Ontario are better locations for businesses. Areas of Canada that are farther away from these core markets must pay higher transportation costs to ship their goods and services to markets. This discourages businesses from setting up in locations on the **periphery** (areas outside core markets).
Available Resources	Strong economies are built on the resources that are available. Resources include both physical resources, such as minerals and forests, and human resources, such as a skilled workforce and the ability to build successful businesses. Areas with poor physical resources will not have the finances to build colleges and universities, develop training programs, or encourage businesses.
Government Actions	Some provincial and municipal governments do not have the resources to overcome the obstacles to a strong economy. They cannot put in place the programs needed to solve the disparity problems.

FIGURE 14.6

FIGURE 14.6

The Harbour of Lunenburg, Nova Scotia
One human resource that Lunenburg has is its historical significance and charm. Lunenburg is developing a sustainable tourist industry based on its preserved past.

One government policy to try to reduce regional disparities is the use of equalization payments. These are payments the federal government gives to less wealthy provinces. These provinces can use the money to accomplish their own goals. Most years, eight provinces get equalization payments. You will notice from Figure 14.7 that Ontario and Alberta do not get these payments. This is because they are considered wealthy and not in need of federal government help.

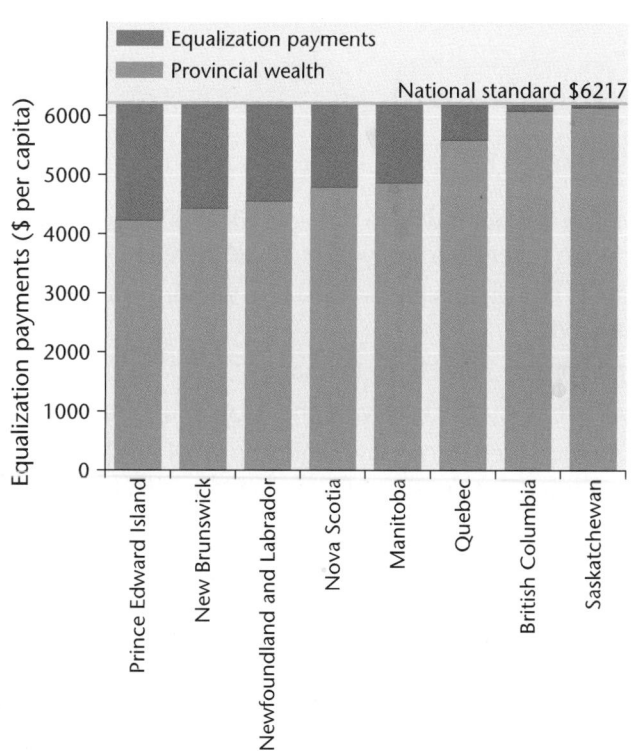

FIGURE 14.7

Equalization Payments, 2004–2005
These payments bring up the wealth of these provinces to that of the rest of Canada. Which province gets the largest equalization payment?

There are loud critics of equalization payments. Why, they argue, should tax dollars from Ontario and Alberta go to economically weaker provinces? If people want to enjoy greater wealth, they should pick up and move to where the jobs and opportunities are. This debate has been going on in Canada for many years.

FIGURE 14.8

Evidence That Supports and Opposes Equalization Payments
Which point of view do you think is strongest? Why?

Evidence That Supports Equalization Payments	Evidence That Opposes Equalization Payments
• Weaker provinces can afford more services with equalization payments. • The equalization payments are used to fund education and health care programs. The federal government can then have a say in how these programs are run. • The country as a whole is strengthened because all Canadians share the nation's wealth.	• Equalization payments are general payments to provinces. Not everyone in poor provinces is poor, so why should richer people benefit from the payments? • The payments lead to dependence on the federal government. • The higher taxes needed for equalization programs mean that businesses will be less able to compete globally.

 LITERACY SKILL

Using Rapid Writing

Rapid writing is a good way to get your ideas on paper. It is helpful when you are suffering from writer's block. Here are the rules:

- Write as fast as possible on the topic without editing or correcting your work.
- Don't lift your hand from the paper.
- If you are really stuck, rewrite the topic as a sentence.
- Start when the teacher says, and stop when told.
- Count the number of words you wrote in the rapid-writing activity.

Your teacher may ask you to share your writing with others.

CASE STUDY

Regional Disparities in Toronto

So far we have talked about the regional disparities among the provinces. Disparities also exist within cities. Large urban areas almost always have disparities: in the quality of housing, in the available shops and services, in the level of safety. In the early 2000s, United Way of Toronto studied the pattern of poverty in that city. Its findings were published in a report titled *Poverty by Postal Code*. The organization discovered that there was a very tight connection between where people lived and their chances of being poor. Figure 14.9 shows the pattern of poverty for the city of Toronto.

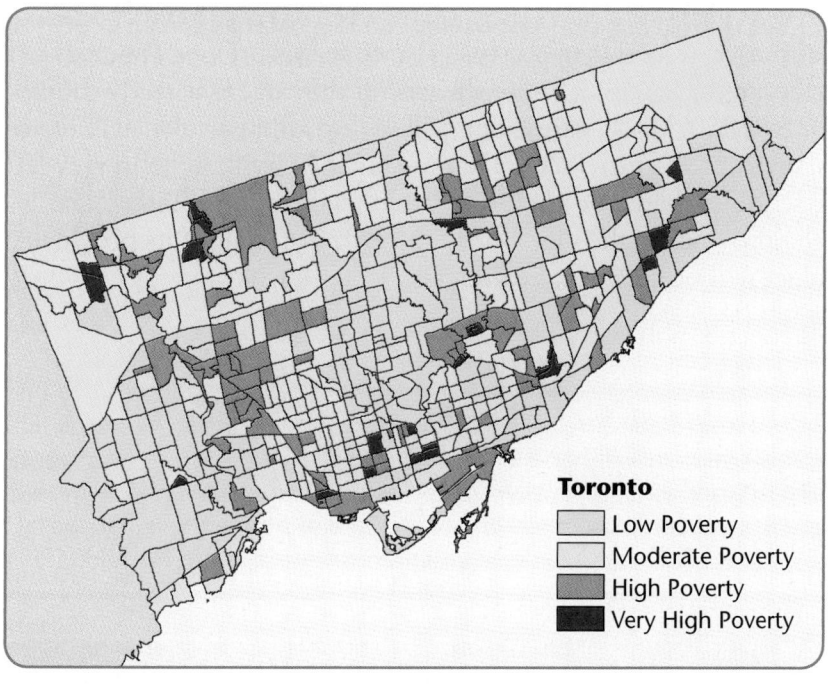

Toronto
- Low Poverty
- Moderate Poverty
- High Poverty
- Very High Poverty

FIGURE 14.9

Family Poverty Rates in the City of Toronto, 2001
Which colour shows the worst poverty?

3. Write a definition for the term *regional disparities.*

4. Use the ideas of core and periphery to identify parts of Canada that are suffering from regional disparities.

5. Why can internal migration be seen as one indicator of regional disparities?

6. Complete a three-minute rapid-writing activity on the topic of equalization payments.

The Health Care Crisis

In recent years, the news media have been saying that Canada's health care system is in a crisis. The concerns are not about the quality of the care, but about the *cost* of the care. One study showed that by 2050, health care alone will use up all the provincial income for seven of the provinces. That means there will be no money left for schools, roads, or any other provincial responsibilities. Ontario is the province in the worst position. By 2011, half of its provincial budget will be spent on health care.

FIGURE 14.10

Health Care Spending Per Person in Canada, 1990–2003
What was the level of spending for the year you were born?

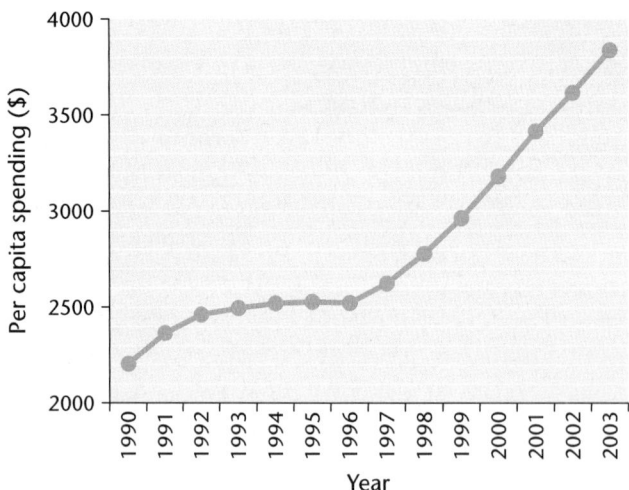

Why is this crisis occurring? Here are four important reasons:

- **The Aging Population:** Canadians are getting older on average (see pages 94–96 in Chapter 9). This is partly because we are living longer. Canadians have one of the longest life expectancies in the world. Older people tend to put more demands on the health care system than younger people do.

- **New Medical Challenges:** There are new threats to the health of Canadians all the time. In some cases, these are threats from outside the country, such as new strains of flu viruses. In other cases, these threats are homegrown. A good example is the increasing number of "superbugs." These are drug-resistant diseases that are particularly deadly for the old and the very young.

- **Health Care Fraud:** Costs are driven up by people who take advantage of Canada's medical care system without helping to pay the costs. For example, people have used fake health cards to get health care that they are not eligible for.

- **Higher Standards:** Canadians are used to a high-quality health care system and complain if standards drop. For example, recently in Ontario the government began to deal with long "wait times," the length of time a patient has to wait to get tests or treatments. People in Ontario feel that waiting weeks or months for such things as hip replacement surgery is unacceptable.

> **FAST** *Fact*
>
> Most Canadians in the southern part of the country rarely have to travel more than 25 km to see a family doctor. People in northern locations have to travel much greater distances.

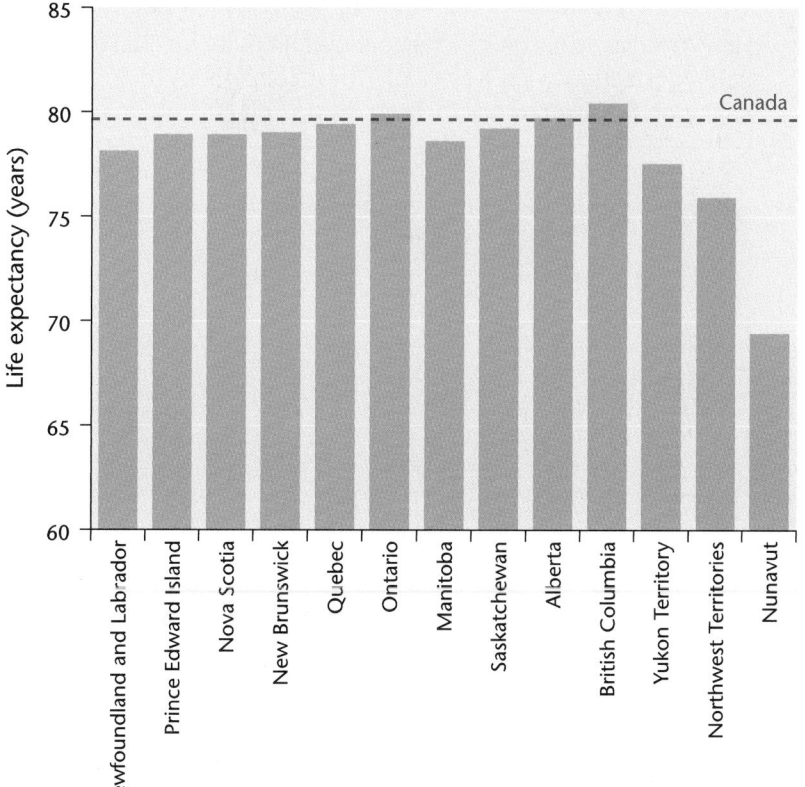

FIGURE 14.11

Average Life Expectancy at Birth for Canadians, 2001
What might be a reason for the low life expectancy in Nunavut?

GEOCAREERS

Paramedic

When someone has a medical emergency, paramedics are often the first medical help that person gets. Paramedics quickly stabilize patients and transport them to hospitals or other services. Understanding the geographic patterns (road systems, traffic flows, and housing patterns) of local areas helps paramedics keep travel times short.

Paramedics must complete a two-year college program and pass a provincial exam. College programs usually require that applicants already have a Standard First Aid certificate and know CPR. In addition, they have to be physically fit and able to communicate well. Ongoing training is required throughout a paramedic's career.

 CHECK IT OVER

7. What is one trend or pattern that shows Canada could be facing a health care crisis?

8. Why are longer life expectancies making the health care crisis worse?

9. How much are you concerned about wait times for medical treatment? Rate your concerns on a scale of 1 (not concerned) to 5 (very concerned). Give reasons for your rating.

THINK IT OVER

Knowledge and Understanding

1. Complete an ideas web that shows some important ideas about the causes and outcomes of regional disparities.

2. Provide one example or illustration to show how regional disparities affect the economic health of communities.

3. Explain how an aging population makes the health care crisis worse.

Thinking and Communication

4. Typical internal migrants in Canada are
   - 25 to 34 years old
   - university educated
   - unmarried

   Give reasons why people with these characteristics are more likely to move than other people.

5. Suppose you are a government official in a province experiencing negative net migration. What are three things that you could do to try to slow down the movement of people in your province to other provinces?

6. Are you likely to become an internal migrant because of regional disparities? Make up a chart that shows the advantages and disadvantages of moving from where you live to another part of the country. What is your conclusion?

PERFORMANCE TASK

Comparing Ecozones

Key Words

ecozones
comparison chart
documentation
bibliography

In this performance task you will learn to

◢ *illustrate regional differences using the concept of ecozones*

◢ *use the methods and tools of geographic investigation to understand Canada's ecozones*

Introduction

The physical and human systems within Canada work together to give us the quality of life we enjoy. One way to see the connections among the systems is to look at ecozones. Ecozones are regions of Canada that are broken down into land and water zones with the same characteristics. Ecozones include both human and physical characteristics, such as landforms, climate, soil, vegetation, wildlife, and human activity. We will focus on the land ecozones.

FIGURE PT2.1

Canada's Land Ecozones

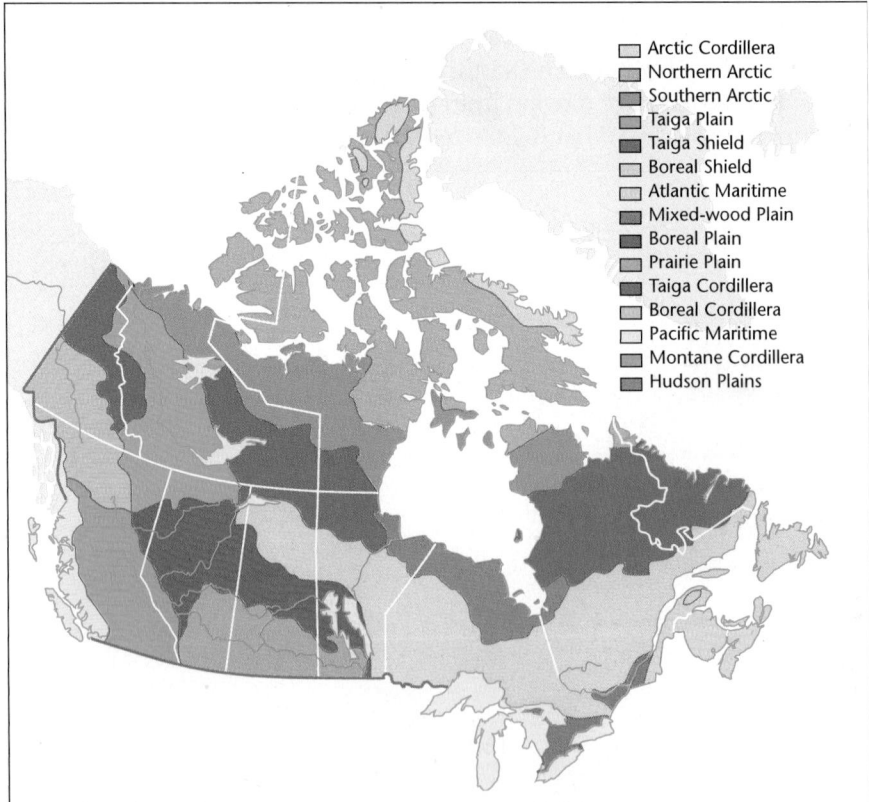

- Arctic Cordillera
- Northern Arctic
- Southern Arctic
- Taiga Plain
- Taiga Shield
- Boreal Shield
- Atlantic Maritime
- Mixed-wood Plain
- Boreal Plain
- Prairie Plain
- Taiga Cordillera
- Boreal Cordillera
- Pacific Maritime
- Montane Cordillera
- Hudson Plains

Mountain High Maps ® Copyright © 1993 Digital Wisdom, Inc.

Performance Task Assignment

Your job is to compare the ecozone you live in with one other ecozone. You are doing this so that you can determine which is the better ecozone in which to locate a new national park.

Step 1   Ask your teacher to explain how you will be evaluated on this assignment.

Step 2   Determine the ecozone you live in. Choose one other ecozone to compare to your own.

Step 3   Review the purposes of national parks by checking the list of points on page 49.

Step 4   Find information that will help you to understand the characteristics of the ecozones. There are many good Web sites you can access on the Internet. Your search words could be *ecozones*, *Canada*.

Step 5   Organize your collection of information by preparing a comparison chart. Your comparison chart might have these headings:

Decide which characteristics to record by thinking about the purposes of national parks.

Characteristics	Your Ecozone	The Other Ecozone

Step 6   Record information in your chart. Make sure that you give full documentation of your sources; that is, that you supply all the references you used. Ask your teacher for a good way of recording your information. Source information is included in your bibliography.

Step 7   Find a picture from each ecozone. The picture should show some of the important characteristics you are noting. Make sure to record the sources of your pictures.

Step 8   Review the information you have collected and decide whether you have enough information to make a good decision about where to locate the new national park. If you can't decide, you may need to find and record more details.

Step 9   Make your decision and write a short summary paragraph in which you give some of the reasons for your decision.

Step 10   Share your research findings. Make up a poster or a Web site that includes

- a map showing the two ecozones that you investigated
- your two pictures
- your completed comparison chart
- a bibliography of your information sources
- your summary paragraph

Unit

3

Environmental Challenges

Overall Expectations

In this unit you will learn to

◢ explain the relationship between sustainability and stewardship

◢ assess the impacts of human systems on the natural environment

◢ relate lifestyle choices to Canada's economic and environmental well-being

◢ identify changes in energy and explain how they could affect the lives of Canadians

◢ apply the concepts of stewardship and sustainability to a current issue

◢ communicate the results of geographic inquiries

It is important to understand how people affect the natural environment and how the environment affects people. With this knowledge we can protect the environment we live in.

Chapter 15

Aboriginal Peoples and the Environment

Key Words

inuksuk

Elders

traditional ecological knowledge (TEK)

oral histories

In this chapter you will learn to

- ◢ *explain the relationship between sustainability and stewardship*
- ◢ apply the concepts of stewardship and sustainability to Aboriginal culture
- ◢ describe the role of Aboriginal peoples in protecting the environment
- ◢ identify some aspects of traditional ecological knowledge
- ◢ explain how traditional ecological knowledge influences how Aboriginal peoples interact with their environment

Introduction

Have you ever tried to build something out of rocks? It's very difficult. The rocks are uneven and they don't seem to stay where you put them. So how do Inuit do it? You have probably seen a picture of an inuksuk built by Inuit. You may have seen an imitation of an inuksuk along a shoreline or highway.

The traditional purpose of an inuksuk is to act as a marker or signpost to guide Inuit across the featureless North. It could show directions, it could point to areas where shelter could be found, or it could provide a warning that something dangerous is ahead. In Canada's North, an inuksuk is a welcome sight. It tells travellers that they are not alone, that someone has been there before them.

FIGURE 15.1

Inuksuk at Aupalaqtuq Point, Nunavut
The inuksuk (pronounced *in-ook-shook*), meaning "likeness of a person," often have a particular purpose or meaning. What do you think the purpose of this inuksuk might be?

In this chapter we will see how the inuksuk reminds us of the Aboriginal peoples' close connection with the natural environment. We will focus on these topics:

- traditional knowledge held by Aboriginal peoples about the environment
- how traditional knowledge is passed from one generation to the next by oral histories

CHECK IT OVER

1. Have you ever built an inuksuk? If you have, explain why you did it. If you haven't, tell why someone who is not Inuit might build an inuksuk.

2. Why do you think Inuit create a direction symbol or signpost out of stone?

Traditional Ecological Knowledge

Traditional ecological knowledge (TEK) is the knowledge that Aboriginal peoples have learned through direct contact with the environment. It includes a detailed understanding of plants, animals, and other natural things. TEK represents a oneness between people and their natural environments. This is why Aboriginal peoples act as stewards or caretakers of their environment. They take care of the environment by not using more than they need. The environment in turn provides for them. Being one with the environment means things in nature such as animals, rocks, trees, and water (and even humans) have a spiritual connection to one another. Animals and birds are often given human characteristics and are greatly respected by Aboriginal peoples.

Animal	Meaning	Animal	Meaning
eagle	strength, courage	owl	secrecy
coyote	intelligence, stealth	rabbit	quick thinking
fox	cunning, cleverness	wolf	death, rebirth

We can find this strong relationship between Aboriginal peoples and their environment in the art and artifacts that are left by the Aboriginal peoples. The totem poles of the Haida from British Columbia provide a good example.

FAST *Fact*

Recent events reveal how important the inuksuk is as a symbol of Canada's Aboriginal peoples. In November 2005, 20 Aboriginal veterans of the Second World War, accompanied by **Elders**, or spiritual leaders, visited First and Second World War sites in Europe. Their visit was called a "Calling Home Ceremony." Its purpose was to return the spirits of fallen warriors to their homelands and put them to rest with their ancestors in Canada. An inuksuk was placed at Juno Beach Centre, the site of the Canadian D-Day landing in 1944. This inuksuk will serve as a permanent reminder of Canada's Aboriginal peoples' service to their country.

FIGURE 15.2

Human Characteristics Given to Animals by Aboriginal Peoples
Can you think of other animals that we refer to in ways that give them human characteristics?

FIGURE 15.3

A Totem Pole in the Queen Charlotte Islands, B.C.
The totem pole often tells a story about the people who made it. What is one image from this carving that you can identify?

3. What shape does a traditional inuksuk take? Why do you think that this is so?

4. What are some of the purposes of an inuksuk? Can you think of other reasons to build an inuksuk?

5. If you were to carve a totem pole, what animals or features would you put on it? Why would you use those particular animals or features?

Oral Histories

How do the Aboriginal peoples share their traditional ecological knowledge? It is done through oral histories. This is the telling of stories or passing on of information from one generation to the next. These histories are not written down or recorded in books. They are taught by the Elders in a community to the young. There is great honour in Aboriginal communities for those who can remember the stories told by the Elders so that they can be passed on to the next generation.

FIGURE 15.4

The Telling of a People's History
Oral histories are passed from one generation to the next when Elders tell their histories and stories to the young.

Traditional ecological knowledge that is passed on through oral histories has the following characteristics:

- It is often told through stories.
- It is most often told by Elders.
- It is used in teaching young children and youths.
- It is mainly passed on through descriptive stories.
- It is also learned through observation and hands-on experience.
- It is based on data collected over a long period of time in one location.
- It passes environmental wisdom from one generation to the next.

FIGURE 15.5

Characteristics of Traditional Ecological Knowledge
Does your family or cultural group have something similar to Aboriginal peoples' traditional ecological knowledge?

CASE STUDY

A Hunter's Story

This is an account of a First Nations Elder:
When I was young, we used to hunt all the time. We used to hunt moose, bear, caribou, ducks, geese. We hunted all the time. You had to hunt until you killed something. Sometimes we went hungry, but mostly we had country food all the time.

It's hard to hunt moose. You have to follow the tracks until you find the animal. Moose are smart. You have to be careful because they watch everything, and they run away fast. I shot my first moose when I was fifteen. I didn't know a lot about hunting, so an old man took me out in the bush. I saw some moose tracks. I was real excited because I wanted to shoot that moose. The old man ignored those tracks. He didn't even say anything; he just kept on walking. We walked for a long time, and we found more moose tracks. The old man said there was a moose here, so we went into the bush, and we found it and I shot it. I was happy. It was a good feeling because we took it back and everyone had fresh meat. That old man knew how to hunt and he showed me how to hunt.

In those days, everyone used to travel together and everyone would help each other. If someone killed a moose, they would share it with everybody. Today, people don't share as much as they used to. That was important in the old days—if you had meat, you never refused to share it with anybody. If you didn't share, then the hunting was no good. That's why people respected a good hunter, because he always shared everything.

CHECK IT OVER

6. What do you think is the main point in "A Hunter's Story"?

7. Can you think of a story from your family that conveys a message that would be worth telling your children in the future?

How important is traditional ecological knowledge? It is becoming more and more significant as we become more concerned with saving the environment and the things around us. Below are two examples of traditional knowledge being used along with scientific knowledge to address environmental issues. They show the growing importance of TEK.

1. In the mid-1990s, the Canadian Arctic Resources Committee was identifying the impact of human activities on the duck populations in the Hudson and James Bay areas. Inuit hunters were able to provide detailed information about the location of the ducks, their nesting habits, and their eating habits. This information was vital in developing an environmental plan to protect the ducks if there were an oil spill in the area.

2. The Belcher Islands project draws on traditional ecological knowledge about the feeding activities of reindeer in the area, and how they breed. The project also learned from the methods Inuit use to hunt reindeer. This information was combined with science to develop a plan to manage a herd of reindeer recently introduced to the Belcher Islands.

Literacy Strategy

Viewing a video

Making sense of the information presented in a video requires that you reflect on what you see by asking yourself the following questions:
1. What was the message?
2. What questions do I still have?
3. How do I see the video connecting to my world?

 LITERACY SKILL

Tips for Watching Videos

There are a number of steps that are useful to follow when watching a video in the classroom.

1. Record the title, source, and date of the video. This will allow you to refer to the video in the future.

2. Identify the purpose of the video. Your teacher will explain why the video is being shown. You can see how the video fits into the lesson.

3. Record the information from the video. Often there will be a video guide for you to complete which will highlight the main points of the video. Your teacher will likely provide time during the video for you to record information on your worksheet. The teacher may emphasize key terms, ideas, or examples. He or she may show important segments of the video twice, if necessary.

4. Find a personal connection to the video. If you can connect your personal experiences to the video ("I heard about this on the news…"), the information will have more meaning for you.

5. Relate the significance of the video to your current studies. Your teacher may lead a discussion or debate so you can react to and discuss the content and opinions presented in the video.

CASE STUDY

Bill Reid, Aboriginal Artist

Bill Reid was born in Victoria, British Columbia, in January 1920. His mother was Haida and his father of European descent. He was raised and lived most of his life in British Columbia. When he died in March 1998, after a 30-year struggle with Parkinson's disease, he left a legacy of art ranging from the tiny to the huge—in wood carving, silversmithing, goldsmithing, printmaking, and sculpture.

Bill Reid introduced the great art traditions of the northwest coast Aboriginal peoples to modern audiences. He brought modern ideas to Aboriginal traditional art. He also helped to inspire and teach young Haida artists. Bill Reid's work has helped to build lasting bridges between First Nations and other peoples.

You may even have an example of Bill Reid's art in your pocket! The Haida sculpture in Figure 15.6 is an example of Bill Reid's work. It is featured in the centre of the most recent edition of the Canadian $20 bill.

FIGURE 15.6

Bill Reid's *The Spirit of Haida Gwaii* Sculpture
Why do you think Reid's work was chosen to be displayed on Canadian money?

GEOCAREERS

Wildlife Technician

Wildlife technicians study and observe animals to help scientists with research. They collect information on animals, plants, seeds, water, and soil. These findings help them learn about animal populations in the wild. Wildlife technicians support scientists in wildlife management and animal biology. They do this by collecting scientific samples and analyzing them. Geography prepares students for this career by covering topics such as physical systems, and teaching skills such as map and air photograph interpretation and research skills.

CHECK IT OVER

8. Sometimes researchers do not take oral histories into account when they are investigating an issue. Can you suggest two reasons why they might not include oral histories in their research? Can you think of two reasons why they should?

9. If you were given the opportunity to design one of the bills (such as the $50 bill) for the Canadian government, what images of Canada would you include? Why would you choose those images?

THINK IT OVER

Knowledge and Understanding

1. List three examples of how the Aboriginal peoples of Canada identify with their environment.

2. What are some lessons that all Canadians can learn from traditional ecological knowledge?

3. What are two ideas Aboriginal peoples have about the environment that you could make part of your own life? Explain your answer.

Thinking and Communication

4. Suppose you were asked to create a Web site or a poster display to show the idea of traditional ecological knowledge. Make a list of 10 images that you would include. Your images could include pictures of people doing things, picture of objects that have been built, or copies of works of art.

5. Imagine that you are writing a letter to a friend who lives in another country. In a short paragraph, explain to your friend what traditional ecological knowledge is.

How Big Is Your Ecological Footprint?

Chapter 16

Key Words

- ecological footprint
- stewardship
- sustainable development
- zero waste

In this chapter you will learn to

⊿ *explain the relationship between sustainability, stewardship, and an ecological footprint*

⊿ compare the ecological footprint of a typical Canadian with that of people from other countries

⊿ judge Canada's environmental stewardship based on the size of the average Canadian's ecological footprint

⊿ explain the relationship between stewardship, sustainability, and change in Canada's use of resources

Introduction

Suppose you were part of a group hiking in one of Canada's national parks. One of your group challenges you to walk 100 m through a section of natural forest without disturbing anything. No problem, you think, and start out. You step carefully and push gently through the shrubs and small trees. At the end of the distance, you look back along your path—not bad, barely any branches broken and only a few plants damaged.

But then your friends help you to look closer and you are surprised by the damage that you see. Some ways you disturbed the natural environment include

- compacting (pressing down) the soil where you stepped
- squashing small insects and amphibians
- killing tiny plants just starting to grow
- breaking off flowers before they had a chance to be pollinated
- scaring wildlife

You realize that your movements had a far greater impact than you thought—you have an ecological footprint.

Literacy Strategy

Creating mental images
When you visualize (create mental pictures) during reading, it helps you to understand what you are reading and later helps you to remember what you read. As you read, create a "mental movie" that highlights what you are reading.

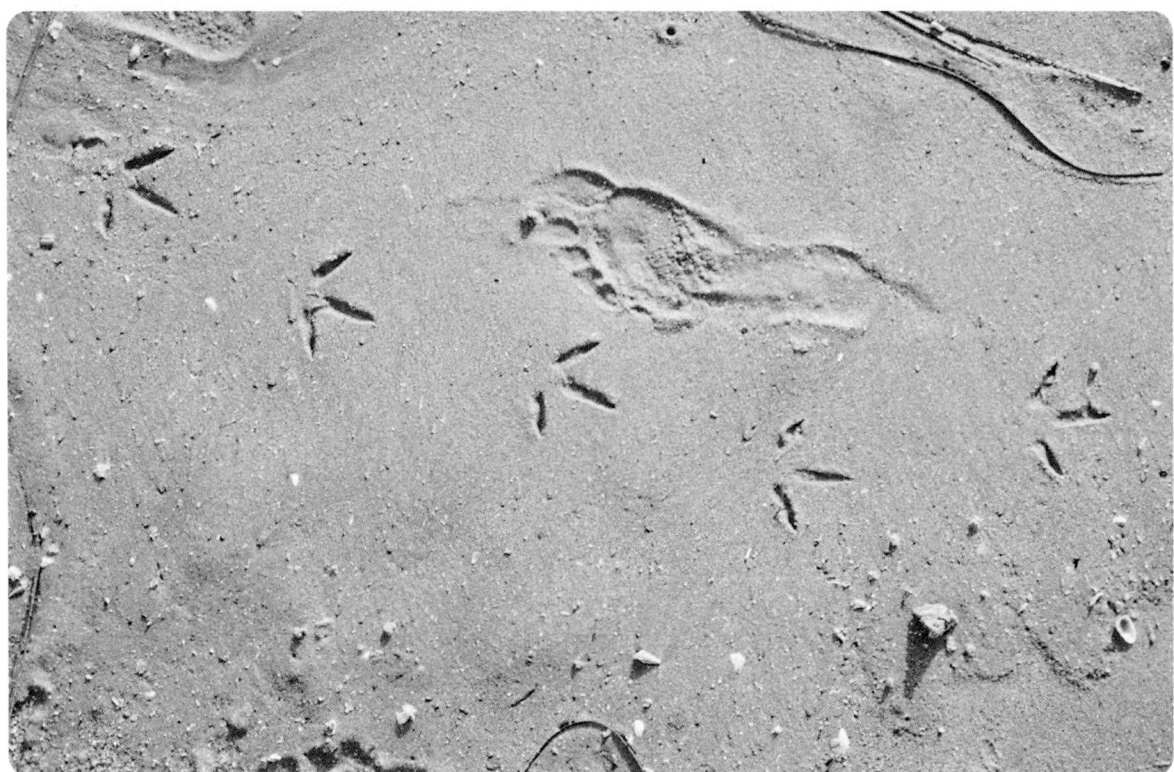

FIGURE 16.1

Footprints in the Sand
Walking across a beach
has an impact on the
environment. Our
day-to-day living also
changes natural systems.

In this chapter we will look at

- the idea of an ecological footprint
- how Canada's ecological footprint compares to that of other countries
- what it means to be an environmental steward

CHECK IT OVER

1. List five ways that you have an impact on natural systems.
2. Identify one way that you could cause less damage to the environment.

Footprints on the Environment

Our ecological footprint is a way to think about how an individual or society leaves an impression on the place where we live. The idea was developed by a Canadian, Dr. Bill Rees, at the University of British Columbia. It refers to the amount of the earth's surface that is needed to produce all the energy and resources that each of us uses. It also includes all the land needed to absorb all the waste we make.

The global average ecological footprint is 2.8 hectares (ha) of land per person. The average Canadian uses 7.7 ha—we have a much bigger footprint than most other countries in the world. These amounts are calculated using surveys to get the average. Figure 16.2 shows you some of the factors that are considered.

Household or Individual Footprint	City, Town, or Region Footprint
• amount and types of food eaten • amount and type of electricity used • size of house or apartment • amount of goods bought • fuel efficiency of home and vehicles • distance travelled by car, transit, bike, and foot	• population density • average household size • consumer spending • energy use • urban land use

FIGURE 16.2

Information Used to Calculate an Ecological Footprint
How does the size of your home affect your ecological footprint?

Examples of Heavy Footprints	Examples of Light Footprints
sport utility vehicles (SUVs)	bicycles
12-lane freeways	gravel roads
coal-fired electrical plants	solar power
commuters by car	public transit, e.g., subway
driving to school	walking to school

FIGURE 16.3

Heavy and Light Ecological Footprints
Why is walking to school "lighter" than driving to school?

Interpreting Cartoons

Cartoons are humorous drawings in newspapers, in magazines, and on Internet sites. They entertain and often challenge readers by making a comment on a current event. The caption sometimes explains the event. Look at Figure 16.4 to see how the cartoonist shows the idea of an ecological footprint. Identify the symbols or images that are shown in the cartoon. Describe the main point of the cartoon.

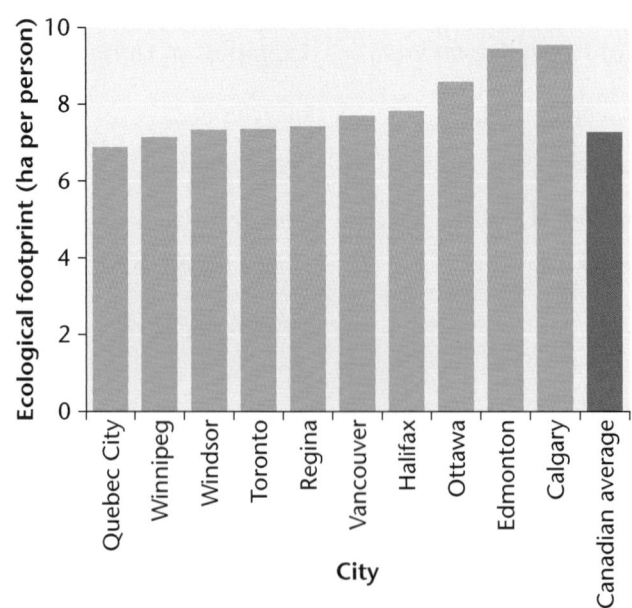

FIGURE 16.4

Visualizing the Idea of an Ecological Footprint
Do you think this cartoon is effective? Why or why not?

FIGURE 16.5

Ecological Footprints for Selected Canadian Cities
In which province are the top two cities located?

Source: *Ecological Footprints of Canadian Municipalities and Regions*, 2005, p. 21. Prepared for The Federation of Canadian Municipalities by Anielski Management Inc.

GEOCAREERS

Soil Conservationist

Soil is the thin layer of mineral and vegetable matter that covers most of the surface of the planet. The work of the soil conservationist is to save and protect this life-supporting layer. Soil damage can come from

- wind and water erosion
- poor use of fertilizers
- over-farming
- salt buildup

Soil conservationists usually work for governments, conservation groups, and agricultural businesses. Geography provides these specialists with the background and knowledge to perform such tasks as

- locating where soil types occur using mapping skills
- describing climate and weather patterns, which have an important role in how soils form
- analyzing patterns of land use that can harm soils and create soil erosion

 CHECK IT OVER

3. Explain what your ecological footprint is.
4. Explain why ecological footprint measurements are given as hectares.
5. Give one suggestion for how you might have a lighter ecological footprint for each of these aspects of your life:
   - transportation
   - waste
   - energy use
   - food
6. Create a diagram to show two people, one with a light ecological footprint and one with a heavy ecological footprint. Add labels to show the actions or belongings that create light or heavy footprints.

A Global View of Ecological Footprints

Over 6.5 billion people live on our planet. The human footprint is found everywhere. (See the Case Study: Human Footprints in Antarctica on the opposite page.) Scientists and businesspeople are exploring the last remote frontiers on Earth, such as the polar regions and jungle lands, in a race to find resources, species, and spaces. Human activity has disturbed nearly 75 percent of Earth's surface. According to the National Geographic Society, we are using 40 percent of the land's capacity, 35 percent of the ocean's capacity, and 60 percent of the fresh water capacity of Earth. We must look at ways to ensure that humans and their standard of living have a future.

FIGURE 16.6

Ecological Footprints for Selected Countries
How does Canada compare to the world average?

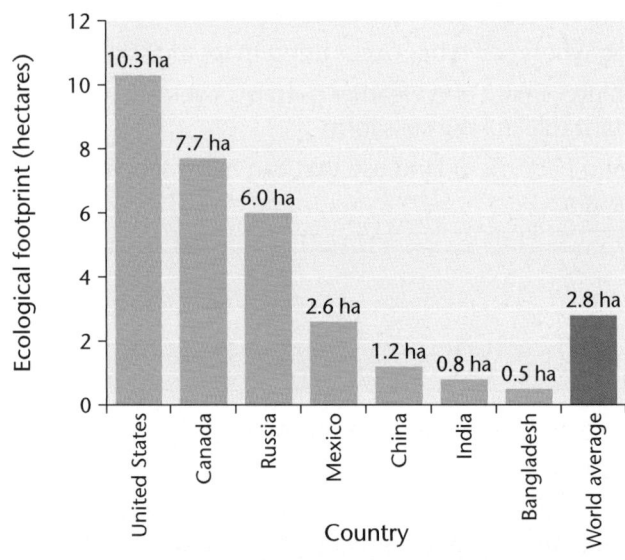

FIGURE 16.7

The Border Between Canada and the United States
This satellite image shows the border between Montana (lower half) and Alberta and Saskatchewan (upper half). In Montana, wheat is grown in fields, while in Canada, cattle graze on range land. How do these examples show ecological footprints?

CASE STUDY

Human Footprints in Antarctica

Antarctica is a continent surrounding the South Pole that has few human ecological footprints. A number of nations signed a treaty in 1961 making this uninhabited area a World Reserve. Today, 44 nations have agreed to this treaty designed to keep the continent as a reserve devoted to peace and science. The treaty forbids

- military activities
- nuclear testing
- the disposal of radioactive waste

The treaty encourages scientific research of

- penguins
- whales
- ice formation
- the ozone layer

Seven nations have staked land claims here, but the treaty is holding. Ecotourism is a popular and growing activity. Tour operators agree to be very careful how they conduct their tours so that ecological footprints in the area remain light.

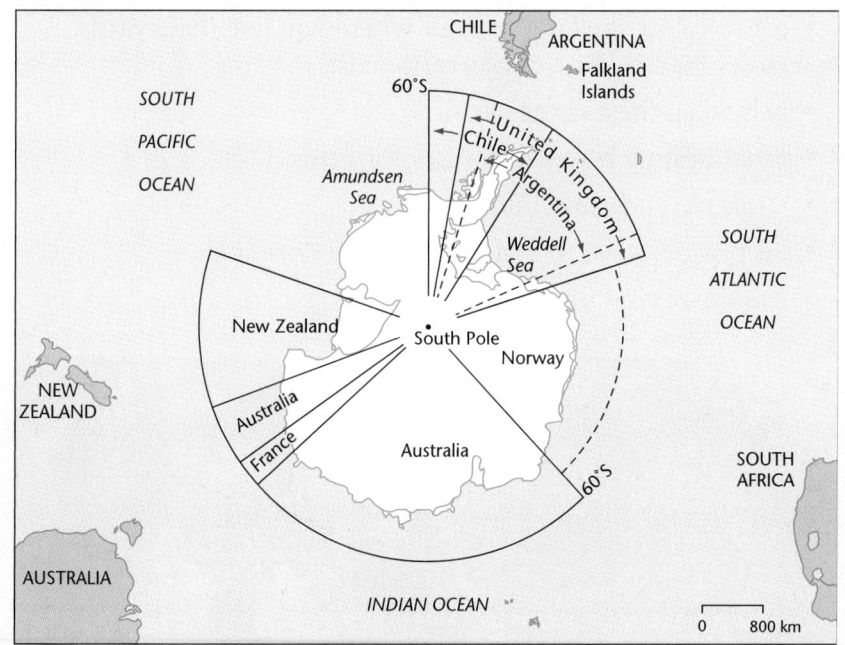

FIGURE 16.8

Territorial Claims in the Antarctic
Why do you think France and the United Kingdom have claims on Antarctica?

7. Explain why humans leave ecological footprints even in places where there are few people.

8. What geographic pattern can you find in the graph in Figure 16.6? You may need to look up the locations of these countries in an atlas to see a pattern.

9. How might an international treaty reduce ecological impacts in Antarctica?

Becoming an Environmental Steward

Parents and guardians care for children. This is similar to the roles found in stewardship of the environment. Stewards are the guardians of the land. They protect the land where they live and they also care for Earth as a whole. If everyone made a personal choice to become a steward of Earth, most environmental problems would start to disappear. To be a steward, you can do the following:

- get to know the land around where you live (backyards, parks, hydro lines, conservation areas)
- help keep these areas clean
- build nesting boxes or houses for birds
- plant trees, shrubs, and flowers
- keep waterways free of garbage and chemicals
- use waste containers in public areas

FIGURE 16.9

Becoming a Steward of the Environment
What are these people doing to improve the environment?

16

Each province has many agencies that act as official stewards. For example, in Ontario, conservation authorities are the stewards of watersheds. They

- protect the sources of all rivers
- test and monitor ground water, especially well water
- protect shorelines from erosion and destruction
- protect downstream users from pollution and waste runoff coming from upstream
- shelter wildlife, birds, animals, and fish

On a world scale, stewardship is organized through the United Nations. The UN groups try to solve the world's environmental problems. Figure 16.10 shows some of the efforts that have been made in global environmental stewardship.

FAST Fact

Germany is one of the leading nations of **zero waste** laws. Its laws make sure all parts of products are 100 percent recyclable, for everything from soda pop to Mercedes Benz cars!

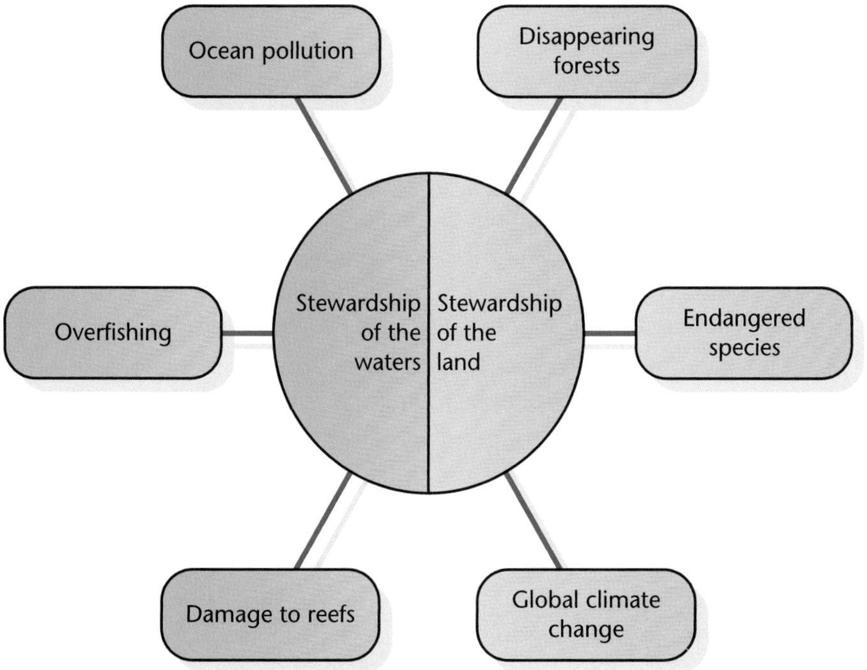

FIGURE 16.10

Global Efforts at Stewardship of the Environment Which efforts do you think might be most important to Canada's environment?

Some non-governmental organizations, such as Greenpeace and the World Wildlife Fund, also work as stewards of the environment.

Sustainable development is one of the most promising ideas to help solve environmental problems. This means that people work together to encourage development that meets the needs of, or sustains, today's standard of living but does not hinder the ability of future generations to meet their own needs. In other words, your grandchildren will live as well as or better than you do. In forestry, for example, sustainable development means that another tree is planted for every tree that is cut down. In this way, the forest stock is sustained—it never decreases—for future generations. Sustainable development provides the framework for linking economic prospects with environmental protection.

CHECK IT OVER

10. Give one reason to explain why getting to know the area around you is an important part of being an environmental steward.

11. If zero waste laws were in force in Canada, how do you think your life would be different? Explain your points.

12. Explain how sustainable development is part of being a steward of the environment.

THINK IT OVER

Knowledge and Understanding

1. Describe how you contribute to Canada's heavy ecological footprint.

2. Suggest ways of showing others how to reduce their ecological footprint. Give one strategy you might use for each of the following: with your friends, at home, and at school.

3. Make up three statements that compare Canadians' ecological footprints to those of people in other parts of the world.

4. Based on your own experience and research, give three examples of efforts that governments use to try to protect the environment.

Thinking and Communication

5. Create a collage to show pictures of the ways that humans leave a footprint on the environment.

6. Use the Internet and other resources to find out what your community or area has done to reduce its impacts on the environment. Prepare a poster or Web page to show the information that you have found. Include a bibliography.

7. Research the idea of sustainable development. Create a cartoon, diagram, or picture to show this idea visually. Write a short paragraph to explain how this image shows sustainable development.

Canada's Energy Situation: Are We Going to Run Out of Power?

Chapter 17

Key Words

- renewable energy sources
- non-renewable energy sources
- conventional energy sources
- alternative energy sources
- fossil fuels
- wind farm
- bitumen
- muskeg
- overburden
- surface mining
- reclamation

In this chapter you will learn to

◢ *identify current or anticipated changes in energy and explain how they could affect the lives of Canadians*

◢ *apply the concepts of stewardship and sustainability to analyze Canada's energy situation*

◢ identify the locations and determine the relative importance of Canada's major energy sources

◢ use criteria to evaluate alternative energy sources and conservation strategies

◢ explain the change in Canada's consumption (use) of energy and other resource-use practices

Introduction

A buck twenty-five! Yup, the price of gas at the pumps in Toronto in September 2005 was $1.25. Drivers were paying about 40 percent more for gas than a year earlier. Why? Some people said it had something to do with Hurricane Katrina and the damage to oil refineries in Texas. Others accused the gasoline companies of overcharging consumers. Yet other people blamed high taxes for the sudden increase in gasoline prices. Fortunately, gas prices returned to the levels they were at before the hurricane, but it makes you think. How high can energy prices go?

FIGURE 17.1

The Highest Gasoline Price in Toronto in 2005 The price of gasoline hit $1.25 in 2005 after Hurricane Katrina shut down several large U.S. oil refineries. Why do you think the price of gas increased?

Energy prices are connected to energy supply. If there isn't much energy available, prices go up. Will we ever completely run out of energy? What types of energy sources do we have in Canada and how long will they last? This chapter will try to answer some of these questions. We will look at these topics:

- Canada's current energy supplies
- alternative energy sources for this country
- large-scale energy projects
- sustainability and stewardship of energy supplies

 CHECK IT OVER

1. What are three ways you use energy?
2. What are two ways higher energy costs may affect you?

Canada's Energy Sources and Uses

There are many different ways to look at energy and energy sources. In Canada, we can put energy into two simple categories:

- **renewable energy sources:** energy supplies that can be replaced after they are consumed, for example, solar power or wind power
- **non-renewable energy sources:** energy supplies that are limited and cannot be replaced once they are used up, for example, oil and natural gas

We can also view energy sources as conventional energy sources or alternative energy sources. Conventional energy sources are the more common sources of energy found in Canada. They include flowing water, fossil fuels, and uranium. Alternative energy sources include solar, wind, tidal, biomass, geothermal and, more recently, hydrogen. These sources are being developed to replace the conventional ones. Alternative energy sources are renewable and usually do not harm the environment.

FAST Fact

Nearly 5 percent of Canadian jobs are tied to getting or distributing energy. Energy exports make up 5 percent of our total exports.

CHECK IT OVER

3. What types of energy are used in your home? Are they renewable or non-renewable sources?

4. Copy the chart below into your notebook. Complete the chart with as many types of energy sources as you can think of. List them in the proper location in the chart.

	Renewable Energy Sources	Non-Renewable Energy Sources
Conventional Energy Sources		
Alternative Energy Sources		

Energy is used in a number of different ways. Take a look at Figure 17.2.

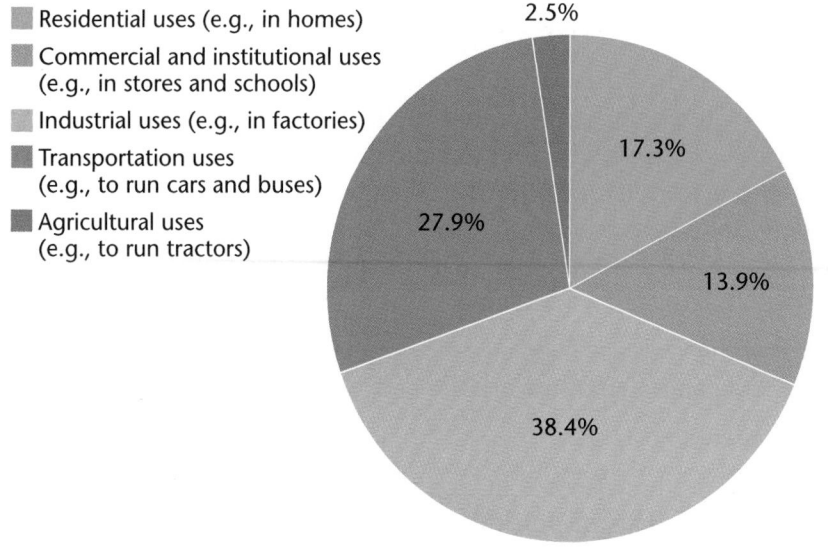

- Residential uses (e.g., in homes)
- Commercial and institutional uses (e.g., in stores and schools)
- Industrial uses (e.g., in factories)
- Transportation uses (e.g., to run cars and buses)
- Agricultural uses (e.g., to run tractors)

2.5%
17.3%
27.9%
13.9%
38.4%

FIGURE 17.2

Energy Use in Canada, 2003
What are the two largest types of energy use in Canada? Give two examples of each of these types of energy use.

Fossil Fuels

Fossil fuels such as coal, oil, and natural gas are minerals that were formed from the remains of plants and animals. Fossil fuels are found in sedimentary rock areas. These areas are found all over Canada.

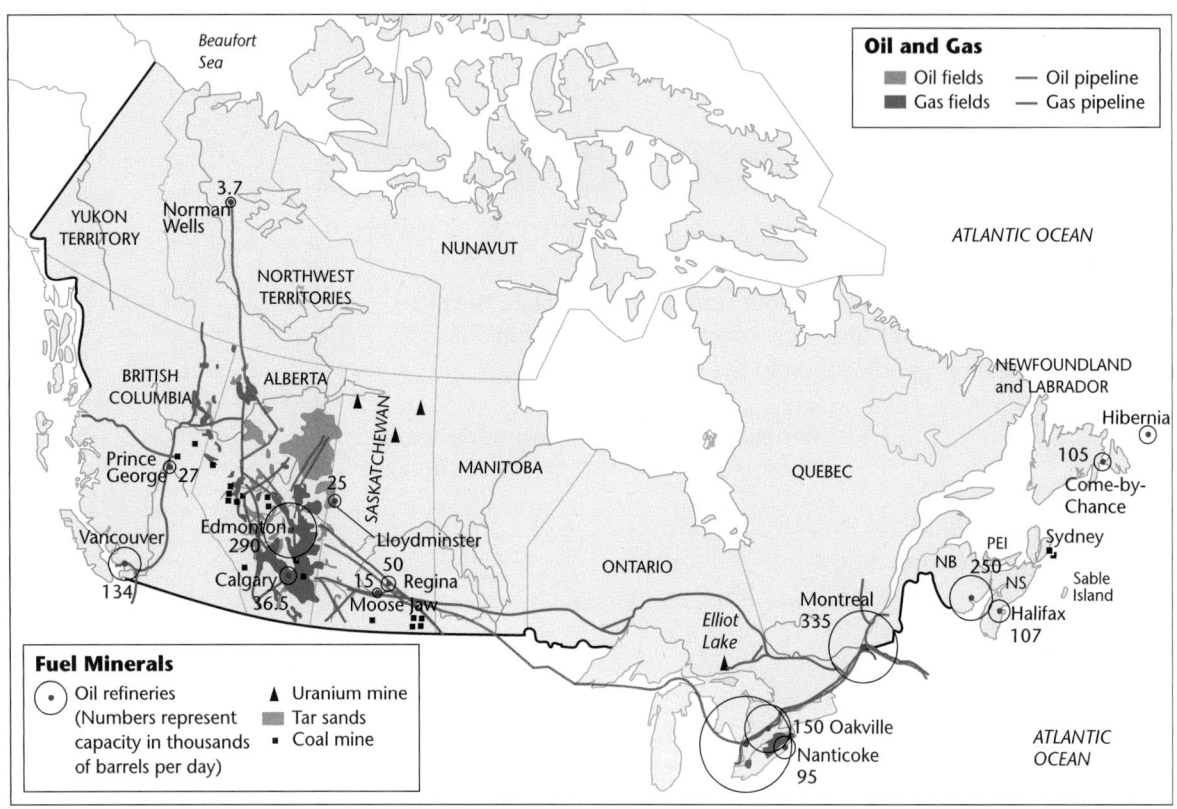

FIGURE 17.3

Fuel Minerals of Canada
Which province or territory has the most fossil fuels? Which province or territory has the largest oil refinery capacity?

Hydroelectric Energy

Hydroelectric power is an important type of electricity in Canada. Hydroelectric power is generated by flowing water. The flowing water turns the turbines. These machines convert the flowing water into electricity. In Ontario, Niagara Falls is an important source of hydroelectricity.

There are both advantages and disadvantages to the production of hydroelectricity. Two advantages of hydroelectric plants are

- flowing water is free
- there is no air pollution

Two disadvantages are

- they are often located far from the areas where the electricity is needed. This means it costs more to transport the electricity.

Also, the people who live in these remote areas have to move because their land has to be flooded.

- they cost a lot of money to build

FIGURE 17.4

The Adam Beck Generating Stations 1 & 2, Niagara Falls, Ontario
How does electricity from this plant get to customers?

Nuclear Energy

Nuclear energy is another important way to produce electricity in Canada. Nuclear reactors produce heat by splitting uranium atoms. This heat converts water into steam, which spins a turbine or generator to make electricity.

FIGURE 17.5

The Pickering Nuclear Power Plant
This nuclear power station is a source of energy for southern Ontario. Did you know that about 50 percent of the power used in Ontario comes from nuclear power generation?

There are also advantages and disadvantages to the production of nuclear energy. Two advantages are

- Canada has an abundant source of uranium, which is needed for the nuclear reactors
- nuclear power plants do not produce air pollution

Two disadvantages are

- radioactive materials can be very hazardous to human health
- waste products from nuclear power plants remain dangerous for 100 000 years

CHECK IT OVER

5. Can you think of a major disadvantage of using fossil fuels as an energy source?
6. Reread the section called Hydroelectric Energy. What are other advantages of using hydroelectricity as an energy source?
7. Nuclear power plants use radioactive materials. Do you think it is safe to live near one of these plants? Why or why not?

LITERACY SKILL

Skimming and Scanning to Identify New Words

Skimming is very useful because it allows you to understand the main ideas of a text in a very short time. It helps you to determine the article's focus. One simple way to skim a chapter is to follow these steps:

1. Read the first paragraph or introduction.
2. Read the first sentence of the rest of the paragraphs.
3. Read all of the final paragraph or conclusion.

Scanning allows readers to get information from a text without actually reading it. A good example of scanning is looking for a number in the telephone book. You scan when you want to find answers to specific questions. Follow these steps:

1. Decide what you are looking for.
2. Decide where you should look for the information.
3. Move your eyes quickly down the page until you see the answer.
4. Read what you found just to be sure it is the right information.

Scanning can also be used to identify words you do not know. Look down this page and write down any unfamiliar words. Then look them up in a dictionary. Guess what? You will be using the technique of scanning to find the words in the dictionary!

Alternative Energy Sources

Conventional energy sources have been around for a long time and are used by most people. Yet, they can be expensive and are often harmful to the environment. In the past few decades, people have begun to take a serious look at alternative energy sources. Several types of alternative energy sources are discussed below.

Solar Energy	Solar energy takes the heat from the sun and turns it into a useful form of energy. Solar panels on the roof of a house can produce energy to heat the water in a swimming pool. Many calculators and watches use energy from the sun.
Wind Energy	Wind energy is produced by moving air. Sailboats and old-fashioned windmills have used wind energy for centuries. Today, wind energy is used to produce electricity. For more information about wind energy, see the Case Study on page 180.
Tidal Energy	Tidal energy is produced by the flow of tides. When the tide comes in to shore, the water can be trapped in reservoirs behind dams. When the tide goes out, the water behind the dam is released. This flow of water can be used to turn a turbine to produce electricity. The Bay of Fundy, on Canada's east coast, is one of the best areas in the world to produce tidal energy.
Biomass Energy	Biomass energy is produced by burning organic material, stuff we usually think of as garbage. Examples are dead trees, branches, yard clippings, even used tires and livestock manure. When this material is burned, it heats water to produce steam. The steam is then used to turn turbines and produce electricity.
Geothermal Energy	Geothermal energy is produced by using heat from the earth. A geothermal power plant is like a regular power plant except the steam or hot water in the geothermal power plant is heated by the earth. No fuel is burned to turn the water into steam. If you have ever visited a hot spring like the one in Banff National Park in Alberta, you have seen geothermal energy in action.

FIGURE 17.6

Alternative Energy Sources
Can you use any of these sources in your home?

Wind Energy

Recently, wind energy has been used in a new way: to produce electricity. The wind turbines, as they are called, can be as high as a 25-storey building, with blades as long as a football field! To work efficiently, a wind turbine must have wind speeds above 19 km/h. Wind has to be this strong to turn the turbines fast enough to generate electricity. To make electricity, the shaft of the turbine must be connected to an electrical generator. A **wind farm** is made up of many wind turbines located in the same area.

FIGURE 17.7

A Wind Farm at Cowley, Alberta
Some people think wind turbines are an eyesore on the landscape. What do you think?

Wind turbines and wind energy have many advantages:

- Wind energy is clean. It does not produce air pollution.
- Wind is continually renewed. It is not used up like oil and gas and will always be available.
- Once a wind turbine is installed, the only costs are maintaining it. The energy to run the wind turbine is free.
- Wind energy does not produce carbon dioxide or any other hazardous wastes. This reduces the total amount of greenhouse gases, lessening the effects of global climate change.
- A wind turbine takes very little farmland out of production.

 CHECK IT OVER

8. Name one advantage of each type of alternative energy source.
9. Can you think of some disadvantages of developing wind energy?
10. Are there any windmills or wind farms in your area? Why or why not?

GEOCAREERS

Clean Energy Researcher

Clean energy researchers are environmental engineers who specialize in alternative and renewable energy sources. They often work in teams with other professionals. They do research and calculations in labs and offices to develop innovations in the field of clean, renewable energy. Clean energy researchers analyze our energy needs and plan environmentally friendly solutions. For example, a clean energy researcher in a windy coastal region might research wind generators and then write a report recommending a plan to develop a wind turbine.

Energy Megaprojects

Energy megaprojects are large construction projects built to develop an energy resource, such as building a hydroelectric plant or constructing a site for extracting a fossil fuel. This section of the chapter will investigate two energy megaprojects in Canada: the Hibernia Oil Field and the Athabasca Oil Sands.

Hibernia Oil Field

The Grand Banks off the coast of Newfoundland and Labrador were once known for their great numbers of codfish. Today, a different resource is being developed. Oil deposits were discovered here in 1979. The Hibernia Oil Field is 315 km east of St. John's, Newfoundland and Labrador, in approximately 80 m of water. It began producing oil in 1997. In 2005, the Hibernia Oil Field produced over 74 million barrels of oil. The oil field is in the ocean, which means building and anchoring drilling rigs has been a major challenge.

FIGURE 17.8

Hibernia Offshore Oil Rig
This rig has to be large enough to withstand storms in the Atlantic Ocean.

There have been a number of environmental concerns about the development of offshore oil wells. In the case of Hibernia, three issues were raised:

- **Atlantic storms:** The oil rigs have to be constructed to be able to withstand these frequent and often violent storms.
- **Icebergs:** The Hibernia Oil Field is located in what has been called "iceberg alley." The potential damage from large icebergs hitting the oil rigs is a concern.
- **Oil spills:** There are major fears about oil spills in the area. Such spills can result from damage done by storms or icebergs, or from storing and transporting the oil to the refineries onshore.

Athabasca Oil Sands

The Athabasca Oil Sands (sometimes called the Tar Sands) cover an area of approximately 40 000 km^2 in northern Alberta. Oil sand is made up of sand and other rock material that contains a heavy oil called bitumen. The sand is composed of over 70 percent sand and clay, 10 percent water, and up to 18 percent oil.

FIGURE 17.9

The Location of the Oil Sands in Northern Alberta
The location adds to the problems of extracting the oil. Can you think of two problems that must be overcome because of this location?

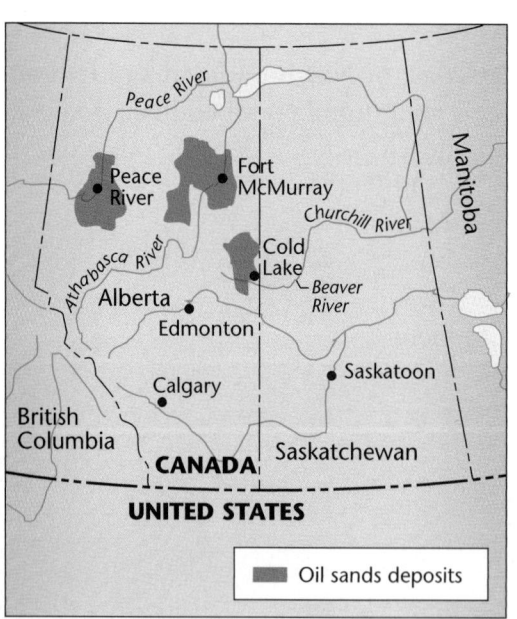

The Athabasca Oil Sands contain approximately 1.7 trillion barrels of bitumen. It is the largest oil resource in the world. Unfortunately, with current technology, only a small portion of the resource can be recovered.

How do the oil companies get the oil out of the ground? First, the muskeg and the overburden must be removed to expose the deposits of oil sand. Muskeg is a swamp or bog in northern Canada. The water-soaked earth and soil must be drained and removed. Beneath the muskeg is a layer of rocky, clay-like material called overburden. It too must be removed to reveal the tar sands.

The current method of mining the oil sands is surface mining. Surface mining is used in oil sand areas that lie under 75 m or less of overburden material. Only 7 percent of the Athabasca Oil Sands deposit can be mined this way. Most of the oil sands lie underneath more than 75 m of overburden and will have to be mined using different mining techniques.

The most common method of surface mining is the truck-and-shovel method:

1. The shovel scoops up the oil sands and dumps them into a heavy hauler truck.

2. The oil sands are mixed with water and pumped through a pipeline to the extraction plant.

3. The oil is separated from the sand by a process called the hot water treatment. This process cleans the bitumen off the sand.

4. The oil is sent to the refineries for final processing. This process is very time-consuming and expensive.

FIGURE 17.10

Digging Up the Athabaska Tar Sands in Alberta
The removal of the oil sands requires very expensive and very large equipment. How might the use of these large machines harm the environment?

Surface mining is very damaging to the environment. It can damage the quality of water as well as forest habitats for birds and other animals. Sometimes mountaintops are removed, which causes the slopes to weaken. This can cause landslides.

Oil companies must submit an environmental impact assessment to the government. There are a number of environmental concerns. The most important issue is land reclamation. This means that the whole area that was mined must be returned to a productive natural state. The land could be reclaimed as a forest, grassland, or wetland.

 CHECK IT OVER

11. How many years after it was discovered did Hibernia start producing oil? Why do you think it took that long?

12. List three ways that surface mining is bad for the environment.

13. If Canada could develop the oil sands to their full potential, do you think the price of oil and gas would go down? Explain your answer.

Sustainability, Conservation, and Stewardship

This chapter has focused on the ways energy resources are used and some of the problems that result because of that use. This final part of the chapter will explore how the concepts of sustainability, conservation, and stewardship are necessary to maintain these resources.

Sustainability, or sustainable development, is development that meets the needs of the present while still allowing future generations to meet their needs. Sustainable development means following these guidelines for energy production:

- We must take care that we don't use up all our energy sources. We need to leave some available for the future.

- We must not allow our energy use to pollute or harm the environment. We want our children to be able to enjoy the outdoors.

Conservation means something quite similar. Conservation is reducing our consumption of renewable and non-renewable resources and making sure they are available for other people and for the future.

Stewardship is a way we can all help to reach the goals of sustainability and conservation. Stewardship is managing the environment and natural resources carefully and responsibly for the benefit of everyone. In other words, each one of us must do our part in taking care of the environment.

CHECK IT OVER

14. Make a diagram to show the connection among these three ideas: sustainability, conservation, and stewardship.

15. What are three actions that you might take to help Canada have a more sustainable energy future?

 THINK IT OVER

Knowledge and Understanding

1. Can you think of some disadvantages of developing solar energy?

2. Where do you think most of the wind farms are found in Canada? Why?

3. Describe how mining companies recover oil from the Athabasca Oil Sands.

4. Oil companies must reclaim the land they used after they are finished mining. What are three things that the land could be used for once it has been reclaimed?

Thinking and Communication

5. Why do you think wind energy is becoming the most important alternative source of energy?

6. Think of three reasons that the government should invest more money in research about alternative energy sources.

7. Most of the energy megaprojects in Canada are run by private companies. Should the government have more control over our energy resources? Why or why not?

8. What are some things that you can do to act as a "steward" for the environment?

Chapter 18

The Greater Toronto Area's Greenbelt Plan

Key Words

urbanization

Greenbelt Plan

environmentally sensitive lands

escarpment

moraine

aquifers

In this chapter you will learn to

◢ apply the concepts of stewardship and sustainability to a current issue

◢ describe the role of key stakeholders in protecting the environment

◢ describe the views of key stakeholders on a local environmental issue

Introduction

Look at Figure 18.1. Try to find a baseball diamond. Try to find a skateboard park. Give up? Don't feel too badly. In some urban areas, houses are being built so fast that the other necessities of urban living are being forgotten.

FIGURE 18.1

The Livable City?
Is this what we want our cities to look like? What seems to be missing from this picture?

This chapter will look at the ideas of sustainability and stewardship in one part of Canada, the Greater Toronto Area (GTA). The GTA refers to the City of Toronto, plus the four urbanized regions that surround it and are tightly connected to it: Durham, York, Peel, and Halton. We will look at

- some characteristics of the Greater Toronto Area
- one plan that has been developed to protect natural systems
- different points of view on the plan

CHECK IT OVER

1. List five words that describe your reaction to Figure 18.1.
2. Give two reasons that cities might be growing so quickly.

The Roles of Governments

Who is involved in planning a city? All levels of government play important roles. See the text box below for information about the roles of the various levels of government in Canada.

FIGURE 18.2

Levels of Government in Canada
Depending on the issues, all levels of government may have a role in protecting the environment.

Level of Government	Description	Responsibilities
municipal government	This level of government is responsible for a municipality. Cities, towns, townships, and counties are types of municipalities.	Municipal governments make bylaws to manage activities, such as policing, within their boundaries. They also provide services such as waste management, roads, parks, and recreational facilities.
provincial and territorial government	This level of government is responsible for a much larger geographic area: a province or territory.	Provincial governments pass laws concerning such things as pollution, highways, natural resources, and energy supply. Provincial parks and wilderness areas are administered by provincial governments.
federal or national government	This level of government ties all of Canada together.	Decisions by this level of government affect the whole country. Some areas of responsibility are fisheries and oceans, the environment, immigration, and communications. The federal government also deals with international issues.

Each level of government must consider many factors when making decisions.

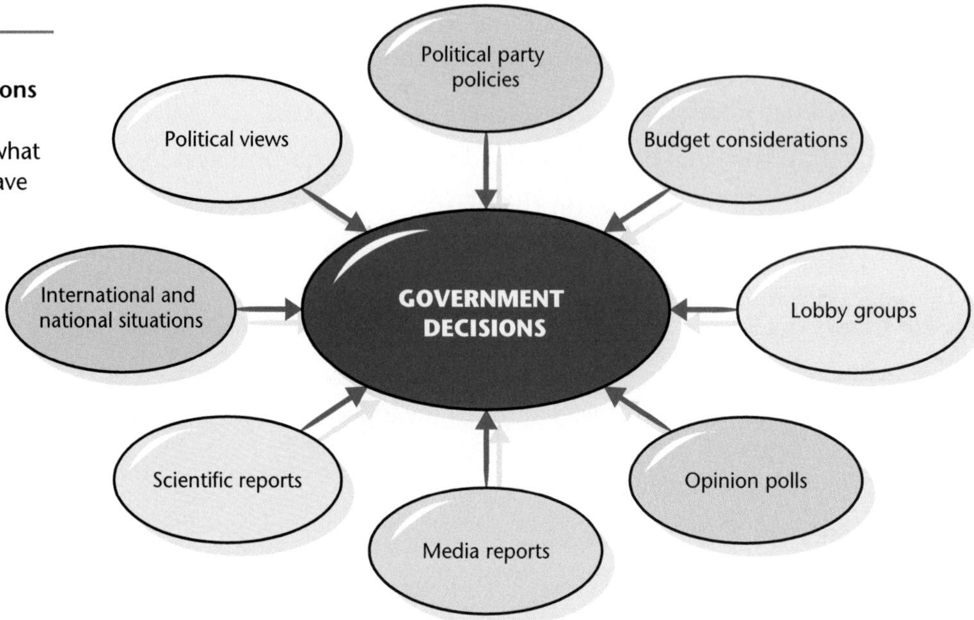

FIGURE 18.3

Factors Affecting Government Decisions
Select one of these factors and discuss what influence it might have on the government.

The Greater Toronto Area

The Greater Toronto Area is not a level of government. It is an organization that brings together municipal governments and the provincial government (see Figure 18.5). The different levels of government discuss problems and issues that affect them all.

One of the largest problems for the GTA is that it has grown very quickly over the past several decades. The increasing population growth has put the physical environment in the GTA at risk. Much of the green space in the GTA is being lost to urbanization—it has been developed into cities.

Municipality	Population 1996	Population 2001	Percent Population Change	Average Earnings
Durham Region				
Clarington	60 615	69 834	15.2	$48 811
Oshawa	134 364	139 051	3.5	$43 726
Whitby	73 794	87 413	18.5	$52 996
Ajax	64 430	73 753	14.5	$48 731
Pickering	78 989	87 139	10.3	$53 739
Scugog	18 837	20 173	7.1	$48 301
Uxbridge	15 882	17 377	9.4	$49 603
Brock	11 705	12 110	3.5	$38 028
York Region				
Markham	173 382	208 615	20.3	$54 218
Whitchurch-Stouffville	19 835	22 008	11.0	$59 379
Richmond Hill	101 725	132 030	29.8	$54 076
Aurora	34 857	40 167	15.2	$66 295
Newmarket	57 125	65 788	15.2	$51 928
East Gwillimbury	19 770	20 555	4.0	$56 109
Georgina	34 777	39 263	12.9	$41 183
King	18 223	18 533	1.7	$72 993
Vaughan	132 549	182 022	37.3	$52 582
Peel Region				
Mississauga	544 382	612 925	12.6	$48 770
Brampton	268 251	325 428	21.3	$44 029
Caledon	39 893	50 595	26.8	$56 490
Halton Region				
Oakville	128 405	144 738	12.7	$71 023
Milton	32 104	31 471	−2.0	$52 158
Halton Hills	42 390	48 184	13.7	$52 781
Burlington	136 976	150 836	10.1	$56 649
City of Toronto				
Toronto	2 385 421	2 481 494	4.0	$50 522

FIGURE 18.4

Population Growth in the GTA Between 1996 and 2001
What are the names of the four regions that surround the City of Toronto?

CHECK IT OVER

3. a) Name the five municipalities of the GTA that had the largest population in 2001.

   b) Why do you think these areas had so many people?

4. a) What areas of the GTA did not grow quickly from 1996 to 2001?

   b) Why do you think these areas did not grow?

FIGURE 18.5

The Greater Toronto Area
How would you describe the location of the City of Toronto in the GTA?

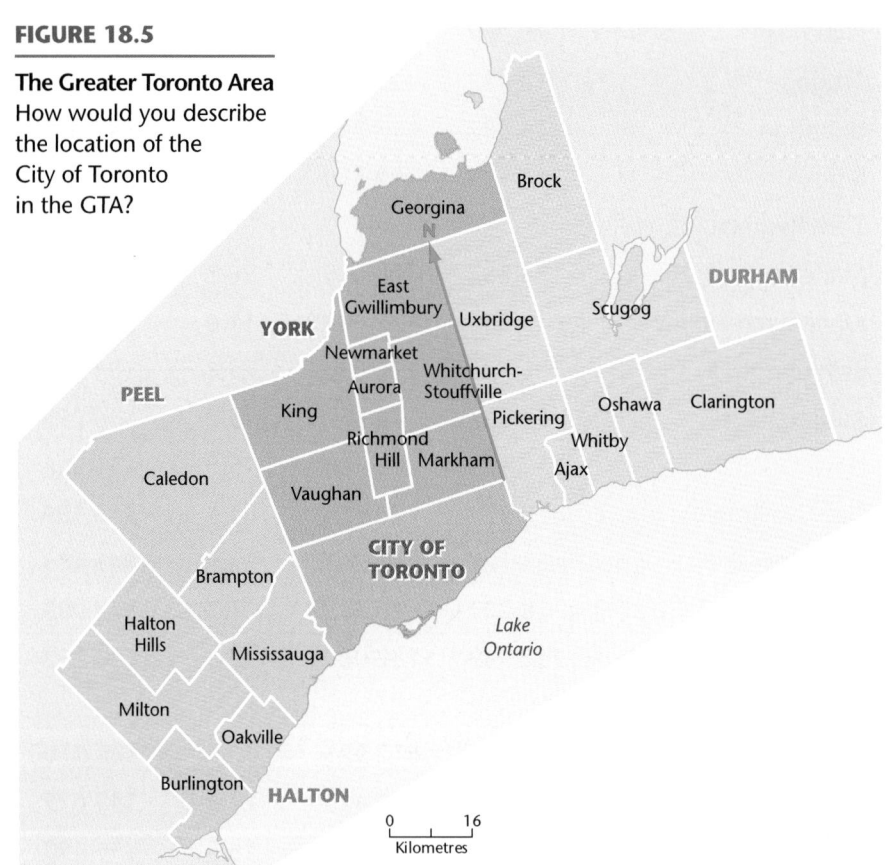

The Greenbelt Plan

The Greenbelt Plan covers over 720 000 ha of land in southern Ontario (see Figure 18.6). It stretches from the Niagara Peninsula in the southwest to Rice Lake in the east. It includes some of the most environmentally sensitive lands and best agricultural lands in the province. The Greenbelt Plan will protect lands from major urban development, while meeting the needs of growing communities.

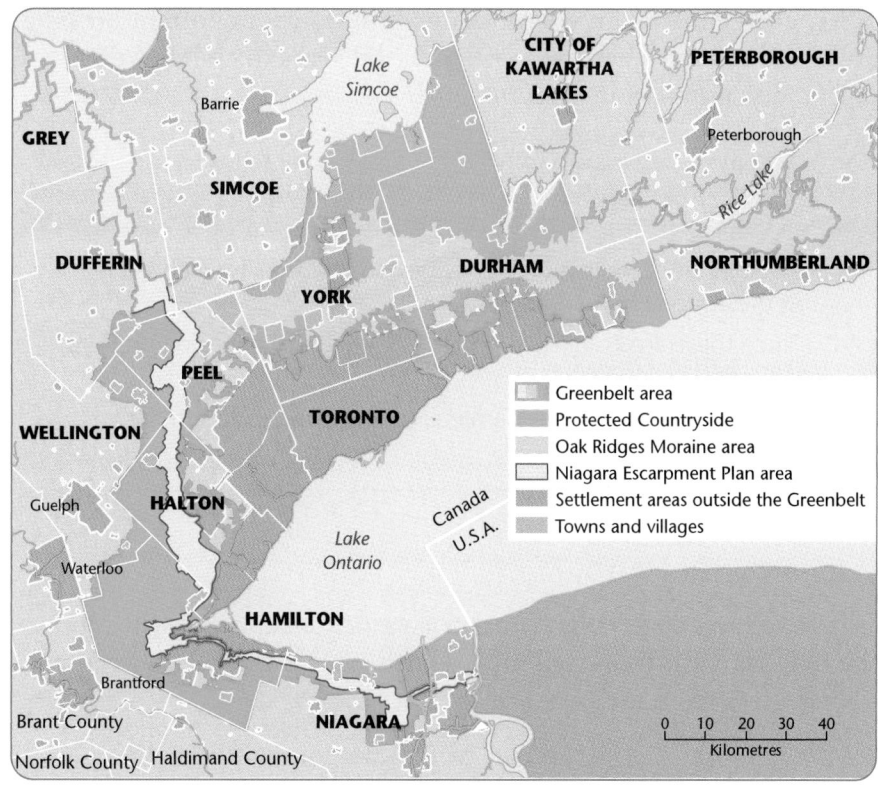

FIGURE 18.6

The Greenbelt Plan
Name one major Ontario city that is not included in the Greenbelt Plan.

Map legend:
- Greenbelt area
- Protected Countryside
- Oak Ridges Moraine area
- Niagara Escarpment Plan area
- Settlement areas outside the Greenbelt
- Towns and villages

The Greenbelt Plan provides permanent protection to the agricultural land and the ecological features (such as streams and ponds, trees and plants) in this area. Three major areas are protected by the Greenbelt Plan:

- the Niagara Escarpment (governed by the Niagara Escarpment Plan)
- the Oak Ridges Moraine (governed by the Oak Ridges Moraine Conservation Plan)
- the "Protected Countryside"

The Protected Countryside is made up of three areas:

- **Agricultural Land:** prime agricultural areas, rural areas, and specialty crop areas (including the Niagara Peninsula's grapes and fruit, and the Holland Marsh area of fruit and vegetables north of Toronto)
- **Natural Land:** important landform areas and water resource systems such as the Niagara Escarpment and the Oak Ridges Moraine
- **Settlement Areas:** the hamlets, villages, and towns in the Protected Countryside

The Greenbelt Plan was developed to protect important farming areas and sensitive natural systems in the years to come, even during fast population growth.

 CHECK IT OVER

5. What kinds of recreational activities do you think could take place in these Greenbelt areas?

6. Since these areas are now protected, what activities do you think will not be allowed?

7. List four or five different hamlets, villages, and towns in the Greenbelt area.

Is Everybody Happy?

Whenever any major plan is put forward, some people will support the new plan and some will not. This is true of the GTA Greenbelt Plan. In favour of the plan are

- the Ontario government, which came up with the plan
- environmentalists who have been calling for the protection of green spaces

Opposed to the plan are

- developers
- farmers

It is not a surprise that the developers are against the plan. They will not be able to build as many houses, which means they may lose money. It is surprising, though, that many farmers are opposed to this plan. Shouldn't the farmers in the Greenbelt area be pleased that their agricultural land is being preserved? They look at it differently. The plan preserves the farmers' land for agriculture, but what happens when a farmer wants to sell his or her farm to the developers and make money for retirement? That option is no longer available.

FIGURE 18.7

Farmers Protest the Greenbelt Plan
What actions are these farmers taking to show their unhappiness with the plan?

LITERACY SKILL

Looking for Bias in Sources

Every time we read about things in the newspaper or in textbooks, or when we research on the Internet, we should be aware that there may be bias in the information that is presented. *Bias* is a point of view put forward to influence a reader's opinion. How can we know whether what we are reading is biased? We can look for clues that would suggest that there is some bias in the material.

Type of Bias	Explanation
exaggeration	The material makes special claims—"biggest," "richest"—without providing actual information.
overgeneralization	The material makes general statements or uses stereotypes.
charged words	The material makes comments about people that are hurtful or promote hate.
prejudice	The material picks on particular groups or people, especially making negative comments.
inclusion/exclusion	The material does not give the whole picture—it does not put forward all sides of the issue.
opinion versus fact	The material fails to distinguish between what is opinion and what is fact.

FIGURE 18.8

Detecting Bias in Research Sources
How would you define the word *bias*?

Oak Ridges Moraine

One part of the Greenbelt Plan is the Oak Ridges Moraine (ORM). The moraine was formed by glaciers about 12 000 years ago during the last ice age. It stretches about 160 km from the Niagara Escarpment in the west to the Trent River in the east. The moraine is home to more than 900 plant species and is one of the last protected areas for birds and animals in southern Ontario.

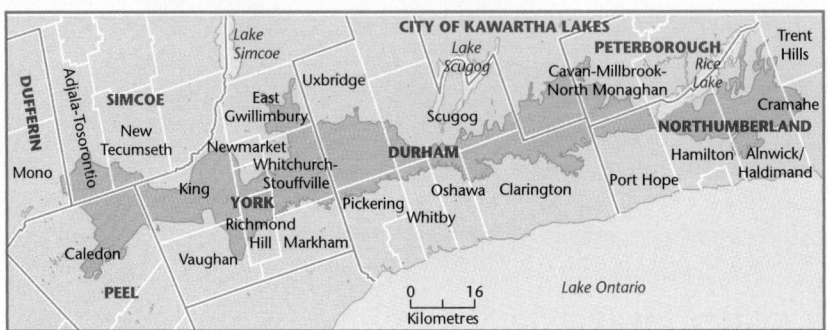

FIGURE 18.9

The Oak Ridges Moraine
Describe the Moraine's location in the GTA.

The Oak Ridges Moraine shows the conflicts that can occur over land use. People want to live in this area because it is close to the GTA. However, housing developments, and the removal of sand and gravel to build these developments, have put great pressure on the land. The habitats of hundreds of plant and animal species are at risk.

Equally important is the effect of development on the water resources of the Moraine. The ORM acts as a rain barrel. It collects rainwater and fills up the groundwater aquifers (underground layers of rock that store water). In the Oak Ridges Moraine, aquifers feed the region's wetlands. More than 65 streams and rivers flow north and south from the moraine into southern Ontario. These are sources of water for many residents of southern Ontario. Development could have a negative impact on these water sources.

Under the GTA's Greenbelt Plan, a significant part of the Oak Ridges Moraine is protected from further development.

GEOCAREERS

Land Use Planner

Land use planners create land development plans that meet people's needs while preserving the natural environment. Land use planners decide how to build communities based on environmental and human needs. First, they take the time to understand what residents, community groups, politicians, and businesspeople want in their communities. Then land use planners develop strategies for action. This action may include

- preparing plans for environmental protection such as wildlife preserves, national and provincial parks, and watersheds (regions that drain into a body of water)
- making land use plans for housing, farms, and transportation systems

Land use planners can work for real estate agencies, not-for-profit organizations, architects, or the government.

 CHECK IT OVER

8. **a)** What are two groups that have opposed the Greenbelt Plan?

   b) Why do these groups not like the plan?

9. What are the goals of the Greenbelt Plan?

10. What is your opinion of the Greenbelt Plan? Do you think it is a good idea or a bad idea? Give reasons for your opinion.

 THINK IT OVER

Knowledge and Understanding

1. **a)** Name the five areas of the GTA with the highest percentage growth in population between 1996 and 2001.

   b) Why do you think these areas grew so quickly?

2. What are some recreational activities that you might participate in on the Niagara Escarpment?

3. Do you think it is important to protect the Oak Ridges Moraine?

Thinking and Communication

4. If you were part of the government, how would you make the farmers understand why their farmland is included in the Greenbelt Plan?

5. Where do you predict future population growth in the GTA will be? Why?

Literacy Strategy

Persuasive writing
Persuasive writing is used to convince others to think like you do. There are many ways to suggest that others see something your way. You can use

- a brochure (written details to highlight your position)
- an advertisement (written and visual words and pictures to persuade)
- a speech (spoken emotional words to convince)

Making a Difference at Home

Key Words

municipality

water meter

reduce

reuse

recycle

In this performance task you will learn to

▲ *relate current lifestyle choices of Canadians to the prospects for sustaining Canada's environmental well-being*

▲ *communicate the results of geographic inquiries*

Introduction

All of us face environmental challenges because of the damage our society is doing to our ecosystems. The decisions we make every day affect the environment around us.

Performance Task Assignment

In this performance task you will use the knowledge you have gained in this subject to help your household and community become more environmentally friendly.

Step 1   Decide which one of these topics you want to focus on:

- conserving household water
- conserving household energy
- reducing household waste

Step 2   Find out what your municipality has done or is doing about your topic. You may need to use the Internet, or your teacher might direct you to some other useful sources. Remember to record the source information for each of your sources.

Step 3   Use the information in this textbook to find out what *could* be done to improve your topic. Put this information together in a research file.

Step 4   Decide on two actions that your municipality *should* take to improve your topic, using the information from your research file. Think of a visual way to show your ideas, such as a diagram or a collage. Be sure to give reasons to explain why you have made your decisions.

Step 5 Write out a short presentation that you might give to your classmates. Your presentation topic is "In what ways do the lifestyle choices of Canadians affect the environment?" Include evidence that you discovered during your research to answer the question.

Step 6 Hand in a one-page written summary, a research file, a visual showing two actions, and written presentation materials.

Water Recycling: Only a very small part of the water supplied to our homes is used for "high-quality uses," such as drinking, preparing food, brushing teeth, or bathing. Water from dishwashers, showers, and washing machines could be recycled to flush toilets, one of the biggest uses of water in our homes.

Water-Wise Gardening: Homeowners can reduce water use by planting drought-resistant species, collecting water from downspouts (pipes that carry water down from the roof gutter), and using compost and mulch to help soil hold moisture.

Water-Conserving Devices: Low-flow showerheads and low-flush toilets can significantly reduce household water use.

Water Metering: Install a **water meter** (measures amount of water used). Doing so has been shown to reduce water use by 20 to 50 percent.

◀ **FIGURE PT3.1**

Ways to Reduce Residential Water Use

Improve Insulation in Homes: Caulking and sealing the ceilings, walls, and floors of your home can reduce the amount of cold air that enters.

Reduce Losses and Waste: You can save a lot of energy by repairing dripping taps, switching off lights, turning down thermostats, and so on.

Use Energy Star Appliances: Some appliances such as refrigerators, washing machines, and dishwashers have been designed to be energy efficient.

Buy Energy-Efficient Homes: Houses that are thoughtfully designed need much less energy and have very small amounts of waste.

◀ **FIGURE PT3.2**

Ways to Reduce Household Energy Use

▼ **FIGURE PT3.3**

Ways to Reduce Household Wastes

Reduce and Reuse	• Buy items with as little packaging as possible. • Buy products that you know can be recycled or reused.
Recycle	• Make sure all your recyclables go to the recycling box. • Keep up to date on materials that your municipality recycles.
Compost	• Use a backyard composter if you live in a house. • If you live in an apartment, check to see how recyclables are managed.
Detoxify Your Home	• Check with your municipality to see how you can dispose of hazardous wastes, such as old paints and unused cleaners. • Buy environmentally safer products. Read labels so that you know what you are getting.
Speak Up	• Get involved in an organization that advocates for the environment. • Speak out when you see your family and friends developing poor waste habits.

Unit

4

Canada and the World

Overall Expectations

In this unit you will learn to

▲ *report on how Canada influences and is influenced by its connections with other countries*

▲ *identify the economic connections between Canada and other countries*

▲ *explain how current global issues affect Canadians*

▲ *communicate the results of geographic inquiries*

▲ *use the tools of geographers to gather, organize, and evaluate information about a Canadian issue*

Canada plays many roles in the world, from giving aid to developing countries to helping protect the world's environment.

199

19 Comparing Qualities of Life

Key Words

quality of life

indicators

consumption

pollution

Canadian
  International
  Development
  Agency (CIDA)

In this chapter you will learn to

◢ report on how Canada influences and is influenced by its connections with other countries

◢ analyze how choices you make can have an impact on other parts of the world

◢ compare the lives of people in Canada to other parts of the world

◢ describe how Canadians use resources and create pollutants compared to other parts of the world

Introduction

Canada is blessed with resources that make this country a great place to live. These include an inviting geography, interesting people, and healthy ways of life. Here is how these resources make our lives better:

Geographic Factors	People	Lifestyles
• plenty of space and open land • clean lakes and rivers • scenic mountains • farmland • trees, minerals, oil, and other natural resources • shorelines on three oceans	• educated • skilled • bringing customs and cultures from all over the world	• schooling for all • government services such as health care • fair prices for a large selection of goods and services • safe and clean cities, towns, and villages

These three factors allow Canadians to enjoy a high quality of life. For most Canadians, a high quality of life means that we do not worry about where our next meal will come from or where we will find shelter for the night. When we go shopping, there are goods and foods from all over the world to choose from, and prices are usually reasonable.

This chapter looks at the quality of life in Canada and how it compares with the quality of life in other nations in the world.

The topics that will be considered are

- indicators of quality of life
- how geography shapes our quality of life
- consequences of our quality of life

CHECK IT OVER

1. What are three things that you would like to have that you think would improve the quality of your life?

2. Brainstorm five ways that show Canada has a higher standard of living than many other countries in the world.

Indicators of Quality of Life

As Canadians, we have many resources available to us. That means we can make satisfying choices in our daily lives. The satisfaction we get is called quality of life. Quality of life results from having

- material wealth, such as comfortable homes, good food, and effective transportation
- non-material wealth, such as feeling safe in our communities, feeling optimistic about the future, and knowing our human rights are protected

FAST *Fact*

A baby born in Lesotho, Africa, is expected to live 36 years. A baby born in Switzerland is expected to live 82 years.

FIGURE 19.1

Different Qualities of Life
What do the Canadians in this picture have that many Africans do not have?

Canada was ranked
number one on the
Human Development
Index from 1994 to
2000. In recent years,
our ranking has slipped.
However, we are
consistently among
the top five countries.

Geographers try to measure the qualities of life of people around the world. They study indicators, or markers, to measure quality of life. The indicators are used to get the Human Development Index (HDI). The HDI measures and ranks, among other things

- *life expectancy:* the number of years that a male or female can expect to live in the country in which he or she was born

- *primary school enrollment:* the number of children going to kindergarten or Grade one in a country, and how many are boys and how many are girls

- *Gross Domestic Product (GDP):* the amount of money a country makes, including wages and earnings

Country	Area (square km)	Population	Life Expectancy (female/male)	Primary School Enrollment (female/male)	Gross Domestic Product (per capita)	Human Development Index
Brazil	8 574 215	178 470 000	73/64	97%/96%	$7 770	medium
Canada	9 984 670	31 753 000	82/77	100%/100%	$29 480	high
China	9 596 961	1 304 196 000	73/69	93%/92%	$4 580	medium
Democratic Republic of the Congo	2 344 858	52 771 000	43/41	34%/35%	$650	low
Haiti	27 750	8 326 000	50/49	n/a	$1 670	low
India	3 287 263	1 065 462 000	65/63	76%/91%	$2 670	medium
New Zealand	270 534	3 875 000	81/76	98%/99%	$21 740	high
Russia	17 075 400	143 246 000	73/61	99%/99%	$8 230	medium
Switzerland	41 284	7 169 000	82/76	99%/99%	$30 010	high
Thailand	513 115	62 833 000	74/65	85%/87%	$7 010	medium

FIGURE 19.2

Human Development Index for Canada and Selected Countries
According to this chart, which country do you think has the lowest quality of life? the highest? Why might the United Nations want to measure the qualities of peoples' lives around the world? (Note: *per capita* means "per person.")

Destination	Chosen Most Often by People in
Canada	U.S., France, China
U.S.	India
Australia	Britain, Canada, Germany, Netherlands
Britain	Poland, Spain
Germany	Turkey, Russia
China	Pakistan
France	Lebanon
Japan	Indonesia
United Arab Emirates	Jordan

FIGURE 19.3

Lands of Opportunity
Quality of life helps to shape how others think about a country. This chart shows the results of a survey when people in different countries were asked, "Where would you go to lead a good life?"

Other indicators are also useful for assessing quality of life, such as

- how many children die before the age of five
- how many people live on less than $1.00 per day
- how many people have clean drinking water every day
- how many people can read and write
- how many people have HIV/AIDS
- how many people do not have enough good food to eat on a daily basis

FIGURE 19.4

Other Indicators of Quality of Life
Can you think of some countries that would have a low quality of life based on these indicators?

 CHECK IT OVER

3. Explain how each of the indicators given in Figure 19.4 shows something about quality of life.

4. What are three indicators used by the United Nations to develop the Human Development Index?

5. Define what an *indicator* is.

6. Read the Fast Fact on page 201 and look at Figure 19.2. How does the information about Switzerland in the table explain why the Swiss baby has a greater life expectancy than the baby from Lesotho?

Geography and Quality of Life

The high quality of life enjoyed by Canadians is partly built on things we get from other places in the world. A product is made from resources. These resources may come from countries such as Brazil or Russia that are rich in natural resources. The resources are shipped to countries like China, Mexico, and Thailand that make and assemble goods. These goods are shipped out to Canada in box-like containers loaded on huge cargo ships. When they arrive in Canada, trucks and trains deliver the containers to stores near you.

When you buy a product, money goes back to the source country. Part of the money you spend makes its way back to the other countries involved in making the product. Canadians want good value when we spend our money—to improve our quality of life—but we also want to be fair to the people in other countries who worked to make the product. In this way, workers and business owners in other nations will make wages and profits that allow their qualities of life to improve.

Here are some ways to make sure our spending power ripples out in a way that is fair to other countries:

- Pay fair prices for authentic handcrafted items from developing nations (pottery, clothing, carvings).
- Do some research and buy clothing from brands that do not use "sweat shops." These are factories that provide poor working conditions and employ workers who are underpaid or underage.
- Support Fair Trade organizations. These organizations promote fair prices for products like coffee and tea, so that the workers in the farm communities growing the crops can have decent wages.

Every dollar spent by Canadians can have a worldwide impact.

FIGURE 19.5

Fair Trade Coffee
By encouraging fair trade in products around the world, Canadian consumers can help to improve the quality of life in other countries. What fair trade goods do you buy?

CHECK IT OVER

7. Make a flow chart to show how a dollar you spend can have a positive effect around the world.

8. Give two reasons to explain why it is important that you not buy clothing, shoes, sporting equipment, and other products made in "sweat shops" in other countries.

Consequences of Quality of Life

Another area of concern is the consumption of resources by Canadians. We consume a very high percentage of the world's resources to support our lifestyles. Part of our success in gaining a high quality of life is offset by how much waste we create. This waste comes from packaging, wasted food, and unused chemicals. These dirty our air and water. We buy products we do not need. These all create pollution problems that can take away from our quality of life.

Consuming so much can often create shortages in other areas of the world. Developing countries cannot afford to compete with richer countries. Canadian foreign aid workers, who work for such organizations as the Canadian International Development Agency (CIDA), a government agency, try to correct this imbalance. They do this with money, information, training, and peacekeeping missions to areas in need around the world.

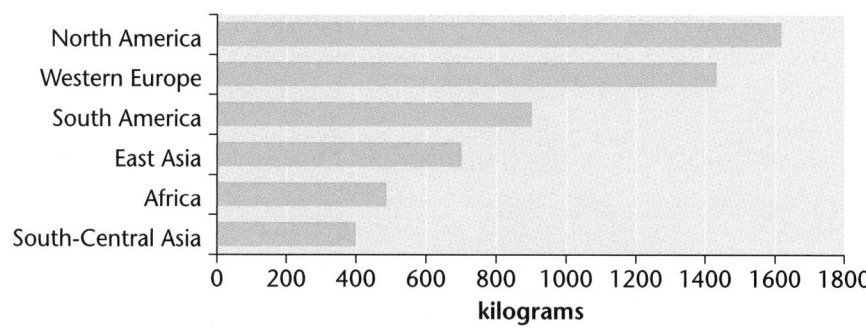

Annual Per Capita Consumption of Food
vegetables, meat, eggs, milk

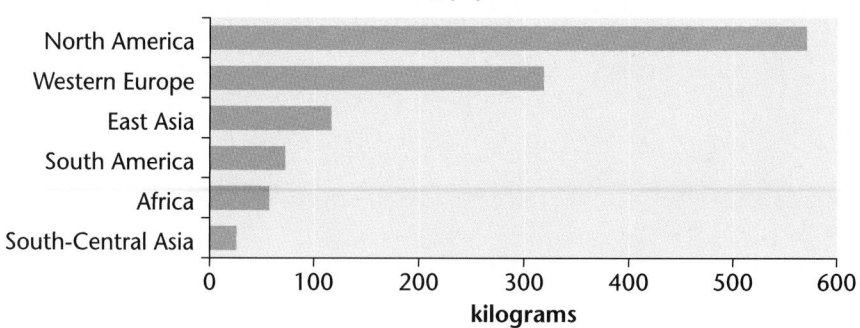

Annual Per Capita Consumption of Fibre
clothes, paper

FIGURE 19.6

Consumption of Selected Goods in Canada
How does consuming goods affect our quality of life in both positive and negative ways?

(continued)

FIGURE 19.6 (continued)

**Consumption of
Selected Goods
in Canada**
How does consuming
goods affect our quality
of life in both positive
and negative ways?

Annual Per Capita Consumption of Wood
construction, burning

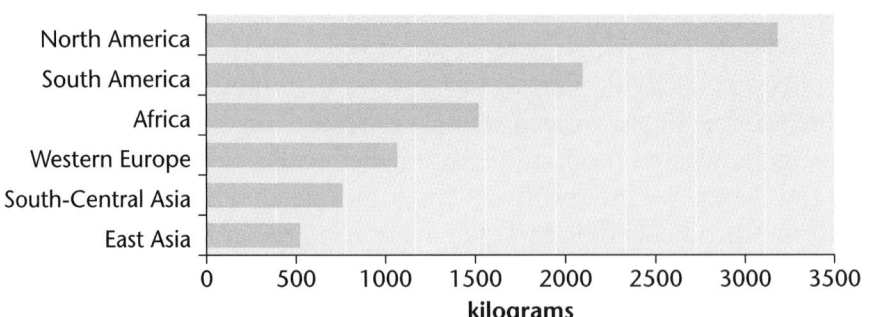

 GEOCAREERS

International Aid Worker

Government departments such as CIDA, as well as the United Nations, help developing nations with a huge variety of projects. These projects help people in developing countries improve their quality of life. Geography can help people get work in these fields. This is because Geography uses statistics to show patterns emerging in a nation. Governments take surveys and official censuses of their people all the time. This helps them to plan new developments in the country. If you are good with numbers and statistics, you could have job opportunities overseas. The pay is often low but many feel the experience is priceless.

FIGURE 19.7

A CIDA Worker in Ghana
In what ways might this worker benefit
from working in developing countries?

CASE STUDY

Democratic Republic of the Congo

The Congo is a war-torn nation of over 50 million people in the heart of Africa. It is right beside the equator in the tropical rainforest jungles of the famous Congo River. It ranks very low on the Human Development Index because ruthless leaders have stripped away its wealth. War and killing have marked the Congo's recent history. It has very few health and education services.

Canadians are interested in this country because it has rich natural resources such as high-grade copper and cobalt. Canadian mining companies have opened mines here despite the dangers. If the companies are successful, people of the Congo will get work in the mines. They will earn wages and improve the quality of their lives.

Vodacom, a South African company, is installing towers to allow cell phone use. Cell phones help developing nations communicate. Their governments do not have to build the network of telephone poles and wires that we have in Canada. Vodacom sold phone service to about 50 000 customers in the first six months. It has over 135 000 users, and that number is growing.

The Congo is a nation trying to put a stop to war, danger, and poverty so that it can improve its quality of life.

FIGURE 19.8

A Cellular Phone Store in the Democratic Republic of the Congo
Why are cell phones popular in developing countries?

Drawing Maps

Maps are very useful tools for Geography students. With some practice, you can read maps like books. Maps show information in a visual way. Drawing maps is a useful skill for communicating information. It is often said that a picture is worth a thousand words. To practise this skill, draw a map of the Democratic Republic of the Congo's borders. Then add the main channel and the branches of the Congo River. You should be able to see a connection with the shape of the river basin and the borders of the country.

CHECK IT OVER

9. How does Geography help an international aid worker?
10. Explain how technology can help a developing nation like the Democratic Republic of the Congo.

THINK IT OVER

Knowledge and Understanding

1. Examine Figure 19.2. Think of reasons why people would choose to live in another country. Select one country in the world and explain why you would like to live there.
2. Explain how a higher standard of living can create waste and pollution.
3. What is CIDA and what are some things that it does to try to improve qualities of life around the world?

Thinking and Communication

4. Select one indicator from Figure 19.4. Write a paragraph to analyze how that factor influences quality of life.
5. Create a poster or PowerPoint presentation to show how paying a fair price for goods from other countries benefits people in those countries.

Buying and Selling: Canada's Trade Picture

In this chapter you will learn to

◢ identify the economic connections between Canada and other countries

◢ describe Canada's role in major international organizations

◢ judge how well Canada promotes international well-being

Key Words

trade

exporting

importing

tariffs

international trade

World Trade Organization

globalization

competitive advantage

Introduction

Let's say you have something that your friend Raheem wants. You can arrange to give, trade, or sell it to him. If it is a thing, such as a basketball, you can sell it to him for cash or trade it for something you want, such as a football. You are buying or trading goods. If you help Raheem with his Geography homework and he trades with you by downloading a new ring tone to your cell phone, you are trading services.

Countries also have trade partnerships. Buying and selling goods and services are key aspects of Canada's trade with other nations. Trade is important in understanding our relationships with these partners. Canada is one of the world's leading trading nations. We rely heavily on our international relationships to support our way of life.

This chapter will focus on these topics:

- Canada's trading partners
- the products that we buy and sell
- the advantages of being a trading nation

CHECK IT OVER

1. a) Make a list of five products you buy in a year.

    b) Make a list of five services you buy in a year.

2. Identify three items you have bought that came from other nations.

FIGURE 20.1

The Value of Trade for the Top Ten Trading Nations, 2004
How does Canada compare with the United States?

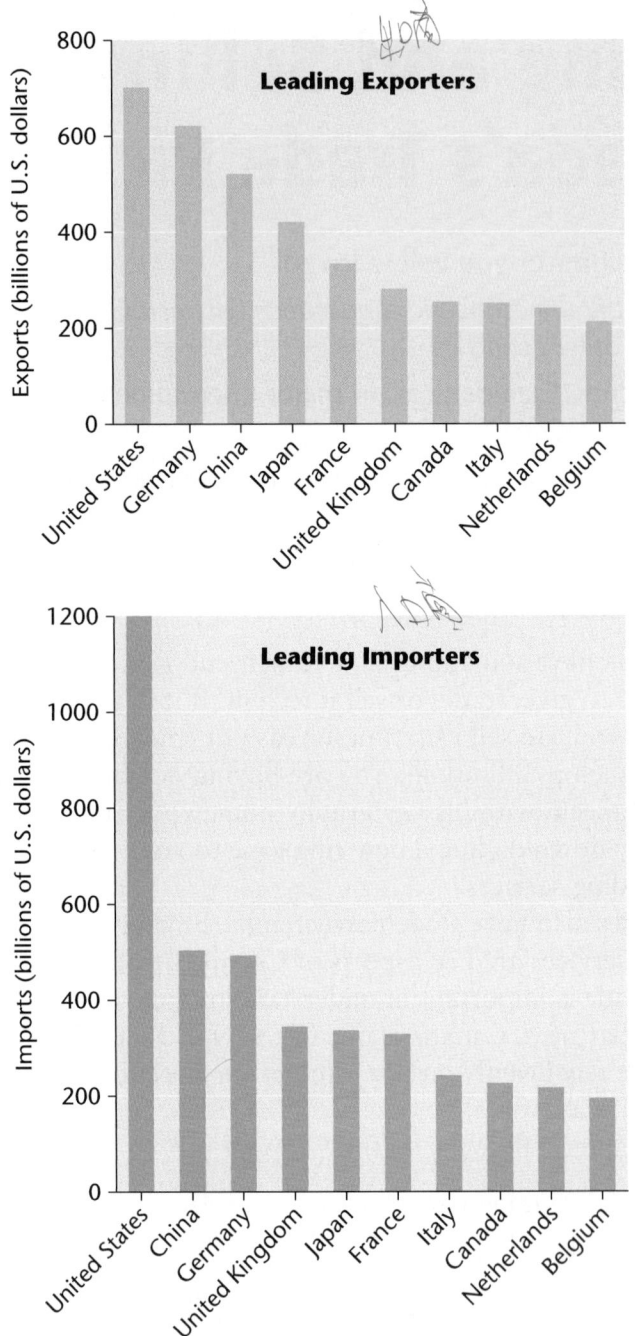

Canada's Trade Partners

Trade involves two things: selling goods and services to another country (also known as exporting) and buying goods and services from another country (also known as importing). Exporting and importing form the basis for international trade.

Canada is a member of the World Trade Organization (WTO). The WTO oversees and keeps track of all the world's trading patterns. It has over 145 members who are involved in 95 percent of the world's trade. The WTO's main job is to make it possible for countries to trade easily and effectively. Most of its efforts are to encourage the globalization of world trade. When businesses open branches, outlets, stores, or other operations in other countries, it is called *globalization*.

imports:	goods or services brought into one country from another country
exports:	goods or services sent out from one country to another country
balance of trade:	the dollar difference between the value of the goods and services that a country exports and the value of the goods and services that it imports
trade surplus:	when a country has more exports than imports
trade deficit:	when a country has more imports than exports
tariffs:	taxes that a government puts on imports (to make the imported goods more expensive so that people will buy locally made goods)
free trade:	when no tariffs are applied to any goods and services
balance of payments:	a financial statement of a country's total payments to and receipts from other countries

FIGURE 20.2

Trade Words
Why do countries want to have a trade surplus?

FIGURE 20.3

A Container Ship in the Port of Vancouver, British Columbia
Sealed boxes called containers are an effective way to move goods to Canada from other countries and to ship our products around the world. What are some reasons that containers are so effective?

Canada's main trading partner is the United States for both imports and exports. In fact, the trade between these two nations makes up the largest trading partnership in the world. Our connection with the large and powerful U.S. economy is a great advantage to Canadian industries. The U.S. provides a market for

- raw materials such as oil and gas
- manufactured goods such as automobiles
- services such as testing for mineral content in rocks or water quality

FIGURE 20.4

Canada's Top Ten Export Destinations, 2004
The destinations are the countries where Canada's goods or services are going. Which country is the largest export destination?

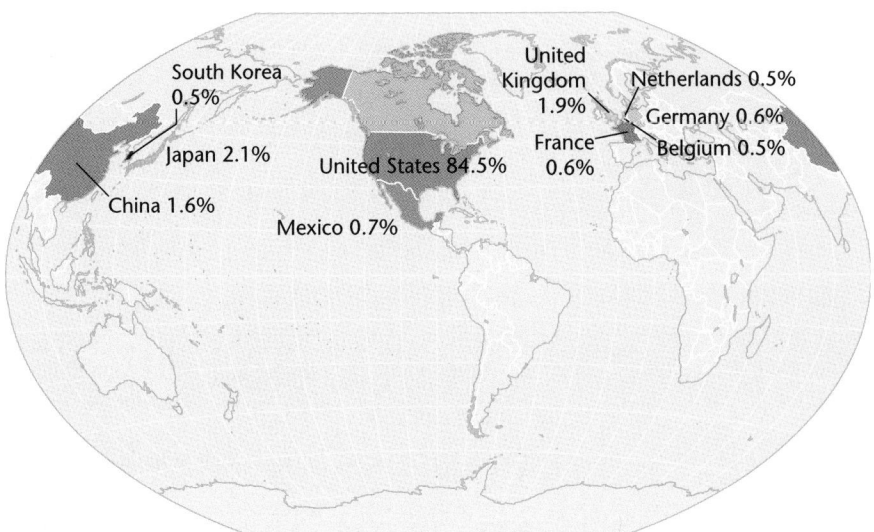

Percent of total Canadian exports

FIGURE 20.5

Canada's Top Ten Import Sources, 2004
The sources are the countries that are providing the goods or services. Look at Figures 20.4 and 20.5. Which country provides the most goods and services?

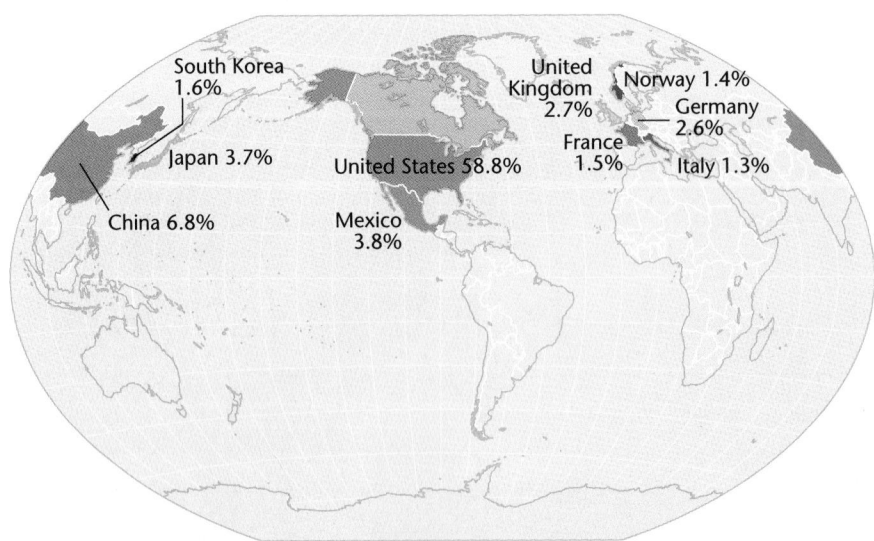

Percent of total Canadian imports

At the same time, this close connection puts Canada at risk. Canada relies heavily on its trade relationship with the United States. If there are declines in the amount of goods and services the American market needs, Canadian trade suffers. Our government's solution is to have more trading partners. European countries such as France and England are long-standing trading partners. Canada is increasing its trade with China and Japan every year. Emerging nations around the world (for example, South Africa and Brazil) are potential partners for the future.

CASE STUDY

Trade in China and India

China and India have taken two different directions to upgrade their standard of living. Their economies are specializing in very different products for sale to world markets.

China is very good at making consumer goods cheaply because their wages are quite low. The workers are skilled and efficient, so goods, such as clothing and electronic products, are produced and exported at a low cost.

India has followed a different path. It has a highly educated work force that has a good knowledge of the English language. It has chosen to provide services, such as call centres and computer help desks. When you call to ask a question about your new computer, world telephone systems simply direct your call to a help line in India. A trained worker answers your question at a much cheaper labour rate than in North America.

Each of these countries is earning trade dollars to spend on much-needed Canadian exports of wheat or oil products.

CHECK IT OVER

3. Name three ways that the American market helps Canadian businesses.

4. Identify three other countries that Canada trades with.

5. Explain briefly how China and India have taken different paths to develop their economies.

Products Canada Buys and Sells

Canada imports goods we cannot produce ourselves. In the winter, we buy fruits and vegetables from countries with warmer climates because it is too cold here for our farmers to grow them. We also import goods from other countries because they are cheaper (for example, clothing) or because they are made better (for example, watches).

FIGURE 20.6

Reasons for International Trade
Why has Canada become one of the world's top trading nations?

Labour costs are lower in developing countries. (Sports shoes are made in Asian countries where wages are much lower.)

Materials are not available or are too expensive in Canada. (Mexico produces glass products bought by Canadians.)

Why are goods and services imported into Canada?

Canada's climate is not suitable for some products. (By weight, bananas are the best-selling fruit in Canada, even though we can't grow them.)

Canadian corporations have not developed the required expertise. (Precision lens for optical equipment is often imported from Europe, particularly Switzerland.)

Being located next to the world's largest consumer market gives Canada an advantage. (Sales of agricultural products like hogs are made possible by relatively inexpensive transportation costs.)

Canadian businesses have developed superior skills and technologies. (Canadian telephone and telecommunication technologies are in demand around the world.)

Why are goods and services exported from Canada?

Available natural resources make up a large part of our exports. (Canada's vast forests mean that we produce large quantities of forest products.)

Historical development of Canada's industries and businesses has kept us linked by trade to other countries. (Canada's automobile industry is an important part of the continental auto industry.)

The Canadian market is fairly small. It makes sense not to produce every single item we need. It is better to focus on things we can produce well in Canada. Then we can trade these items for items that other countries produce better or more cheaply. This is the competitive advantage that businesses want. If a country produces items well, it can exchange them for specialized items around the world. Canada has a competitive advantage for these reasons:

- **Abundant natural resources:** We have a rich supply of soil, fresh water, oceans, forests, and minerals for our natural resource industries.

- **Skilled workers:** We have workers who are highly literate, educated, and technically skilled in making complicated machinery such as automobiles.

- **A good communications system:** Our advanced telephone and satellite equipment and services allow us to run businesses efficiently.

FAST *Fact*

Cows, cars, and gas— these three products powered Canada to its highest trade surplus level in 2005. In August 2005, Canada exported $37.9 billion and imported $32.4 billion in trade for a surplus of $5.5 billion in one month!

FIGURE 20.7

A Unit Train of Coal Heading for the West Coast for Export to Asia
What might be another product that is hauled by unit trains (trains that transport a single product from one point to another)?

CHECK IT OVER

6. Name three competitive advantages that Canada has.
7. Read the Fast Fact. Explain how Canada gets a trade surplus.
8. Look at Figure 20.7. Why are trains used to haul materials like coal?

Advantages of Being a Trading Nation

When nations trade with each other, countries see good things happen to their economy and way of life. Goods and services can be created in certain countries and exchanged with others. If tariffs, or taxes, are kept low, then free trade lets these goods move around the world. The first written agreement to cover these issues was the General Agreement on Trade and Tariffs, or GATT, in 1946. This agreement removed tariffs and set up trade rules for the nations that signed the agreement.

Sometimes countries join other trade groups. Canada joined the North American Free Trade Agreement, or NAFTA. NAFTA allows free trade on most goods and services among Canada, the United States, and Mexico.

When you buy something, you make a choice that affects Canada's trade patterns. If you want those new running shoes at the cheapest price, they will be made in a country with low wages and imported into Canada for you to buy. Your personal choices often determine what Canada buys from, or trades with, other nations.

 GEOCAREERS

Import Buyer

Many businesses employ import buyers or purchasing agents to get the goods and services that they need from other countries. The buyer or agent tries to get the best price for the resources that the company requires. The buyer may have to travel to the place where the goods or services are coming from to make the deal. Training in Geography will help you

- understand the culture and ways of doing business in that nation
- know the best way to transport the goods and services into Canada
- know who the competitors are and where to go for other suppliers

LITERACY SKILL

Interpreting Plus–Minus Graphs

The graph in Figure 20.8, World Trade in Goods by Region, shows the annual percentage change in value of imports and exports in 2001 by world geographic area. The percentage is shown on the *x* axis. The change is either an increase or a decrease. For example, Latin America's exports and imports are decreasing. The imports are shown in one colour and the exports in another. Being able to read a bar graph like this one means you can see which areas are gaining ground and which ones are losing ground in their trade.

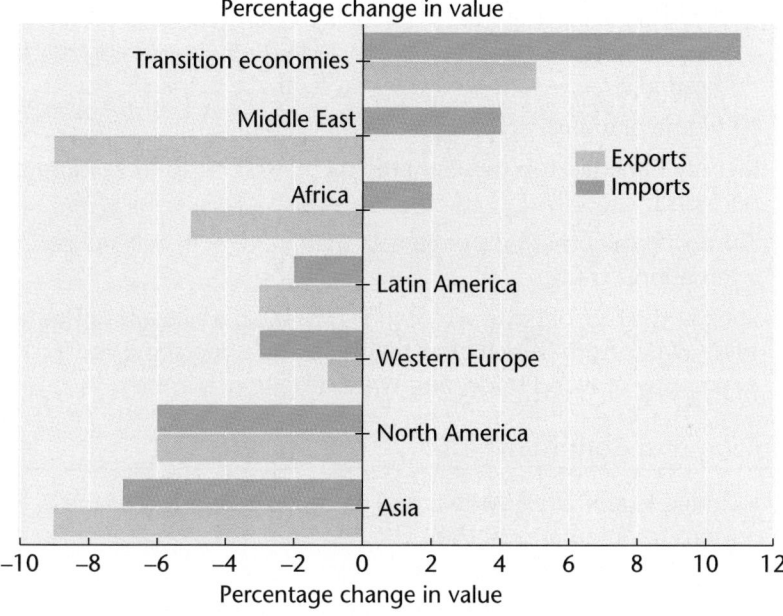

FIGURE 20.8

World Trade in Goods by Region, 2001
Transition economies are countries (such as Russia and China) that are changing very quickly, from poor to relatively rich. How does North America compare to other parts of the world?

CHECK IT OVER

9. How does Geography help a person to be a better import buyer?

10. Identify three ways that your personal choices in buying goods and services can influence Canada's trade patterns.

THINK IT OVER

Knowledge and Understanding

1. Look at the plus–minus graph in Figure 20.8.
   a) Explain how this graph works, including how percentages are used in it.
   b) Name one plus region and one minus region.

2. Identify Canada's top three import partners and top three export partners.

3. Think of three other jobs or careers that are directly related to international trade.

4. Look at the box of trade words in Figure 20.2. Make a list of other trade words from this chapter that help you understand the geography of world trade, and write definitions for them.

Thinking and Communication

5. Examine Figure 20.6. Write a one-paragraph summary of the reasons for international trade.

6. Using Figure 20.1, create a table showing the approximate value in dollars of the imports and exports of these world leaders in trade.

7. Suggest how Canada must develop in the area of trade to maintain its standard of living.

Travel and Tourism

In this chapter you will learn to

- ◢ *report on how Canada influences and is influenced by its connections with other countries*
- ◢ judge how well Canada
  - ■ responds to global challenges
  - ■ promotes international well-being
- ◢ understand how your personal choices have an impact on the global community
- ◢ know how Canadian society influences cultures in the "global village"

Key Words

tourism

cultural and historic sites

factors of tourism

economic benefits

environmental impacts

Introduction

Young people often travel during their spring break. From secondary school to college students, young tourists hit the road in search of warm beaches or other destinations. You may have plans to travel yourself. Here are some reasons why young people travel:

- school exchange programs
- hiking trips with an organization, such as Scouts or Adventurers
- family trips to visit relatives or see sights
- band trips
- sports competitions

FIGURE 21.1

Young People on Spring Break
Why do you think these travellers wanted to visit another country?

This chapter will focus on travel and tourism and the ways tourism builds connections among people. We will look at these topics:

- the global and Canadian patterns of tourism
- factors that affect tourism
- the impacts of tourism

CHECK IT OVER

1. **a)** What are three reasons why young people travel?
   b) Why do you travel?
2. List three trips that groups in your school have taken recently.

Travel Patterns

Tourism is a form of world trade. People travel to another part of their own country or another nation to see new and interesting things. It is a trade in services. Many kinds of services are involved. Tourism and travel make a lot of money for the places attracting visitors. In fact, international travel is one of the fastest-growing parts of many economies around the world. Both the number of tourists and the amount of money they spend are rapidly increasing.

FIGURE 21.2

Reasons for Travelling
Can you think of any other reasons why people would travel?

People travel for many reasons:

- *learn about the world*
- **do business with other regions**
- compete in sports
- **explore a new place**
- visit an historic site
- learn a new language
- *get a new job*
- take a relaxing holiday
- *go on a retreat to a spa or health club*
- **follow a hobby**

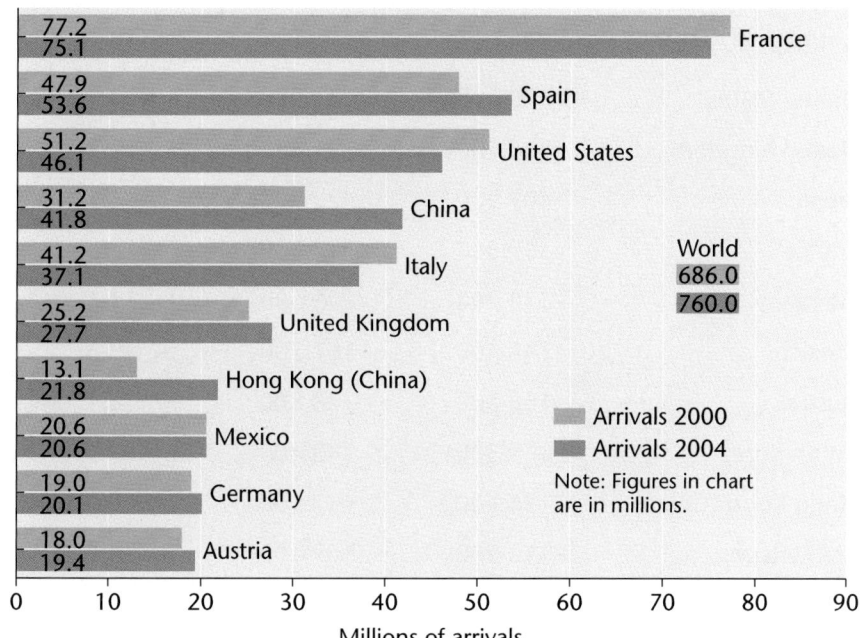

FIGURE 21.3

Top Countries for Tourist Arrivals
As tourists enter a country, they are counted as *arrivals*. What does the difference in numbers between 2000 and 2004 tell you?

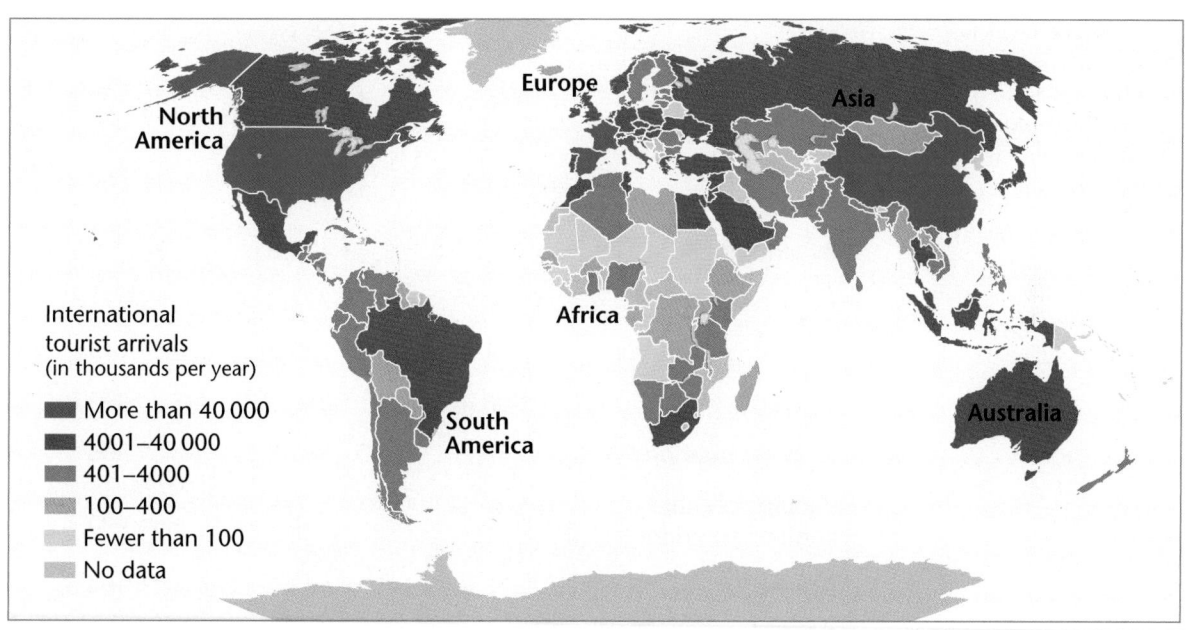

FIGURE 21.4

International Tourist Arrivals, 2005
Which countries in the world attract the most tourists?

Chapter 21: Travel and Tourism   **221**

FIGURE 21.5

Trips to Canada of More Than One Night
Why do you think fewer people are travelling to Canada from some countries?

Country of Origin	2001	2002	% Change
United States	15 570 000	16 167 900	3.8
United Kingdom	826 100	721 300	−12.7
Japan	409 900	422 800	3.1
France	357 300	312 300	−12.6
Germany	330 200	293 500	−11.6
Mexico	148 400	161 200	8.6
Australia	158 500	148 800	−6.1
South Korea	139 300	143 400	2.9
Hong Kong (China)	125 400	117 900	−6.0
Netherlands	113 900	107 100	−6.0

FIGURE 21.6

Nonresident Travellers Entering Canada
What kind of transportation do most travellers coming to Canada use?

	2001	2002	2003
	'000s		
Total nonresident travellers	**47 146.6**	**44 896.3**	**38 902.6**
U.S. residents entering:	42 871.3	40 878.2	35 509.4
By automobile	35 202.0	33 423.8	28 749.2
By plane	4 228.2	4 224.0	3 912.9
By train	131.0	120.7	114.2
By boat	868.4	886.2	873.8
By other methods	756.9	641.3	566.5
Residents of other countries entering:	4 275.4	4 018.1	3 393.2
By land	618.8	533.1	404.5
By air	3 565.6	3 402.9	2 906.7
By sea	91.0	82.0	82.0

GEOTECHNOLOGY

Global Positioning Systems

Global Positioning Systems and the Internet play a huge role in the travel business. Airplane passengers can see their flight position during the trip. Using satellite relays, air traffic controllers on the ground know the exact position of the plane. NavCan is the agency in Canada that guides flight traffic, especially on the busy routes from North America to Europe.

LITERACY SKILL

Making Connections Among Sources of Information

Geography uses several formats to present information. These are called geo-tools. They include

- maps
- tables
- graphs
- charts
- photos
- words

Often ideas found in one source add to patterns you see in another source. These build on the main idea in a third source. When you are doing research, stop to reflect on the ideas and try to make connections among the sources of information. Look at Figure 21.3, a bar graph, and Figure 21.4, a map, and look for connections between them.

Literacy Strategy

Making connections
As you read, try to make connections between the text and yourself. For example, consider what you can do to help improve the quality of life of people in developing countries. Making connections will help you better understand the text.

FIGURE 21.7

The Eiffel Tower in Paris, France
Why might tourists come here?

One reason that people choose to travel is to see cultural and historic sites. One of the top destinations for people travelling to see cultural and historic sites is Europe. These sites include

- historic buildings and monuments (for example, the Coliseum in Rome, Italy, and Stonehenge in England)
- museums and galleries (for example, the Louvre Art Museum in Paris, France, which exhibits the "Mona Lisa")
- churches (for example, Westminster Abbey in London, England, and Notre Dame in Paris, France)

People also visit Europe for the food, shows, scenery, shopping, and other attractions.

We have seen that there are many reasons why people travel. There are also reasons that people choose not to travel. Some factors of tourism have a direct effect on holiday or travel plans.

- **Age:** When you are young, some travel choices may not be possible because you do not have the money, your parents or guardians have not given their consent, or you are not old enough. When you are older, health and physical conditions can limit travel.
- **Time:** Free time or holiday time is a major factor when you are in school or you are working. You must travel when the holiday schedule of your school or company allows it.
- **Money:** You need to budget for trips. Travel money must come out of what is left over after you have met your daily needs.
- **Safety:** People want to be safe and secure when taking a holiday. Disease, war, and terrorism are factors that restrict travel.

CHECK IT OVER

3. Read the Fast Fact on page 220. Calculate how much money tourism will earn by 2010.
4. Review the list of factors of tourism. Select the most important factor affecting your life and write three sentences to explain its effects.

Impacts of Tourism

Some parts of the world are attracting more and more travellers. A growing number of visitors are going to Asian countries like China, Japan, and Vietnam to sightsee or for business. Cruise ships are making more calls to ports in Asia. Tourism has many economic benefits for countries. Large numbers of visitors can contribute large amounts of money to an economy, along with other benefits.

Increasing numbers of travellers can lead to more jobs in travel and tourism. In tourist areas there are many types of work to be found. Transportation jobs range from taxi drivers to baggage handlers to immigration officials. In the hotel industry, people work as room service maids, kitchen staff, gardeners, reception desk staff, and managers. Guests need to eat, so restaurants open up, offering selections of local food. Services develop to supply entertainment, tours, and adventures of all kinds. All this tourist activity helps the economy. The travel and tourism workers who are making money from this activity spend their tips and wages on local goods and services for their own families.

GEOCAREERS

Travel Agent

Many people see the career of a travel agent as an ideal job. You get paid to see the world and to travel. Geography is an excellent background for this job because it

- gives you information about different countries and cultures
- helps you understand charts, tables, and maps
- informs you about the types of transportation systems used in world travel
- helps you understand the needs of business travellers

Many high schools offer a Travel and Tourism course in their Geography departments. Community colleges carry on this education with Travel and Tourism programs. Co-op courses are a good way to get experience in this service business.

FIGURE 21.8

A Typical Tourism Industry Photograph What message is suggested by scenes like this? What problems may be hidden from potential tourists?

FIGURE 21.9

Tourism in Perspective
What impacts might this large cruise ship have on the local community?

The World Travel and Tourism Council predicts that people will be making one billion international trips by 2010. Countries must be prepared so they can attract, and handle, their share of tourists. The economic benefits can be well worth their efforts.

Tourist money can have positive effects on more than just a nation's economy. Tigers and elephants are examples of two animals whose habitats are being saved because tourists want to see them in their natural settings. This may save these animals from extinction. Tourism also protects historic sites such as Gettysburg, an American civil war site, from development. As long as people are paying to see these sites, they will not be destroyed. The global village has the power to look after its important tourist attractions and preserve them for the future.

Large numbers of tourists can also have a negative impact. Jet airplanes, large cruise ships, and superhighways move people around the world in greater numbers than ever before. Mass tourism is one of the fastest-growing business activities in the world. This can lead to environmental problems. (See Case Study: Mount Everest in Nepal.)

- Large crowds come to areas that do not have enough services (food, water, toilets) to provide for them.

- Old and fragile attractions like historic buildings are damaged by people crowding around them.

- Fragile ecozones like beaches and trails are damaged by overcrowding, litter, and waste disposal problems.
- Treatment plants can't handle the increase in sewage, so it is dumped raw into natural waterways.
- Garbage disposal dumps are not used or fill up too fast.
- Increased vehicle traffic causes air pollution.
- Attractions such as rock concerts in city squares can result in noise pollution.

CASE STUDY

Mount Everest in Nepal

How could the world's tallest mountain, Mount Everest, be affected by tourism? This stunning natural wonder of the Himalaya Mountains has drawn people for centuries. The people who live around this mountain range, such as the Sherpas of Nepal, worship the mountains as holy sites. More recently, the mountains have caught the eye of tourists interested in mountain climbing. At first the goal was simply to climb to the top of the highest peak. Sir Edmund Hillary and Tenzing Norgay climbed Everest in 1953.

Since then, many more people have gone on expeditions to the Himalayas. Today, more than 27 000 walkers, trekkers, hikers, and climbers come to Nepal to explore the mountains each year. The treks begin at the little airport at Lukla. Its runway has been paved to handle the increased air passenger traffic from Kathmandu, the capital city.

All this activity creates many problems. Tourism's ecological footprint has changed. There have been a number of negative environmental impacts:

- Traffic bottlenecks occur on narrow, steep mountain trails.
- Trails erode under the heavy traffic load of people and yaks (used to carry equipment and supplies).
- Tea houses are overcrowded and short of resources, which have to be carried in to the remote sites.
- The forests of Everest and other mountains have been cut down to provide firewood for making tea and meals for trekkers.
- The soil erodes quickly from the steep slopes after the trees have been cut down. This makes it hard to replant.
- Litter is everywhere. Climbers and trekkers do not clean up after themselves or carry their waste out when their expedition is over.

KEEP is the Kathmandu Environmental Education Project. It is one of several organizations that are working to save the natural beauty of the area before the damage becomes permanent.

CHECK IT OVER

5. How does Geography help you to be a good travel agent?
6. Name five jobs directly related to the travel and tourism industry.
7. How does money spent by tourists help a nation's economy?
8. Describe three environmental problems that result from an increase in tourist activities.
9. a) What does KEEP stand for?
   b) What does this organization do?

THINK IT OVER

Knowledge and Understanding

1. Examine the bar graph in Figure 21.3, Top Countries for Tourist Arrivals.
   a) Which country did the most people travel to in 2000 and 2004?
   b) In your opinion, what are three reasons why tourists like to visit this country?
2. a) Figure 21.5 shows how many tourists from various countries are visiting Canada for more than one night. Which country do most of the tourists come from?
   b) Name four methods that tourists from all over the world can use to travel to Canada.
3. Name six geo-tools used by geographers. (Hint: See the Literary Skill box.)

Thinking and Communication

4. List five ways tourism benefits the place where you live.
5. If you or a family member works in the tourism industry, describe what you know about how the business works. If not, choose a job in the tourism industry that you would like to try, and tell what you think it involves. Write your description in two or three sentences.
6. Make a chart. Compare four problems created by tourists visiting Nepal to four problems created by tourists visiting the place where you live.
7. Use the Internet to search for information about Nepal related to tourist activities. Create a poster or a Web site to show how tourism both helps Nepal and causes problems for this nation. Use a map of Nepal as part of your presentation.

Getting Along With Others: Canada's International Role

Chapter 22

In this chapter you will learn to

◢ *identify how Canada influences other countries*

◢ describe Canada's participation in major international organizations

◢ discuss contributions Canada makes to the world

◢ describe Canada's efforts in promoting international well-being

Key Words

foreign assistance

official development assistance (ODA)

human rights

non-governmental organizations (NGO)

Introduction

A starving child with hunger in her eyes, a flash-flood victim, and earthquake-wrecked houses: we see these images on television when disasters strike around the world. The victims of these disasters often ask Canadians for help. They are seeking food, water, medicine, and money to help rebuild their towns and cities and countries. Canadians are generous in return. Individuals, groups, and the government give these things and more to help people in this global village we all live in.

FIGURE 22.1

Canadians Are Asked for Help
Here is a situation in Sierra Leone, where Canadians have been asked to help reduce the suffering of others. What situations do you recognize?

This chapter will focus on

- how our government helps other countries
- how Canadians contribute through other types of organizations

 CHECK IT OVER

1. When a natural disaster occurs, what are four things Canadians can offer to help a place rebuild?
2. What does the term *global village* mean to you?

Official Assistance: Helping Out in Times of Need

In countries such as Canada, people generally have food, water, shelter, and, to some degree, wealth in the form of money. However, in many developing nations, people are hungry, homeless, and poor. They are often trying to live on less than a dollar a day. Foreign assistance refers to the efforts to help provide financial aid and relief (food, shelter, medicine) to nations in need. This assistance can come from

- governments
- organizations like the Red Cross and World Vision
- corporations
- individuals

The government of Canada gives aid to developing nations through official development assistance (ODA). The Canadian International Development Agency (CIDA) is the government agency that provides this support. Canada sets aside a small portion of tax dollars—about one half of one percent of Canada's gross national product—to be used for foreign aid. Canada currently spends just over $3 billion a year in aid. It has promised to raise this amount to about $5 billion a year by 2010.

ODA helps people in other countries by

- providing clean water and places for waste disposal
- helping build services such as power grids, roads, schools and telephone systems
- protecting human rights and supporting democracies
- saving the environment and wildlife

FIGURE 22.2

CIDA Efforts in Afghanistan
How do efforts like this help to improve conditions for people in developing countries?

Canadian Priorities for ODA, 2003
Afghanistan: number one priority in 2003
Bangladesh
Honduras
Bolivia
Ethiopia
Tanzania
Mozambique
Senegal
Mali
Ghana

FIGURE 22.3

Top Priority Countries for Canadian Aid
On which continent is Afghanistan located?

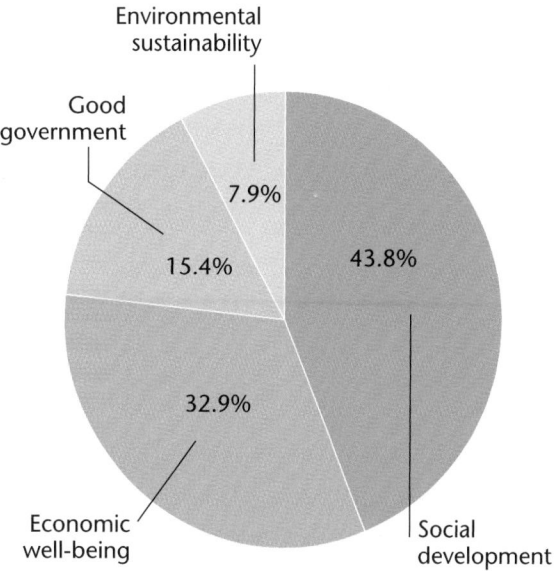

Environmental sustainability

Good government

7.9%

15.4%

43.8%

32.9%

Economic well-being

Social development

FIGURE 22.4

CIDA Spending, 2003–2004
Social development programs focus on such things as improved education, more opportunities for women, and better health care.

CHECK IT OVER

3. a) What is *foreign assistance*?
   b) Where can it come from?
4. a) What do the initials ODA stand for?
   b) How does ODA help people in need?

CIDA and all other Canadian agencies promote basic human rights. This means the right of every human being to enjoy clean air and water, daily food, safety for families, and a peaceful, free life. Human rights also include help with medical problems and the ability to lead a normal life.

Environmental rights issues are closely tied to human rights. People's quality of life begins with their daily surroundings. If there is clean air and water, fertile soil, hope for jobs, and safety, people can live satisfying lives. Canada promotes these goals.

Millennium Development Goals

At the United Nations Millennium Summit in September 2000, world leaders agreed on a set of goals to guide international development efforts. The Millennium Development Goals aim to

- end extreme poverty and hunger
- ensure primary education for all children
- encourage gender equality
- reduce child deaths
- improve the health of mothers
- combat HIV/AIDS, malaria, and other diseases
- ensure environmental sustainability
- form a global partnership for development

These goals are linked to the following targets:

- cutting in half the number of people living on less than one dollar a day
- cutting in half the number of people without access to safe drinking water
- reducing by two thirds the death rate of children under five

The aim is to achieve all these goals by 2015.

FIGURE 22.5

UN Millennium Development Goals
Why have these goals been set?

CASE STUDY

The DART Squad

The Disaster Assistance Response team, or DART, is a Canadian military rapid response team that helps in troubled areas of the world. About 200 soldiers are specially trained for these help missions. DART's four main objectives are

1. **Basic medical care:** A medical aid tent can be set up for treating injuries, dispensing drugs, and doing simple lab tests in emergencies.

2. **Safe drinking water:** A water filtering unit can produce up to 50 000 L of safe water a day.

3. **Repairing damage:** Engineers can fix roads, bridges, electrical systems, and water supply systems.

4. **Communications:** Communication systems allow people to talk to other agencies and help coordinate long-term relief.

The DART team flies into disaster areas such as

- **Pakistan, October 2005:** to help earthquake victims
- **Sri Lanka, December 2004:** to help tsunami survivors
- **Turkey, August 1999:** to help after an earthquake
- **Honduras, October 1998:** to help clean up after a hurricane

FIGURE 22.6

A DART Team at Work in Pakistan
What does DART mean?

FAST *Fact*

The Red Cross works in 183 countries— more than any other NGO.

FIGURE 22.7

Students Participating in a 30-Hour Famine
What are some ways that events like this in Canada help development efforts in other countries?

Helping Out: Non-Governmental Organizations

Many Canadians work to improve living conditions in damaged areas of the world. Organizations such as the Red Cross, World Vision, and Save the Children raise money and supplies for developing regions. These non-governmental organizations (NGO) often involve secondary-school students through programs like World Vision's 30-Hour Famine event. This is an annual event in which teenagers fast for 30 hours and also raise money to help hungry children. The goal is to eliminate hunger in the world.

An estimated 35 000 jobs are created in Canada by ODA and NGO work. Canadian companies provide many of the goods and services to nations in trouble. Counting both ODA and NGO contributions, Canada ranks twelfth in donating foreign aid in the world.

FIGURE 22.8

The Canadian Red Cross Helping After the Tsunami of 2004
Why do Canadians donate to NGOs such as the Red Cross?

 GEO*TECHNOLOGY*

Using GIS to Aid Development Efforts

Geographic Information Systems (GIS) are used to create electronic maps. GIS mapping can plot famine, the spread of illness, and high-risk areas for diseases like HIV/AIDS. GIS maps can be updated quickly to give the latest available data to teams that are responding to emergencies. Medical geography—plotting and spotting disease patterns—is one field that benefits from GIS systems.

 GEO*CAREERS*

NGO Worker

Nurses, teachers, and construction workers are different types of workers who have careers with non-governmental organizations. Wages are often low for field workers. In fact, many are volunteers. However, the experiences and exposure to the world are often priceless. Many religious groups have aid and relief organizations that individuals can participate in.

Geography is good preparation for NGO workers because it enables them to

- know the climate and landforms of the region
- be familiar with the culture of the people
- understand the economy and business types in operation there
- know the needs of the region

NGOs need full-time administrators and fundraisers as well as office and field workers.

8. Explain how GIS mapping can help medical geographers.
9. a) What do the initials NGO stand for?
   b) Who might work for an NGO?
10. How can students help an NGO?

 THINK IT OVER

Knowledge and Understanding

1. a) Describe how much money Canada gives to foreign assistance by percentage and by dollar values.
   b) What is the goal amount for 2010?

2. Name three NGOs discussed in this chapter. Describe their roles in helping people around the world.

3. a) What is GIS?
   b) How can GIS mapping help solve emergencies around the world?

Thinking and Communication

4. Investigate one of the relief efforts by a Canadian DART team. (See Case Study on page 233.) Write a five-point paragraph on their rescue efforts in that part of the world.

5. Many nations are developing quickly, and the Internet and mobile phones have speeded up communication. Give reasons why the "global village" may soon become known as the "global city."

6. Select a recent natural hazard or disaster. Create a photo display or collage to illustrate
   • the type of disaster that occurred
   • the effects of that event
   • the ways assistance was provided to help the people affected
   The display can be in paper or electronic form.

Safety and Global Security

In this chapter you will learn to

▲ *identify the connections between Canada and other countries*

▲ discuss Canada's participation in major international organizations

▲ identify significant contributions that Canada makes to the world

▲ consider Canada's response to global challenges, especially in promoting international well-being

Key Words

safety

security

United Nations

peacekeeping

terrorism

international cooperation

Introduction

Schools are safe and secure places to be. Safety refers to your well-being and health: being free from harm and injury. Security means your surroundings are monitored to protect you from any harm. Your school's teachers, principal, and other staff are there to make sure you are safe when you are at school and that your building is secure from anything that could hurt you.

FIGURE 23.1

Security Features in a Shopping Mall
Cameras and lighting are used to make sure everyone can be seen clearly.

In this chapter we will take some ideas about safety and security and apply them to Canada's connections with the rest of the world. We will consider these topics:

- Canada and the United Nations
- terrorism and its impacts on people

 CHECK IT OVER

1. Explain how this chapter uses the terms *safety* and *security*.
2. What does your school do to provide a safe and secure environment?

FAST *Fact*

Many schools run model United Nations activities in their schools. These special classes often take part in The Hague International Model United Nations every year. The Hague is in the Netherlands and is where the International Criminal Court meets.

The United Nations

The United Nations is the world agency that tries to provide safe and secure places for all citizens in the world. The UN supports

- free speech
- free press
- freedom of religion
- free elections
- equal opportunities for all, whatever their gender, race, or beliefs

Every nation in the world, a total of 191 countries, belongs to this organization. The United Nations has its headquarters in New York City. The quote in Figure 23.2 describes the UN's role in the world.

FIGURE 23.2

From the United Nations' Charter
What might be some reasons that nations have joined the United Nations?

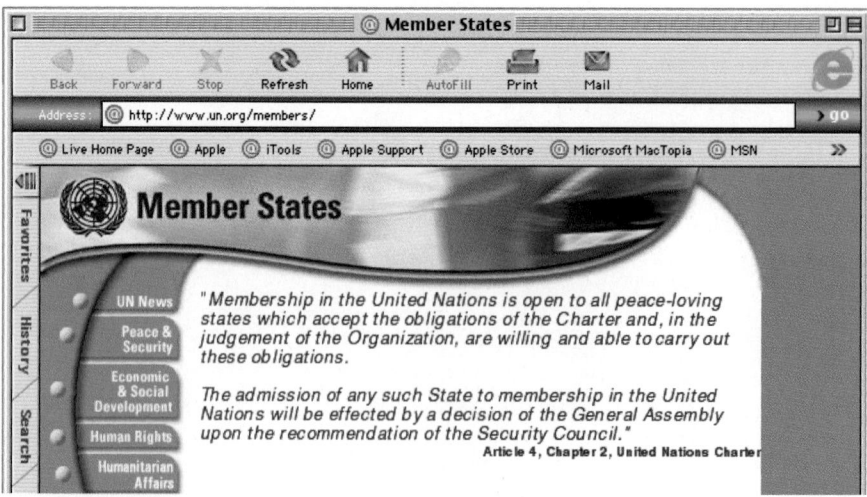

"Membership in the United Nations is open to all peace-loving states which accept the obligations of the Charter and, in the judgement of the Organization, are willing and able to carry out these obligations.

The admission of any such State to membership in the United Nations will be effected by a decision of the General Assembly upon the recommendation of the Security Council."
Article 4, Chapter 2, United Nations Charter

The United Nations runs an International Criminal Court to bring to justice those who commit crimes against other people. These people are criminals who act outside the laws of their own country. Their crimes range from torture, slavery, and murder to trying to kill whole groups of people (genocide).

Peacekeeping is the use of military activity to keep peace between warring states. It is a high-profile activity of the United Nations. Today, civilians are more directly affected by conflicts. This is because these days most conflicts occur *within* states, rather than *between* states. As a result, traditional peacekeeping missions are changing into peacemaking and peace support operations. The goal now is often to achieve and maintain peace. The map in Figure 23.3 shows where current UN peacekeeping missions are taking place.

Peacekeeping is part of Canada's national heritage. Prime Minister Lester Pearson first came up with the idea in 1956 with the United Nations Emergency Force. Since then, Canadian forces have been involved in solutions to conflicts in over 50 situations. Canada regularly provides troops and other resources—including advice on how best to handle situations—to the United Nations.

Canada has a "3-D" policy: defence, development, and democracy. Its goals for foreign aid and peacekeeping missions are based on these 3-D factors. Canadian soldiers are putting these ideals into practice in Afghanistan:

- Canadian soldiers are defending citizens against rebel attacks as a new, democratic government is put in place.
- Military engineers are drilling wells, building roads, and helping with school and medical supplies in this war-torn country.
- Soldiers and other experts are training new police forces.

As a result, Canadians are playing more roles in peace support. These include

- civilian experts, such as human rights monitors
- refugee and child protection experts, and corrections officers to rebuild justice systems
- civilian police to monitor and train local police forces.

FIGURE 23.3

United Nations Peacekeeping, 2005
In what continent do most peacekeeping activities take place? Figures are for peacekeepers from all countries.

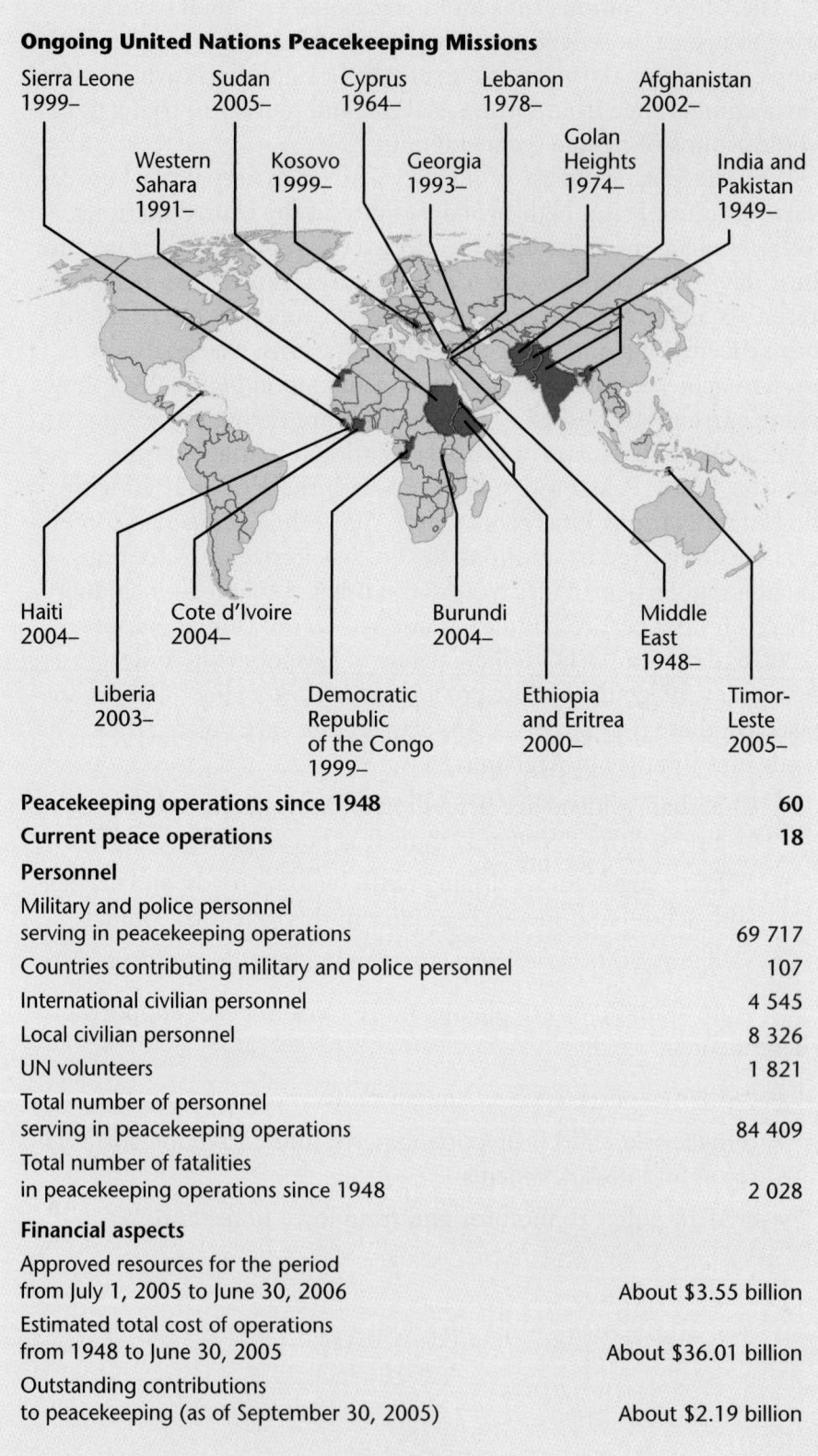

Ongoing United Nations Peacekeeping Missions

Sierra Leone 1999–

Sudan 2005–

Cyprus 1964–

Lebanon 1978–

Afghanistan 2002–

Western Sahara 1991–

Kosovo 1999–

Georgia 1993–

Golan Heights 1974–

India and Pakistan 1949–

Haiti 2004–

Cote d'Ivoire 2004–

Burundi 2004–

Middle East 1948–

Liberia 2003–

Democratic Republic of the Congo 1999–

Ethiopia and Eritrea 2000–

Timor-Leste 2005–

Peacekeeping operations since 1948	**60**
Current peace operations	**18**
Personnel	
Military and police personnel serving in peacekeeping operations	69 717
Countries contributing military and police personnel	107
International civilian personnel	4 545
Local civilian personnel	8 326
UN volunteers	1 821
Total number of personnel serving in peacekeeping operations	84 409
Total number of fatalities in peacekeeping operations since 1948	2 028
Financial aspects	
Approved resources for the period from July 1, 2005 to June 30, 2006	About $3.55 billion
Estimated total cost of operations from 1948 to June 30, 2005	About $36.01 billion
Outstanding contributions to peacekeeping (as of September 30, 2005)	About $2.19 billion

FIGURE 23.4

Soldier Involved in a UN Peacekeeping Operation in Haiti
In what ways does peace-keeping help to improve peace and security?

 GEOCAREERS

Soldier

The Canadian Forces recruiting team often visits schools with information about careers in the Canadian Forces. School guidance counsellors also keep up-to-date files on these careers. Over 100 different jobs are offered in the forces. They all provide training that can be used in civilian life after your forces career is over. Cadet corps offer young men and women the chance to experience military life. The Canadian Forces offer exciting prospects of adventure and travel. However, you must always remember the danger involved in putting your life on the line for your country.

Geography is a good background for these careers because you

- understand landforms and their uses in war settings
- can read maps to locate yourself and strategic sites
- understand the causes and effects of weather and how to survive in extreme conditions
- have knowledge of GIS devices for plotting locations

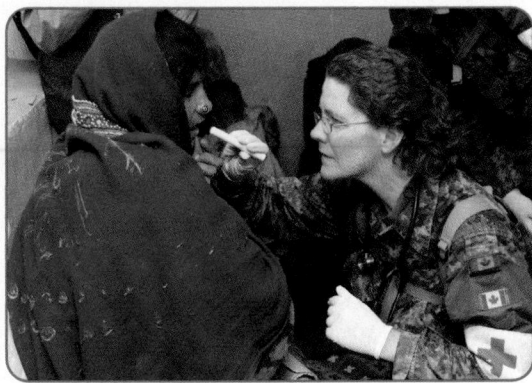

FIGURE 23.5

Peacekeeping in Afghanistan
Why do Canadian soldiers work so much in peacekeeping operations?

3. Identify three ways the United Nations tries to provide safe and secure places for people around the world.

4. Describe the United Nations' peacekeeping activities.

5. What is Canada's 3-D policy for foreign aid and peacekeeping?

CASE STUDY

International Borders

Borders mark the edges of nations. Canada and its neighbour, the United States of America, share one of the longest undefended borders in the world. Canadian border checkpoints are staffed by officers from Canada Customs. Customs officers are the frontline providers of safety and security for a country. They check to make sure that neither illegal goods, such as drugs or weapons, nor people who are criminals get into the country.

Since the terrorist attacks of September 11, 2001, the U.S. has been worried about terrorists crossing the border from Canada into the United States. It has added more electronic surveillance and other devices to prevent further attacks. Americans are now insisting that by 2008 every person entering their country must have a passport. Passports are legal documents that show you are a citizen of your nation. The big problem for U.S. citizens is that only one in every five has a passport. They may want to make a brief visit to Canada or Mexico (who only require a driving licence or birth certificate from U.S. citizens). However, they would not be able to get back into the U.S. They would need a passport to reenter their own country.

FIGURE 23.6

A Canadian Passport
In a world concerned about terrorism, passports have become necessary for people crossing international borders.

FIGURE 23.7

A Border Crossing Point
What safety and security measures do you see in this picture?

Global Terrorism

When ordinary citizens feel unsafe and insecure walking in their own neighbourhoods, they are living in terror. Terrorism is the planned use of injury, murder, or destruction, or the threat of those things, to achieve certain goals. This kind of violence has been around for a long time. Yet after the terrorist attacks against the U.S. on September 11, 2001, the war against terrorism has taken on global importance.

Region	Country	Type of Activity
North America	United States	September 11, 2001. Al-Qaeda attacks government and public buildings in New York City and Washington by hijacking airplanes and crashing them into buildings.
South America	Colombia	February 7, 2003. Car bombs explode in the capital city, Bogota.
Africa	Sierra Leone	1999–2000. UN workers are targeted in an attempt to end peacekeeping missions during a civil war.
Asia	Bali, Indonesia	October 12, 2002. Bombs go off in a nightclub, killing and injuring patrons and tourists.
Eurasia	Russia	September 1, 2004. Chechen rebels kidnap a school, and hundreds of hostages, including school children, die in the standoff.
Middle East	Israel/Palestine	Ongoing for many years, Palestinian uprisings to claim homeland territory in the Gaza Strip result in bombings, shootings, and warfare.
Western Europe	Spain	March 4, 2004. Commuter trains in Madrid are bombed by Al-Qaeda terrorists.
United Kingdom	England	July 7, 2005. Commuter trains in London are bombed by Al-Qaeda terrorists.

FIGURE 23.8

Recent Terrorist Attacks
Few parts of the world have escaped some form of terrorist activity. (Chechen rebels are citizens of Chechnya fighting for independence from Russia.)

LITERACY SKILL

Making Visual T-Charts

A T-chart is often used in an electronic presentation where a photo (or other illustration) is shown on the left side and notes are written on the right side. The purpose of the words in point form is to draw the reader's attention to key features in the picture on the left. Practising this skill will help you make concise points that are clearly illustrated.

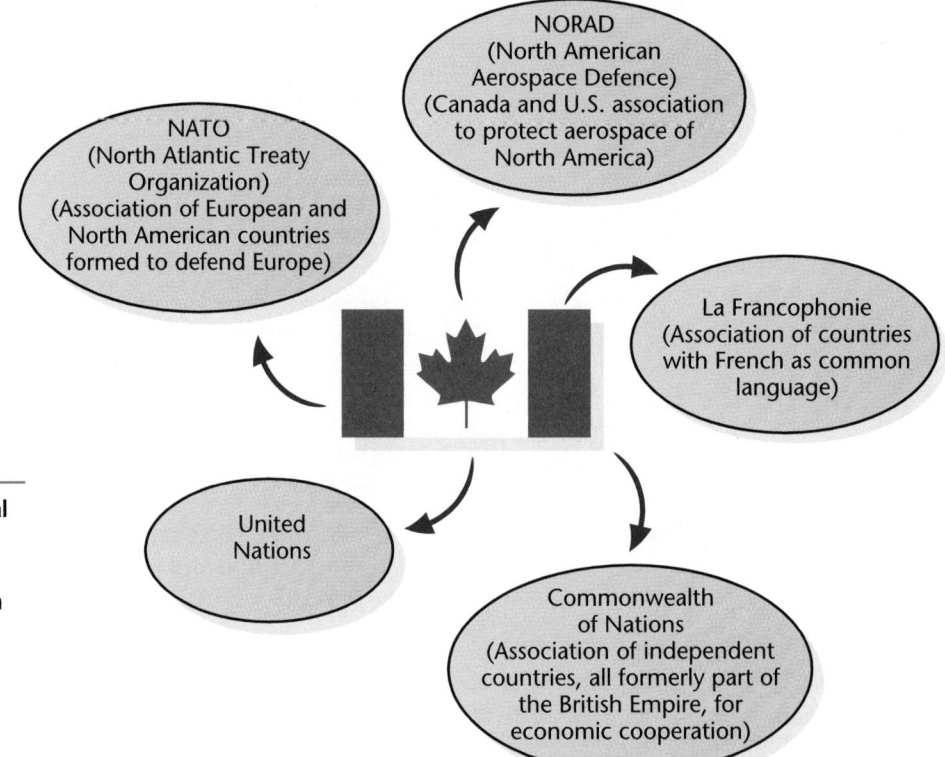

FIGURE 23.9

Canada's International Connections
How do individual Canadians benefit from these connections?

International cooperation happens when nations come together to help end wars and conflicts and to establish peace in war-torn regions. In the global village, the actions of each person or nation can affect everyone else. The 191 nations in the United Nations are working towards a peaceful world.

CHECK IT OVER

6. a) What is terrorism?

    b) Give two examples of terrorist attacks.

7. What is the purpose of international borders?

8. a) What is a passport?

    b) When do you need a passport?

THINK IT OVER

Knowledge and Understanding

1. List four ways Geography can help soldiers in their military careers.

2. What is the purpose of the United Nations' International Criminal Court?

3. Examine Figure 23.3. Describe the location of three UN peacekeeping operations.

Thinking and Communication

4. Write a three-point paragraph to explain how international cooperation contributes to a peaceful world.

5. Describe what happened when you have crossed an international border. How did you feel? If you have never crossed an international border, ask someone who has and find out how he or she felt.

6. Choose a photo or map of a Canadian peacekeeping mission (e.g., Afghanistan). Using a T-chart, show the photo or map on one side. Then use point-form notes on the other side to explain

    • where the problem site is located

    • what the problem in the region is

    • how Canada's peacekeepers are helping to solve the problem

Chapter

24 Canada and the Global Environment

Key Words

Kyoto Protocol

greenhouse gas

global warming

environmental assessment

world reserve

In this chapter you will learn to

◢ discuss the significant contributions Canada makes to the world

◢ compare Canada with the rest of the world in resource consumption and pollution

◢ describe Canada's commitment in responding to global challenges and promoting international well-being

Introduction

The environment allows us and all other forms of life to exist on earth. It provides

- the air we breathe
- the water we drink
- the food we eat
- the energy to fuel our lives
- the raw materials for our goods

Literacy Strategy

Checking your understanding
As you read this long text, stop after each paragraph and think about what you have read by
- asking a question
- clarifying something
- making a comment
- making a connection
- making a prediction
Thinking aloud as you read helps you check your understanding of the text.

The environment also acts as a sink and a drain for wastes. It has the potential to self-clean in just about every situation. For instance, Canada's wetlands act as sponges for all the rain and snow that fall. The wetlands carry that water underground and to other bodies of water. Without wetlands we would have little fresh water.

The danger is that we begin to take these things for granted and start to ignore problems. Without proper care, humans may spoil the earth to a point where it becomes too polluted to support life. We need to manage our resource use so we do not run out of the resources we need. One way countries can do this is by making agreements with other countries about how to protect the global environment.

This chapter will look at the actions Canada takes with other countries to protect the global environment. We will focus on these topics:

- environmental agreements Canada has signed
- goals to reverse global environmental damage
- solutions to environmental problems

FIGURE 24.1

A Natural Environment near Val Marie, Saskatchewan

 CHECK IT OVER

1. Name five things we need to survive on earth.
2. How does our planet act as "a sink and a drain"?

Environmental Agreements

Environmental protection means combining the efforts of every society and individual around the world to save and protect all the systems on earth. This is necessary to ensure life continues into the future.

Canada takes part in many world agreements, such as the Kyoto Protocol. This is an international agreement originally signed in Kyoto, Japan, in 1997, which has, to date (2006), been signed by 161 countries. Its purpose is to reduce global warming by reducing greenhouse gas emissions. These emissions are caused by

- burning oil, gas, and coal
- deforestation

The protocol commits Canada and 37 other industrialized countries to cutting their emissions of greenhouse gases. The goal is for these levels to be at least 5.2 percent below 1990 levels by 2012. To meet this target, the protocol encourages these countries to produce and use energy in more environmentally friendly ways.

FIGURE 24.2

Canada's International Agreements on Environmental Issues
Canada has signed many international agreements to protect the environment. Why do you think so many agreements are needed?

Year	Agreement	Description
1905	The International Joint Commission on the Great Lakes	Canada and U.S. agreement to protect water quality in the Great Lakes
1985	The Great Lakes Charter	Canada and U.S. agreement to protect water quality
1986	Great Lakes Toxic Substance Control Agreement	Canada and U.S. agreement to reduce poisonous substances in the water
1986	Basel Convention on the Control of Transboundary Movements of Hazardous Wastes	Canada and U.S. agreement to prevent dangerous materials from crossing the border
1987	Montreal Protocol on Substances That Deplete the Ozone Layer	agreement of 163 nations to reduce chlorofluorocarbons (CFCs), which are used in air conditioners and refrigerators and which destroy the ozone layer
1992	Rio Conference and Rio Summit	international agreements to protect the global environment and provide for sustainable development
1997	Kyoto Protocol	agreement by 161 nations to reduce world air pollution from levels established in the 1990s
2000	Millennium Ecosystem Assessment	United Nations inspection and record of the world's ecosystems
2001	Stockholm Convention on Persistent Organic Pollutants	agreement of 151 nations to control the use of DDT insect spray and 11 other toxic substances
2002	Earth Summit	ten-year follow-up to the Rio Summit: agreement by United Nations members to continue to work on sustainable development, and to end poverty and environmental destruction

Ecosystem Assessment

Canada was one of the 95 participants in the Millennium Ecosystem Assessment (MA). The study examined some of the most pressing environmental issues, such as

- global warming (the rise in the average temperatures of air and water) caused by greenhouse gases
- dust storms in the Gobi desert
- drinking water shortages in Africa
- vanishing species from the animal kingdom
- dead zones in lakes, rivers, and oceans

The 1300 researchers involved have produced six reports with action plans to reverse harmful trends before it is too late. The Kyoto Protocol (see page 247) is one type of action that is trying to accomplish this.

Calculating Reserves

Until this study, there had not been much data on global environmental issues. The MA study and others will help make further environmental assessments easier. This is because these studies describe the benefits of protecting the environment. Before the study, most companies did not take any responsibility for damage they caused to the environment. Now, companies large and small are aware that they need to be sustainable if they want to survive. For instance, the study predicts that the demand for food will double over the next 20 years. This means agribusinesses (large farming operations) must meet those demands without further damaging the ecosystems, or they risk having no business at all.

One aspect these studies are calculating is the world reserve of each resource. The world reserve is the amount of a resource that remains for human use. For example, as oil is taken from the ground and used up, its world reserve declines.

FIGURE 24.3

Environmental Issues
What role do you think
the golf course plays in
creating the dust storm?
What happens to the
tropical rainforest when
clear cutting is allowed?

CHECK IT OVER

3. **a)** What is the Kyoto Protocol?

   b) What is the goal of the Kyoto Protocol?

4. Write a list of five environmental issues that the Millennium Ecosystem
   Assessment hopes to solve. Which do you think is the most
   important? Why?

5. **a)** What does the term *world reserve* mean?

   b) Why is it important to know about the world reserve for
   each resource?

GEOTECHNOLOGY

Weather Satellites

Weather satellites provide images from space of current weather patterns. Satellites are set in orbits over the earth and send nonstop data to their weather headquarters. The satellites allow these patterns on earth to be instantly tracked, photographed, and reported down to citizens and weather experts alike.

There are two kinds of satellites:

- **Geostationary Satellites:** These satellites orbit 35 000 km above the equator. That means they are moving at the same speed as the earth and can keep above the same spot on the earth. Their main advantage is that receiving antennae on earth can be aimed at the satellite without having to be moved.

- **Polar-Orbiting Satellites:** These satellites orbit over the North and South Poles about 850 km above the earth. Because they are closer, they can cover the entire surface of the earth and bring back higher-resolution images.

Data from weather satellites can also be used to analyze climate change. Scientists study weather patterns over time and identify trends that could affect ecosystems. Armed with this information, scientists can try to protect ecosystems and resources.

Protecting Our Resources

Offering financial incentives is one way of protecting our resources. The Case Study on page 252 gives one example. Another example comes from the Kyoto Accord. One way of decreasing air pollution to meet world standards is by offering financial incentives. By signing the Accord, companies can buy and sell Carbon Dioxide Pollution Credits. Companies producing more carbon dioxide pay a higher fee than those producing less. This system encourages companies to pollute less so they can sell their credits to larger polluters and profit. Those companies will stop polluting when it becomes too expensive.

If these kinds of incentives can be used to combat air pollution, similar solutions can be found for other resources. Worldwide fishing quotas could protect fish stocks because the key stakeholders have a financial reason to protect their investment. Using the Millennium Ecosystems Assessment, values can also be assigned to help protect whole environments. For example, endangered species (such as tigers, elephants, and whales) can be shown to have more value as tourist attractions than they have as items hunted for skins and body parts.

FAST *Fact*

The tropics hold about 50 percent of the world's forests (e.g., tropical rainforest), but they are being cut down at the rate of 25 football fields per minute!

Investing to Protect the Environment

Some resources, such as the oceans and the air, belong to everyone. Other resources, such as rivers, are shared. Protecting the environment in these areas is a problem since no single person owns them.

Panama Canal investment bonds are one example of how this problem can be dealt with. The Panama Canal links the Pacific and Atlantic Oceans, and saves cargo ships many days of travel time. Without the canal, ships would have to travel all the way around South America. The problem is that there is not enough water to keep the canal locks and system filled with water. This is because water runoff from clear-cutting in the forests on either side of the canal makes the supply of water unpredictable.

One solution is for the companies who ship their products through the canal to buy investment bonds from insurance companies. The money from these bonds would be used to buy and plant trees on the deforested mountains around the canal shores. The new forest would slow down the rain runoff and provide a more constant supply of water. The bonds would be repaid in a few years with interest and the shippers would have water in the canal.

Where else could ideas like this pay off?

FIGURE 24.4

Ships Passing in the Panama Canal
The Panama Canal has a strategic location. Why is it so important for ships?

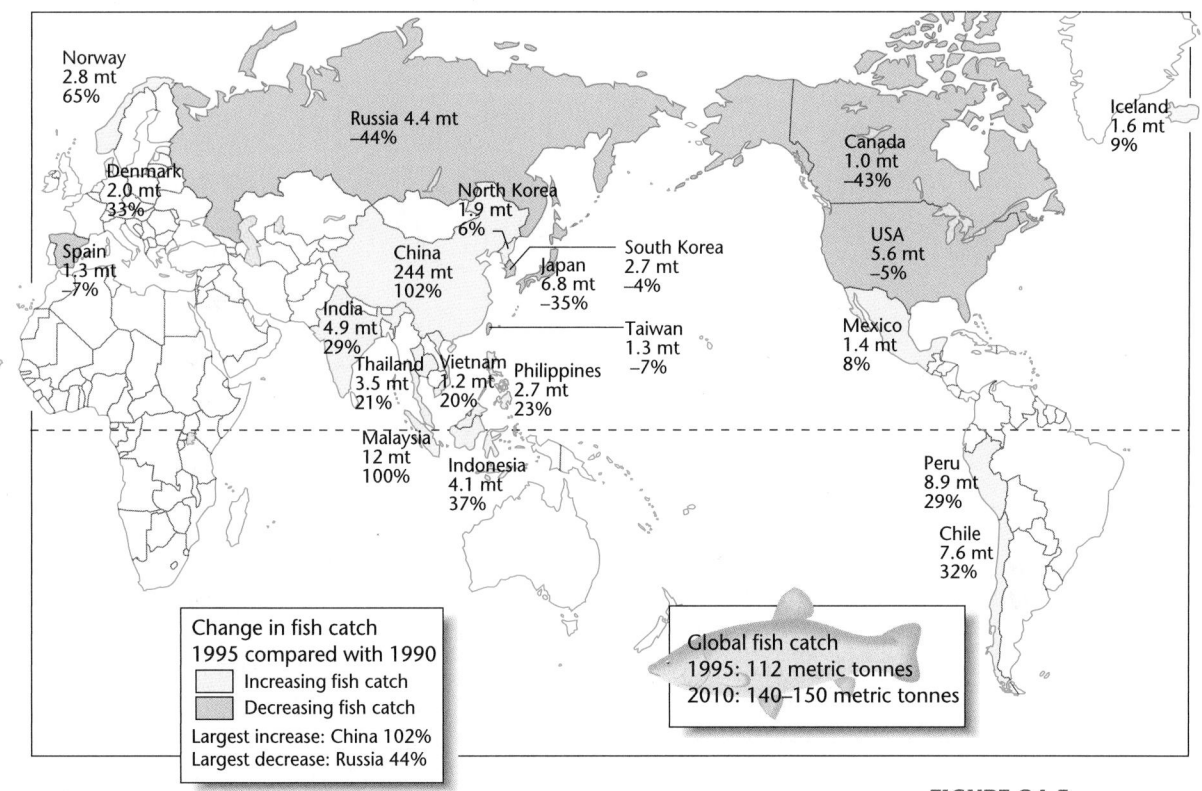

Norway
2.8 mt
65%

Denmark
2.0 mt
33%

Spain
1.3 mt
−7%

Russia 4.4 mt
−44%

North Korea
1.9 mt
6%

China
244 mt
102%

India
4.9 mt
29%

Thailand
3.5 mt
21%

Vietnam
1.2 mt
20%

Philippines
2.7 mt
23%

Japan
6.8 mt
−35%

South Korea
2.7 mt
−4%

Taiwan
1.3 mt
−7%

Canada
1.0 mt
−43%

USA
5.6 mt
−5%

Mexico
1.4 mt
8%

Iceland
1.6 mt
9%

Malaysia
12 mt
100%

Indonesia
4.1 mt
37%

Peru
8.9 mt
29%

Chile
7.6 mt
32%

Change in fish catch
1995 compared with 1990
☐ Increasing fish catch
▨ Decreasing fish catch
Largest increase: China 102%
Largest decrease: Russia 44%

Global fish catch
1995: 112 metric tonnes
2010: 140–150 metric tonnes

FIGURE 24.5

Change in Worldwide Fish Catch, 1995–2010
This map shows increases and decreases in fish catches. Why does the number of fish caught in the oceans need to be controlled?

World protected
spaces 11.5%

World unprotected
spaces 88.5%

FIGURE 24.6

Protected and Unprotected Spaces in the World
Why is there such a small amount of protected space in the world?

FIGURE 24.7

Percentage of Land Protected in Canada
Look at the percentage in 2002. Compare it to Figure 24.7. Why do you think the numbers are so similar?

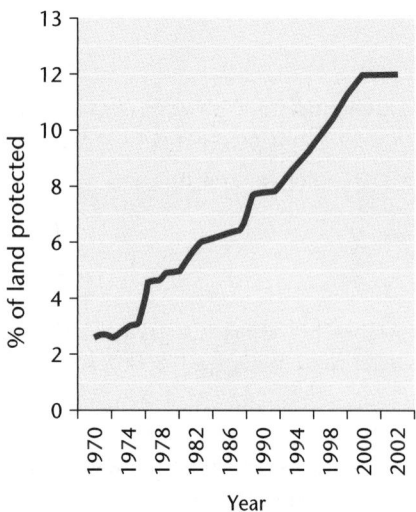

LITERACY SKILL

Constructing Flow Charts

A flow chart is a drawing that shows all the steps for doing or making something. It describes each part and how it relates to the other parts, usually with directional lines or arrows. A flow chart can help you

- understand the complete process
- identify the critical stages of a process
- locate problem areas
- show relationships between different steps in a process

Opposite is an example of a basic flow chart. The shapes show what each step is. For example, an oval is always the beginning or the end of the flow chart.

Start
Approach counter

Action
Order burger

Want fries? — Yes → **Decision** Order fries

No

Want drink? — Yes → **Decision** Order drink

No

End
Pay cashier

Literacy Strategy

How to read a flow chart
When reading a flow chart, look for the subject. The details that flow from the subject show a logical relationship such as cause and effect. By following the flow of the details, you will be able to identify consequences.

FIGURE 24.8

Example of Flow Chart
Flow charts help you to see a problem clearly, in step form.

CHECK IT OVER

6. What percentage of the world's forests are located in the tropics? Suggest one way to reduce the amount of forest being cut down.

7. What are pollution credits?

THINK IT OVER

Knowledge and Understanding

1. Why is the Millennium Ecosystem Assessment important for the environment?

2. Describe the role of weather satellites.

3. Why do we need environmental agreements?

Thinking and Communication

4. a) Explain why it is dangerous for humans to take the earth for granted.

   b) Give an example of what might happen if we did not take any steps to protect the environment.

5. Create a flow diagram to show how buying Panama Canal investment bonds helps to solve an environmental problem.

6. Draw or construct an illustration that shows the impact of tropical rainforests being cut down at the rate of 25 football fields per minute.

Canada and International Sports

Key Words

international sporting events

In this performance task you will learn to

◢ *identify economic and cultural connections between Canada and other countries*

◢ *report on how Canada is influenced by other countries*

Introduction

Canadian athletes participate in many international sporting events against athletes from other countries. These events include the Olympic Games, the Commonwealth Games, and the Arctic Games. Canada will host the 2010 Winter Olympic Games in the Vancouver and Whistler areas of British Columbia.

Canadian athletes do very well in some international competitions such as men's and women's ice hockey and figure skating. However, to compete in Canada, athletes must raise money themselves through part-time work, family support, corporate sponsorships, and government grants. They must devote long hours to mastering their sport. Often, they give up regular jobs and careers.

Performance Task Assignment

Your task is to research and evaluate how Canadian tax dollars are used to support athletes participating in an international sport. You will also compare what Canada does to support its athletes to what another nation does in the same sport.

Step 1   Choose an international sport that Canada participates in.

Step 2   Research how our athletes in that sport are supported with government tax dollars (national, provincial, local levels of government, or sponsorships). Some topics that you may want to include in your research are

- amounts paid to athletes
- sources of money

- support for training
- facilities
- corporate sponsorships

Make sure that you record your source information for your bibliography.

Step 3   Choose another country Canada competes against in that sport. To make research easier, choose a country that uses English as its main language, such as Australia, the United Kingdom, Jamaica, or India. Investigate how the athletes of that country are supported, or paid, so they can compete at the international level.

Step 4   Decide what your answer is to the research question "Should tax dollars be used to support and encourage athletes who compete internationally?" Compose a final argument for your report to evaluate the role of tax dollars and whether it is money well spent in Canada.

Step 5   Prepare your final written or electronic good copy. Add illustrations, if possible, and submit to your teacher.

FIGURE PT4.1

Summer Olympics Gold
Canadian Adam van Koeverden wins a gold medal at the Summer Olympic Games in Athens, Greece, in 2004.

FIGURE PT4.2

Winter Olympics Gold
The Canadian women's hockey team celebrates winning the gold medal at the 2006 Olympic Winter Games in Torino, Italy.

Appendix

Literacy Hints

Note Making

Note making means taking the ideas that are found in information sources, including this book, and recording the information that you need. There are several ways to do this.

T-Notes

T-Notes combine written notes and drawings. Use the format below, or design your own.

Main Title	
Write one or two sentences to describe what this section is about.	
Drawing or Sketch	Subtitles • Write notes in point form here

Point-form Notes (Rough Notes)

Point-form notes involves reading a section, thinking about the main or most important ideas, and recording these ideas in your own words (paraphrasing). Your goal is to record only the most important ideas, using your own words.

Some ideas

- Use chapter and section headings.
- Under each heading, record only key words/ideas.
- Do not write in complete sentences. Use a dash (–) to begin new ideas.
- Use abbreviations.

Example
(Based on Chapter 20)

Canada's Trade Partners
- *Trade*
  - *importing and exporting*
  - *globalization*
- *Partners*
  - *USA largest market for Canadian products*
  - *other partners include China and India*

Products Canada Buys and Sells
- *import what we don't produce ourselves*
- *sell what we produce well: competitive advantage*
- *natural resources*
  - *skilled workers*
  - *communication systems*

Graphic Notes

Graphic notes are also called graphic organizers.

- Create charts, diagrams, or timelines from the information in your notes.
- Add colour.
- Show comparisons visually (with small drawings and maps).
- Be creative in helping yourself see relationships between ideas. For example, use arrows, simple drawings, or colour coding.
- If important material stands out on the page, you will be able to recall it more easily.

Following are examples of different types of charts and graphic organizers.

Organizing main ideas and supporting details

a) Web

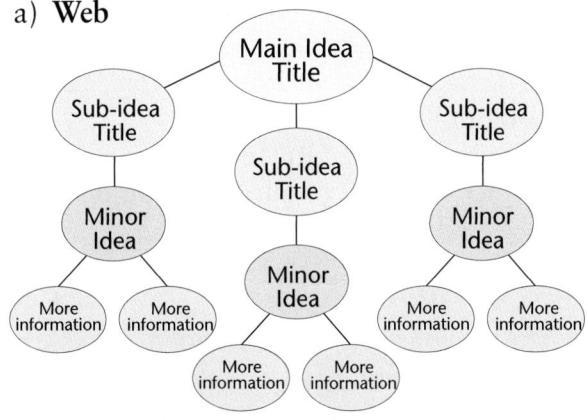

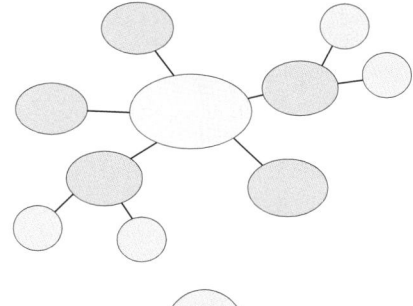

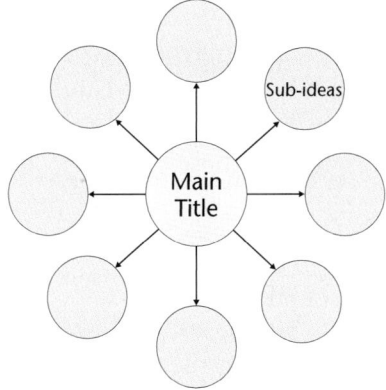

Write the title in the centre and notes in the "donut pieces," one idea per piece. Add to or remove parts from the donut as needed.

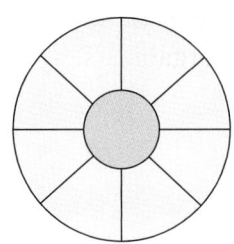

b) Flow Chart

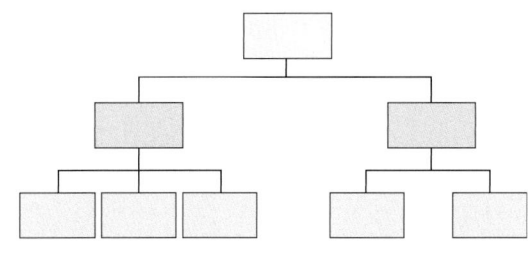

c) **Mind Map**

Mind maps work much like webs. Each idea is placed on a separate line. Each word or idea must be joined by a line to at least one other word or idea. Coloured sketches are often used to represent words or ideas. These sketches will help you remember.

The mind map below is based on ideas and concepts covered in Chapter 9.

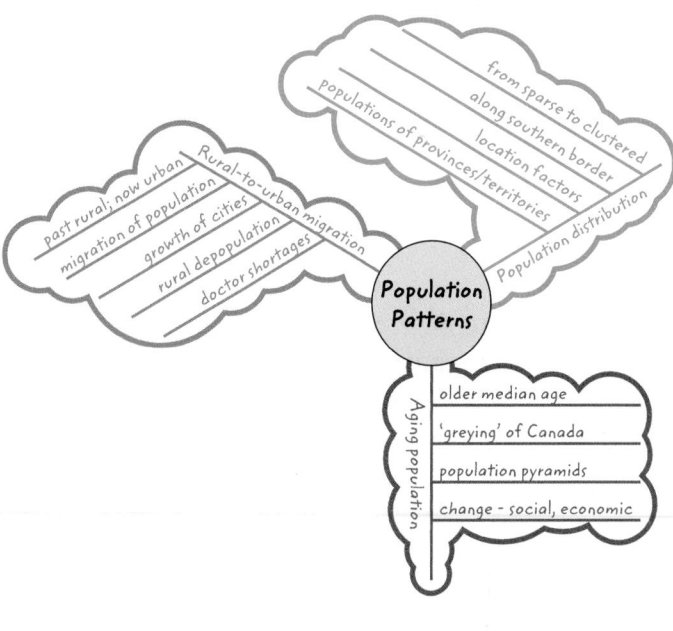

Notebook Organization

Your notebook is your record of the material you have studied. Your notes should be easy to use and to study from.

Organization suggestions

- Keep notes in sequence. Either date them or sort and organize them by topic using dividers in a binder.
- Create a table of contents for each section and chapter.
- Keep the pages in order. Add new information to the back of your old notes.
- Compare your notebook with a partner's to check for items that are missing or out of order.
- Use colours to underline, highlight, illustrate, and code your notes. Colours help you to learn material.
- Use the margins to add diagrams when you study.
- List key words, write out definitions, refer to other sections of your notes, or connect to page numbers from the textbook.
- Develop a vocabulary of terms and unfamiliar words.

Study Skills

It is important to have good study skills and to use them regularly. Study skills will help you learn new material, review, and prepare for exams.

Methods of studying

- Learn by teaching to a friend or parent or guardian.
- Team study. Question each other. Read each other's notes—someone else's way of expressing an idea may stick with you. Ask your partner to explain notes you do not understand. This will help both of you.

- Interview and role-play to understand and be able to explain the point of view of important characters. You may need to write an assignment from someone else's point of view.
- Use practice tests. Review old exams, predict the types of questions you may face, and practise sample answers.

Test questions

Make up your own test questions and share them with others. For example, make the chapter headings into questions that ask the following:

- who
- why
- where
- contrast
- cause/effect
- when
- what
- compare
- describe
- classify

Presentations

In this book, presentation refers to communicating information in visual, oral, or written forms. To prepare and carry out a presentation, follow these steps:

Step 1: Choose one main topic or idea as the focus for your presentation. Everything you do must relate to or provide examples of this main idea.

Step 2: Select a method of presentation from the list of presentation ideas on page 261. Ask your teacher or visit the library to find out how to prepare your presentation if you do not know how.

Step 3: Read about your topic or idea in your textbook. Review any information you already have about it in your research notes.

Step 4: Plan, on paper, how you will prepare your presentation. Establish criteria for how to assess your presentation. See Self-assessment on pages 263–264.

Step 5: Prepare the presentation on the topic or idea you selected.

Step 6: Present your topic or idea to your classmates. Assess your presentation based on the criteria from Step 4.

Some presentation ideas

advertisement	mural
banner	music
booklet	newspaper
cartoon	newspaper article
charades	oral report
chart	painting
collage	pamphlet
collection	panel discussion
comic strip	papier-mâché
construction	photo album
cooking	photographs
demonstration	picture
dance	play
debate	poem
demonstration	poster
diagram	puppet show
diorama	puzzle
display	questionnaire
drawing	radio show
exhibition	riddles
fact file	role-play/drama
fairy tale	scrapbook
flow chart	scroll
game	sculpture
graph	skit
illustrated poem	song
interview	speech
job description	story

letter	survey
magazine	tableau
map	talk show
mask	television show
mime	timeline (illustrated)
mobile	top 10 list
model	Web page
mosaic	written report
multimedia presentation	

Action Plan

1. Date of Presentation _____
2. Describe how you want your part of the presentation to look and/or sound.

   _____
   _____
   _____

3. Plan on paper what tasks have to be done. Assign a completion date for each task.

Task	Completion Date	Done
1. _____	_____	_____
2. _____	_____	_____
3. _____	_____	_____

(add to this list as needed)

Problem Solving

A problem is a difficult question that requires you to consider a number of possible solutions in order to choose the best. For certain kinds of problems (e.g., a math problem), there is one correct answer. However, many problems in life have more than one solution.

Problems ask: Who? What? Where? When? Why? How?

Steps for problem solving

Step 1: Define the problem. Decide what you want to find out.

Step 2: Come up with possible questions and a hypothesis to guide your research. (A hypothesis is a rough guess about the solution, based on what you know.)

Step 3: Research to locate data (information) that relate to your hypothesis.

Step 4: Record the data (information) that relate to your hypothesis.

Step 5: Evaluate the information you have collected by thinking about whether it supports or disagrees with your hypothesis.

Step 6: Arrive at a conclusion by choosing what you think is the best solution—one that makes sense and solves the problem. Think about whether your conclusion agrees or disagrees with your hypothesis.

Problem-solving chart

Problem	Step ①
Hypothesis	Step ②

Research Solution	Data
1.	
2.	Steps ③ ④
3.	
4.	

I think # _____ is the best solution because

Steps ⑤ ⑥

Problem: Greenhouse gases are causing the world to get warmer.	
Hypothesis: We can help the problem by reducing the amount of greenhouse gases we produce.	

Research Solution	Data
1. Pass laws to force people to reduce gases	- people get angry - can't force everyone to do what is right
2. Give rewards to encourage people to take action	- people benefit when they do what is right - people feel good about their decisions - easy to put into action
3. Reduce the amount of energy being used	- fuel-efficient cars - better insulated homes - use public transit
4. Use non-polluting fuels	- develop alternative forms of energy - use renewable fuels - develop vehicles to use different fuels

I think #2 is the best solution because people will be happy to participate. They will receive benefits while helping to solve the problem.

Researching on the Internet

Anyone can publish anything they want on the Internet. No one checks the information for accuracy. Web sites can contain false and inaccurate information. It is always a good idea to ask, "Who produced this information?" when collecting information on the Internet. Information posted on the Internet by a government agency or an institution such as a university is likely to be more accurate than information created by an individual.

Avoid "cut + paste = plagiarize."

When you find useful information on the Internet, it is often tempting to just cut and copy sections from the Web site right into your own document. Copying other people's work without permission and calling it your own is called plagiarism. It is illegal. Record where all information comes from and put quotation marks ("—") around work you take directly from a Web site. Even if you use ideas from a Web site and write the information in your own words, you should still record the online source you used.

Safe surfing

When you are using the Internet, be cautious about personal information you share. *Never* give out personal information (name, phone number, address, credit-card numbers) over the Internet. *Never* agree to meet someone you have met online. If you want to subscribe to an Internet newsletter or register at a Web site, discuss this with your parents or guardians first. Ask them to check out the Web site.

Ad banners appear on almost all commercial Web sites. They are the same as the advertisements you see on television. If you click on ad banners promising you prizes, free products, or chances to win money you will be linked to a Web site that will try to sell you something. *Never* buy anything on the Internet until your parents or guardians have checked out the Web site.

Get your parents' or guardians' or your teacher's permission before looking for information on the Internet. Use only search engines and Web sites they have seen and approved. Tell your parents/guardians and/or teacher about any unusual behaviour or objectionable material you encounter online.

Self-assessment

Self-assessment means evaluating your work or performance to decide how well you have met the expectations of an activity. Check your own work against the ideas in Steps for Self-assessment below. Working with a partner, check each other's work. The goal is for both of you to improve the quality of your work.

Steps for Self-assessment

1. Review the expectations (criteria) for the assignment.
2. List the criteria you will use to assess your assignment.
3. Decide what you have to do to achieve Level 4 (highest rating) for each of the criteria. What would earn Level 3 (next highest rating) for each of the criteria? What would earn a Level 2? a Level 1?
4. Keep the criteria and rating descriptions in mind as you complete your assignment.
5. You may use the sample assessment format shown below. Change the criteria and descriptions to fit the assignment.

Three examples of self-assessment

Self-assessment

Expectations (Criteria)
(Expectations to be decided by the teacher, the student, or both.)

1. _____
2. _____
3. _____

Personal Assessment
Level 1 2 3 4
(Circle one based on above criteria)

Reasons for circling the number I did: _____

_____

Next time, I would _____

_____

This is what I learned about the way I think and work: _____

_____

Assessment by Teacher
Level 1 2 3 4
(Circle one based on above criteria)

Reasons for circling the number I did: _____

_____

Assessing a Group Activity

Performance Expectations (Criteria)

1. Started activity quickly and quietly
2. Demonstrated co-operative attitude
3. Worked quietly and effectively
4. Followed directions and stayed on task
5. Respected ideas, beliefs, and points of view of other group members
6. Was sensitive to the feelings of others
7. Listened to others during discussion time
8. Everyone in group had opportunity to speak
9. All group members worked together to complete the task
10. Ideas/work from each member was included in final group activity

Assessment of the Group
Level 1 2 3 4
(Circle one based on above criteria)

Reasons for circling the number I did: _____

_____

What we learned about working together as a group:

_____

What we would do differently next time: _____

_____

Self-assessment
Level 1 2 3 4
(Circle one based on above criteria)

Reasons for circling the number I did: _____

_____

Teacher Evaluation
Level 1 2 3 4
(Circle one based on above criteria)

Reasons for circling the number I did: _____

_____

Vocabulary

Start a section in your notebook called WordBook. Record in it any new words you want to remember. Several strategies for recording vocabulary follow:

a) WordBook

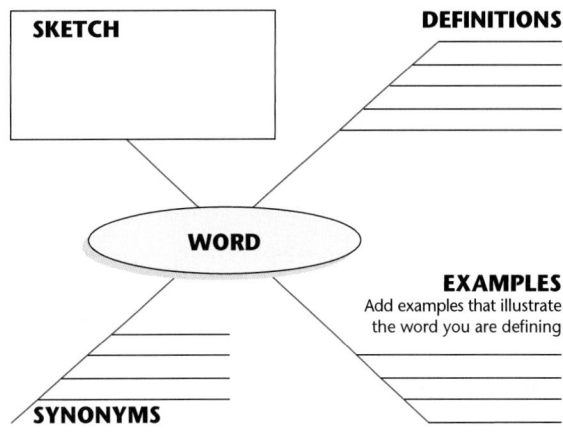

SKETCH   DEFINITIONS

WORD

EXAMPLES
Add examples that illustrate the word you are defining

SYNONYMS

b) Charting

Word		Picture
Definition Write a definition in your own words. Use the information in the textbook, the glossary, or from a dictionary.	**Example** Write examples using the word in context	Draw a simple sketch of the word and colour it. You are not expected to create something artistic. The activity of drawing aids memory.

c) Word Page

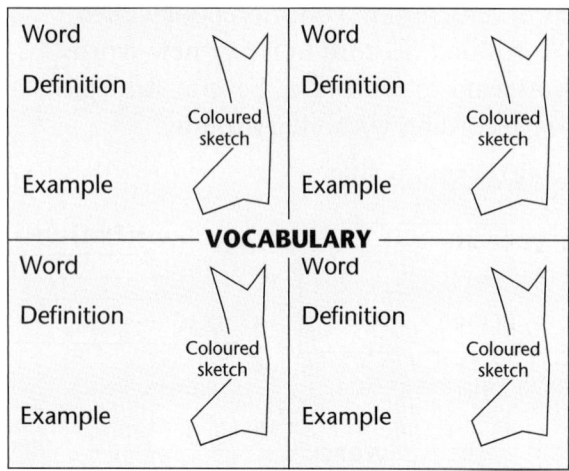

Writing

There are many types of writing. The form in which you write could include any of those described briefly here. Your purpose for writing might include telling, persuading, explaining, reporting, or describing. Think about your purpose and your audience so you can choose the most effective form and words. Challenge yourself by writing in a variety of forms.

Storytelling

There are many ways to tell a story about an incident or series of events. Stories may include your personal thoughts, feelings, and ideas. Stories are often meant to entertain.

1. **Biography**
   - Written account of someone's life
   - Includes information and events from the person's life so the reader can get to know that person
   - Will require research
   - An autobiography is a biography told by the person him- or herself

2. **Diary or Journal**
   - Personal account (description) of daily activities and experiences
   - Each entry begins with the date
   - Includes thoughts, ideas, and feelings

3. **Friendly Letter**
   - Tells about events/information of interest to the person who will receive the letter
   - Can also ask questions, congratulate, comment on events, or tell entertaining stories
   - Intended for someone you know (e.g., a friend)
   - Format includes writer's return address, the date, a greeting, and a closing

4. **Hard News Story**
   - Describes a current event of importance to the readers
   - Answers who, what, where, when, why, and how
   - Factual; may include quotations from people expressing opinions

5. **Historical Story**
   - Story based on historical fact (e.g., people, places, and events) but may also contain fictional parts (e.g., invented characters)
   - Requires research about people, events, and setting (description of place at the time)

6. **Play**
   - A story presented as a dramatic performance
   - Includes title, character and setting description, lines to be spoken by actors, direction about costumes, set/stage design, and actions and expressions of the actors

7. **Short Story**
   - Includes title, description of characters and setting, and conflict (problem)
   - Series of incidents or events take place as characters try to resolve conflicts
   - Climax or point of highest interest comes when the problem is solved. (Note: Problem may be solved in a positive or negative way.)
   - Conclusion

Persuading

Persuasive writing is intended to convince your reader to accept your point of view. Take care to use appropriate language and visuals. Hurting or insulting people will not change their viewpoints.

8. **Advertisement**
   - Announcement or written notice for the public
   - Provides information that is meant to persuade people to act in a certain way (e.g., buy a product, vote for a candidate)
   - Words and pictures should catch people's attention

9. **Brochure/Pamphlet/Flyer**
   - Usually a small booklet or folded sheet providing details (written and visual) that highlight the most appealing features of a place, person, event, or idea

10. **Editorial**
    - An article (short essay) found in most newspapers that expresses an opinion on behalf of the newspaper about a current event or issue in the news
    - Includes facts that support a point of view and strengthen an argument

11. **Essay**
    - An essay is a written composition on a certain subject

- An essay often answers a question beginning with "why," "should," or "to what extent"
- An essay can also be called a position paper

12. **Letter to the Editor**
    - Letter written to a newspaper to express opinions about current events or issues
    - Includes facts that support a point of view and strengthen a position
    - May contain emotional and descriptive words

13. **Political Cartoon**
    - Cartoons are drawings that state an opinion about the subject
    - Cartoonists usually exaggerate features of the subject to create humour
    - The purpose of cartoons is to get readers to look closely at the subject

14. **Review or Critique**
    - An evaluation or judgement of a product or performance (e.g., play, movie, artwork, CD, book)
    - Gives information that supports the writer's claims and opinions
    - Can include emotional and descriptive words

15. **Speech**
    - May serve many different purposes (e.g., entertaining, paying tribute, congratulating); often intended to persuade or convince (e.g., campaign speech)
    - Intended to be spoken to an audience
    - Words should be appropriate for the audience and the situation
    - Planning and practising out loud are needed
    - Volume, expression, pace, posture, and gestures give added meaning and impact to the words

- Point-form notes (cue cards) may be used when presenting but should not be read

Explaining

This type of writing helps the reader understand how to do something and how/why something works as it does.

16. **Instructions/Directions/Manual**
    - Provides a step-by-step order
    - Uses clear language that is easy to follow
    - Uses special terms that relate to the topic and suits the audience (e.g., "sifting" is a suitable term in a recipe)

Reporting

Reports use knowledge gathered from a variety of sources and provide factual information.

17. **Census**
    - A specific count of the people living in an area
    - Might include information about ages, jobs, education, and religion

18. **News Report**
    - Describes a current event or situation
    - Answers the questions who, what, when, where, why, and how
    - Gives factual information as well as peoples' opinions

19. **Newspaper**
    - Newspapers are divided into sections, each dealing with a different topic
    - Newspapers include factual reports and opinion comments

20. **Magazine/Newspaper Feature Article**
    - Provides information about people, places, and events that are of interest to readers

- Usually requires an interview or other research
- Includes visuals

21. **Research Report**
    - Provides detailed information on a specific topic or issue
    - Can be presented in a number of ways

22. **Survey/Poll/Questionnaire**
    - An investigation about a situation or issue
    - Includes clear, specific questions intended for a certain group
    - Poll should allow for responses that are easily recorded and counted (e.g., Yes/No responses)
    - Presents results in graphs, charts, tables, or paragraphs
    - Polls should avoid bias; choose a large, random sample (one in which you can't predict the outcome) rather than just people you expect to answer a certain way

23. **Interview**
    - An interview is a series of questions and answers between two or more people
    - Interview questions are planned in advance to get information about specific topics
    - Interviews may be done in person, over the phone, or online

Describing

Describing can be a part of almost any form of writing.

- Includes details that appeal to the senses (sight, hearing, smell, taste, touch, and balance); these help the reader become involved in the subject
- Make careful word choices that suit the form of writing

Glossary

A

active layer   top layers of soil above permafrost that thaw during summer

advocate for the environment   person who takes actions to try to protect the environment. People who do this try to persuade other people to change their actions so less harm is done to natural systems.

agriculture   the raising of crops and livestock; farming

air mass   large body of air. Air masses have the same moisture and temperature conditions throughout.

alternative energy sources   energy sources that are not commonly used. Alternative energy sources include wind, sun, hydrogen, and tidal power.

aquifers   underground layers of rock that are porous and store water. This water can be reached by using wells.

B

bedrock   solid rock that lies underneath loose material like soil

bibliography   a list of books, articles, Web sites, and other sources about a subject or topic

bitumen   a heavy, almost solid form of petroleum that occurs in natural deposits, such as the Alberta tar sands

boom-and-bust cycles   the up and down swings in economic activity that take place with many natural resource industries. A boom happens when the economy is growing; a bust happens when the economy is in a downturn.

C

Canadian International Development Agency (CIDA)   Canadian government agency that gives official assistance to other countries

census   an official count of the people of a country. In Canada, a complete census is done every year that ends in a one.

census metropolitan area   a city and its surrounding area that contains 100 000 people or more

central business district   the central area of a town or city that contains a concentration of stores and offices

clear-cutting   cutting all the trees in a forested area at the same time

climate   the daily weather conditions of a place averaged over a long period of time

comparison chart   an organization chart that uses columns to show how two or more things are alike and how they are different

competitive advantage   characteristics of a place or activity that give it an edge over other places or activities doing similar things

comprehensive land claims   claims based on continuing Aboriginal rights to lands and resources that cover greater areas of land

consumption   the amount of a resource that is consumed or used up

contingency plan   a set of activities that can be followed in the event of a hazard, such as a natural disaster

convection currents   flows of energy, such as those inside the earth, where heat is moved upward to the surface of the earth

conventional energy sources most common sources of energy. They include flowing water, fossil fuels, and uranium.

core the centre, such as the core of the earth or the middle of a large concentration of people

cultural and historic sites to see these sites is one of the main reasons why people choose to travel

D

demographers scientists who study populations and population patterns

deposition the laying down of material that has been moved from somewhere else. Materials eroded by water, wind, and ice are deposited by physical forces.

discretionary spending money we spend on things we want, rather than things we need

discrimination the recognition of differences and distinctions. Discrimination is based on prejudices that people hold.

documentation the information and evidence that supports an opinion or argument

drainage system network of streams and rivers that drain surface runoff from the land

E

ecological footprint the total human impact on an ecosystem

economic benefits the good things that occur because of economic activities in an area. These benefits include having jobs, being able to afford better health care, and the ability to support social services like education.

economic structure the way an economy is organized. One way to understand economic structure is to break the economy into primary, secondary, and tertiary industries.

ecozones regions based on combinations of natural features (land, climate, etc.) and human activities (land use, transportation, etc.)

Elders the most influential members of an Aboriginal community

emigration the movement of people out of a region, territory, or nation

environmental assessments estimates about the impacts of a proposed action on the condition and value of an environmental area

environmental impacts the changes in the physical systems of a place as a result of human actions

environmentally sensitive lands places where physical conditions can be easily affected in negative ways by human activities

equalization payments money paid by the federal government to provinces with weak economic activity to make sure that all Canadians have a similar quality of life

erosion transportation of broken-down earth materials from one location to another by running water, waves, wind, and ice

escarpment a steep slope or cliff

exporting sending goods and services that are produced in one country to another country

F

factors of tourism conditions that influence the amount and characteristics of tourism

federal government the government of all of Canada that sits in Parliament in Ottawa

foreign assistance an informal name for the help that Canada and Canadians give to other countries

fossil fuels minerals formed from the remains of ancient plants and animals that produce energy. Fossil fuels include coal, natural gas, and petroleum (oil).

fringe urban developments that take place at the edges of cities, on lands that are still partly rural

G

geologic time history of the earth from its formation to the present. Geological time can be divided into major time periods called *eras*.

glaciation accumulation of snow to form a mass of ice, and the movement of the ice

glaciers large ice masses that flow slowly

globalization the process by which most regions of the world have become connected by economics, culture, and financial services

global warming the rise in the average annual temperature of the earth

Greenbelt Plan Ontario plan to provide permanent protection to agricultural land and natural land in the Greater Toronto Area, including the Niagara Escarpment and the Oak Ridges Moraine

greenhouse gas gases such as carbon dioxide that contribute to an increasing average annual temperature

H

hazard a risk or danger

human rights freedoms and rights that belong to all people as defined by the United Nations' Universal Declaration of Human Rights

hythergraph a grid showing temperature and precipitation that is used to compare the climates of two or more places

I

immigration the movement of people into a region, territory, or nation

importing bringing products and services that were made in one country into another country

indicators characteristics that point out something about the conditions within a place or country, such as human rights

industrial heartland the parts of southern Ontario and southern Quebec that contain a large share of Canada's manufacturing activity

infrastructure the networks of transportation, communications, education, and other services that are required for economic and social activities

interaction the process of relating to each other

international cooperation nations working together to try to reach shared goals

international sporting events sporting competitions that involve a number of countries

international trade the exchange of goods and services among the countries of the world

inuksuk a stone structure with the rough outline of a human figure. The inuksuk was used by the Inuit as a landmark as well as to hunt caribou (to spook caribou so they would go to where the hunters were hidden).

K

knowledge workers highly trained and skilled workers who deal with information rather than products

Kyoto Protocol an international agreement to reduce the increasing amounts of greenhouse gases

L

land claims the demands by Aboriginal peoples for ownership and control of lands on which they have traditionally lived

land use the activities that take place on land or the uses to which land has been put

latitude the distance north or south of the equator, measured in degrees

leeward   the side of a mountain facing away from the wind

life expectancies   the average number of years that a person in a given place may be expected to live

M

mechanization   the replacement of human and animal labour with machinery

median age   the age at which half of the population is older and half is younger

meteorologist   a scientist who studies the conditions in the earth's atmosphere. A meteorologist may analyze weather data to help forecast the weather.

metropolitan areas   larger cities plus nearby communities that are tightly connected to the cities

minerals   naturally formed, solid substances with crystal-like structures

moraine   a feature created by materials deposited by glaciers

municipality   a town, city, county, district, or other area that is self-governing

muskeg   a type of vegetation found in swamps and bogs in northern Canada

N

national parks   lands set aside by the federal government in Ottawa for the benefit, education, and enjoyment of Canadians

natural disasters   major natural occurrences that destroy property and take lives, such as floods, fires, and earthquakes

natural vegetation   the vegetation that existed before humans influenced the plants that currently grow there

net migration   the difference between immigration rates and emigration rates (i.e., people who come into a country minus those who leave)

non-governmental organizations (NGO) groups that are not connected to a government, such as the Red Cross

non-renewable energy sources   energy sources that are limited and cannot be replaced once they have been used up, such as coal

O

official development assistance (ODA) the federal government's foreign assistance programs to help developing countries

oral histories   stories, legends, and histories that are passed from generation to generation without being written down

overburden   the unwanted material that covers a mineral deposit

P

peacekeeping   the use of military activity to keep peace between warring states

periphery   the edge or outermost part of a region

permafrost   permanently frozen soil, typically found in high mountains or at high latitudes, such as the Arctic

plates   large pieces of the crust of the earth

plate tectonics   the study of the movements of the earth's plates to understand how mountains, volcanoes, and earthquakes are formed

pollution   the destruction of the purity of the environment

population distribution   the pattern made by where people live within a place or region

Prairie   the region that makes up the southern parts of Alberta, Saskatchewan, and Manitoba. The prairie (without a capital *P*) is a region made up of flat and rolling grassland.

primary industries economic activities that have to do with the harvesting or extracting of natural resources

primary sources sources of information from people who witnessed an event or have firsthand knowledge of a topic

provincial governments governments that look after the affairs of a province

pull factors conditions that attract people to a place, especially a country

push factors conditions that make people want to leave a place, such as their home country, to move to another one

Q

quality of life a measurement of how comfortable life is in a country or place. Quality of life includes material conditions, like good housing, but also includes non-material conditions, like freedom.

quaternary industries a category of economic activities that provide high-level services, such as doctors or professors

R

rain shadow area on the leeward (side of a mountain facing away from the wind) side of a mountain with little precipitation

reclamation restoration, as in restoring land to its original state

recycle reprocess waste materials so they can be used again

reduce make consumer decisions that limit the amount of waste that is created, e.g., packaging

region an area of the earth's surface whose characteristics set it apart from other areas

regional disparities the differences in economic opportunities or living conditions from one part of a country to another

relief precipitation rainfall on the windward (side of a mountain facing toward the normal winds) side of a mountain caused by air cooling as it rises

renewable energy sources energy sources that can be regrown or replenished after they have been used, such as water that is used to make hydroelectric power

reserves areas of land set aside for the use of Aboriginal peoples

resource-based communities towns and communities that depend on extracting or harvesting natural resources for their livelihood

resources available supplies, in Canada especially of trees, fish, and minerals

retail trade sector the part of the economy that sells goods and services to consumers

reuse use existing products or resources more than once, such as refilling drink containers instead of recycling them

river diversions changes that are made to the flow and direction of rivers, often to irrigate croplands

rural having to do with areas outside of town and cities whose economic activities often focus on using natural resources

rural depopulation the loss of people in rural areas as a result of rural-to-urban migration

rural-to-urban migration the changing population distribution patterns as people leave rural areas to live in cities

S

safety the condition of being free from harm or danger

secondary industries economic activities that take products from primary industries and manufacture them into finished consumer goods

secondary sources sources of information that interpret events that have happened in the past

security the condition of being safe from danger or fear

seismologist a person who is trained to study earthquakes and movements of the earth's crust

services economic activities that focus on helping others, such as repairing computers. Services supply something that is useful or necessary.

smog the combination of *smoke* and *fog* in the air

soils complex mixtures of broken-down particles that come from rock, organic materials, water, and air

specific land claims specific complaints that treaties have not been respected by the government

stewardship the activities of someone who is responsible for or looks after the natural environment

subduction zone the area of the crust where one plate slides below another. Earthquakes and volcanoes are often associated with subduction zones.

suburban having to do with land in transition between urban and rural

surface mining open pit mining; a way of extracting minerals from the earth

sustainable development development for which care is taken to make sure that the needs of the present do not reduce the ability to meet future needs

system a set of things or parts that together form a whole

T

tariffs taxes paid to the federal government on goods entering the country

technological change a new development in how scientific knowledge is used for practical purposes, such as computers

telecommute work at home using computer links to one's place of employment

terrorism the use of violence to gain particular objectives

tertiary industries industries that provide services such as personal services or health care directly to consumers

topsoil surface soil that is useful for growing plants because it contains organic material (made of living organisms, such as animal or vegetable remains)

tourism the business of providing services to travellers

trade the selling of goods and services among countries

traditional ecological knowledge (TEK) the knowledge of the environment held by Aboriginal peoples that is part of their culture

treaties official agreements between the federal government and Aboriginal peoples. Many Aboriginal peoples agreed to give up land in exchange for reserves and money.

Tundra the treeless plains of northern North America. The climate is so cold and dry that trees cannot grow.

U

United Nations a worldwide organization whose goals are to achieve world peace and encourage economic and social development

urban having to do with cities or towns

urban functions   activities that occur in towns or cities

urbanization   a process in which more and more of the population lives in cities

utilidors   a large insulated tube mounted on short posts that contains the services that homes need, like water and energy. Utilidors are used in the northern part of Canada to ensure that their heat won't melt the permafrost.

W

water (hydrologic) cycle   the flow of water through the earth and the atmosphere

water meters   measuring devices that record how much water a household or business uses

weather   conditions of the atmosphere at a given time. Weather is usually described using temperature and precipitation conditions.

weathering   breakdown of rocks into small particles by physical processes

wind farm   a group of wind generators that create electricity from moving air

windward   the side of a mountain facing toward the normal winds

world reserve   the amount of a material found in the earth, usually applied to natural resources

World Trade Organization   international organization that sets the rules about how nations can trade among one another and that resolves trade disputes

Z

zero waste   the act of getting rid of unwanted materials in a way that doesn't create any garbage, such as by recycling

zone of ablation   warmer, melting end of a glacier

zone of accumulation   the colder end of the glacier where snow and ice build up

Index

Photo Credits

t=top; b=bottom; c=centre; l=left; r=right

viii (tr) Al Harvey/The Slide Farm, (ct) Victor Last Geographical Visual Aids, (cb) Panoramic Images/ Getty Images; **ix** Dick Hemingway; **x** Courtesy of The Weather Network; **1** Al Harvey/The Slide Farm; **2** www.CartoonStock.com; **7** Daniel Acker/Bloomberg News/Landov; **11** Al Harvey/The Slide Farm; **20** (c) Victor Last Geographical Visual Aids, (br) Panoramic Images/Getty Images; **26** Paul Souders/Getty Images; **32** (t) Ernst Haas/Getty Images, (b) Courtesy of The Weather Network; **38** (l) © J. David Andrews/Masterfile, (r) © John Foster/Masterfile; **45** Al Harvey/The Slide Farm; **48** Copyright © Benita Epstein; **50** Richard Price/Getty Images; **52** © CCRS/CCT 2002; **53** Jim Young/Reuters /Landov; **57** (cr) CP (Jacques Boissinot), (bl) © Reuters/CORBIS/MAGMA, (br) CP/Kelowna Courier (Gary Nylander); **58–59** From *Perspectives: Canadian Geography*, Student Text by DRAPER/ ANDREW. © 2000. Reprinted with permission of Nelson, a division of Thomson Learning: www.thomsonrights.com. Fax: 800 730-2215; **60** With permission of the Royal Ontario Museum © ROM **66** CP (Andrew Vaughan); **68** CP (Andrew Vaughan); **73** Woodruff/Library and Archives Canada / C-004745; **80** Clockwise from top left: © ANTONY NJUGUNA/Reuters/CORBIS/MAGMA, © Reuters/CORBIS/MAGMA, Dick Hemingway, © Photofusion Picture Library/Alamy, Christinne Muschi/ Reuters/Landov, AP; **84** © Michael Newman/PhotoEdit, Inc.; **87** From *Perspectives: Canadian Geography*, Student Text by DRAPER/ANDREW. © 2000. Reprinted with permission of Nelson, a division of Thomson Learning: www.thomsonrights.com. Fax: 800 730-2215; **93** Keith Levit Photography/Index Stock; **95** © Owen Franken/CORBIS/MAGMA; **99** Courtesy of Edmonton Economic Development Corporation; **101** Dick Hemingway; **104** © Larry Fisher/Masterfile; **113** CP (Boris Spremo); **119** © Gunter Marx Photography/ CORBIS/MAGMA; **121** © Paul A. Souders/CORBIS/ MAGMA; **123** © Neil Rabinowitz/CORBIS/MAGMA; **130** (l) © Royalty-Free/CORBIS/MAGMA, (c) CP (Mark Baker), (r) © Royalty-Free/CORBIS/MAGMA; **132** Al Harvey/The Slide Farm; **136** © David R. Frazier Photolibrary, Inc./Alamy; **139** Digital Vision/dv1236089; **145** © Dale Wilson/Masterfile; **154–155** Duane S. Radford/ Lone Pine; **156** Alison Wright/Getty Images; **158** (l)

Omni Photo Communications Inc./Index Stock, (r) Al Harvey/The Slide Farm; **161** CP (Jonathan Hayward). Reproduced with the permission of Bank of Canada; **164** Courtesy of Dr. Alan V. Morgan; **166** © Phil Testemale; **168** Canada Centre for Remote Sensing, Natural Resources Canada; **170** © Gabe Palmer/CORBIS/ MAGMA; **174** Vince Talotta/Toronto Star; **177** By Permission of Ontario Power Generation; **180** Duane S. Radford/Lone Pine; **181** Hibernia Management & Development Company Ltd; **183** CP (Larry MacDougal); **186** CP (Boris Spremo); **193** CP (Derek Oliver); **198–199** © Design Pics Inc./Alamy; **204** AP; **206** © Canadian International Development Agency/Pierre St-Jacques. Reproduced with the permission of the Minister of Public Works and Government Services, 2006; **207** Dino Mahtani/Reuters/Landov; **211** © Scott Gilchrist/Masterfile; **215** © Royalty-Free/CORBIS/ MAGMA; **219** Barbara Walton/EPA/Landov; **223** Johner/Getty Images; **225** Nelson Canada; **226** © Dave G. Houser/Post-Houserstock/CORBIS/MAGMA; **229** CP (Adam Butler); **231** © Canadian International Development Agency/Pedram Pirnia. Reproduced with the permission of the Minister of Public Works and Government Services, 2006; **233** CP (Les Perreaux); **234** CP/Toronto Star (Ken Faught); **235** Wendell Phillips, Canadian Red Cross; **237** Shmuel Thaler/Index Stock; **238** Copyright © United Nations 2000–2006; **241** (t) Source: IS2004-6047, Photo by MCpl John Nicholson, Canadian Forces Image Gallery, National Defence, 2004. Reproduced with the permission of the Minister of Public Works and Government Services, 2006, (b) Source: IS2002-0044a, Photo by MCpl Danielle Bernier, Canadian Forces Image Gallery, National Defence, 2002. Reproduced with the permission of the Minister of Public Works and Government Services, 2006; **242** (l) Photodisc/TR006854, (r) Robert Nickelsberg/ Getty Images; **247** © Tom Bean/CORBIS/MAGMA; **250** (tl) Jose Azel/Aurora/Getty Images, (tr) © Brian Morgan/Alamy, (bl) Robert Marien/Index Stock, (br) © Sally A. Morgan/ Ecoscene/CORBIS/MAGMA; **252** © Danny Lehman/CORBIS/MAGMA; **257** (l) CP/COC(Andre Forget), (r) Bartomiej Zborowski/ EPA/Landov.

Text Credits

18 Figure 2.7: "Geologic Time Scale." From *The ITP Nelson Canadian Dictionary of the English Language* by NELSON CANADA. © 1997. Reprinted with permission of Nelson, a division of Thomson Learning: www.thomsonrights.com. Fax: 800 730-2215; **25** Figure 3.4: This map was taken from *The Atlas of Canada* http://atlas.gc.ca/ © 2005. Produced under licence from Her Majesty the Queen in Right of Canada, with permission of Natural Resources Canada; **49** Figure 6.2: The map was taken from *The Atlas of Canada* http://atlas.gc.ca/ © 2005. Produced under licence from Her Majesty the Queen in Right of Canada, with permission of Natural Resources Canada; **51** Figure 6.4: Reproduced with permission from *The Westerly News*; **69** Figure 7.9: This map was taken from *The Atlas of Canada* http://atlas.gc.ca/ © 2005. Produced under licence from Her Majesty the Queen in Right of Canada, with permission of Natural Resources Canada; **147** Figure 14.9: Reproduced with permission from United Way of Greater Toronto; **152** Figure PT2.1: Mountain High Maps® Copyright © 1993 Digital Wisdom, Inc.; **159** Source: "A Hunter's Story" in *The Learning Circle: Classroom Activities on First Nations in Canada*. Ottawa: Indian and Northern Affairs Canada. 2000. p. 20. Reproduced with the permission of the Minister of Public Works and Government Services, 2006; **165** Figure 16.2: From *Ecological Footprint* produced by the Region of Peel Planning Department, <http://www.peelregion.ca/planning/bulletins/ecological.pdf>. Courtesy of Region of Peel; **190** Figure 18.5: Courtesy of the Greater Toronto Marketing Alliance; **191** Figure 18.6: © Queen's Printer for Ontario, 2005. Reproduced with permission; **194** Figure 18.9 © Queen's Printer for Ontario, 2002. Reproduced with permission; **205–206** Figure 19.6 Courtesy of The Royal Canadian Geographical Society/ Canadian Geographic; **210** Figure 20.1: Reproduced with permission from the National Geographic Society; **217** Figure 20.8: Reproduced with permission from the World Trade Organization; **221** Figure 21.4: Reproduced with permission from the National Geographic Society; **240** Figure 23.3: Copyright © United Nations 2000–2006.